TRANSISTOR AND DIODE NETWORK PROBLEMS AND SOLUTIONS

TRANSISTOR AND DIODE NETWORK PROBLEMS AND SOLUTIONS

HARRY E. STOCKMAN, S.D.

Senior Staff Scientist, National Company, Inc.

Formerly, Professor and Chairman, Electrical Engineering Dept., Merrimack College; and Professor of Electrical Engineering, Lowell Technological Institute

HAYDEN BOOK COMPANY, INC., NEW YORK

Library of Congress Catalog Card Number 67-13011

Printed in the United States of America

To Sonja-May and Harry

Preface

No volume of this type has ever been made available before. Calculations are usually boring, as they require scores of pages of routine manipulations. How can they ever be made interesting? Let us look into the matter.

Most textbooks providing complete problem solutions are usually textbooks on theory that are merely sprinkled with such solutions. One of their common difficulties is that the theory they provide is either insufficient or only a repetition of what the reader already knows. The theory is seldom just what the individual reader requires. Thus the very resolute step of providing no theory at all has been taken in this book; the problem solutions start on the very first page. Included, however, is some information that most readers will need, such as certain tables and formulas. This material has been collected in the appendices in the back of the book in the hope that this arrangement will prove to be the most profitable one. The appendices provide a sort of quick-reference dictionary, presenting common network rules and theorems, condensed twoport theory, and the matrix tables required for the solution of the given problems.

The solutions are to the point, but nevertheless quite detailed, and occasionally more than one solution is given to widen the scope of the text. The standard procedure in using a book like this is for the reader to solve the problem first and then check his own solution against the submitted master solution. Unless the reader makes his own solution independently or at least tries hard to find a solution, the value of this book will be drastically reduced. Sometimes both the problem formulation and the solution appear on the same page, and it is then recommended that the reader cover the solution with a piece of paper in order not to get any hints about the proper techniques by unavoidably glancing down the page.

Although most of the problems employ transistors as active network elements, the solutions are very general. In many problems the active element could just as well have been a tube; as another alternative, the active element may represent a stimulance diode, such as a tunnel diode. Some of the problems actually pertain to tunnel diodes. In a nutshell, the text covers active network theory, with the problem solutions demonstrating the modern way of solving network problems.

The first problems provide a review of common network calculations, including passive networks. The use of the Steinmetz-Kennelly Symbolic Method and the engineering-slanted version of the Laplace Transform Method is demonstrated. Then come problems on function sources, a subject largely neglected even in the most modern textbooks on network theory. Here, and elsewhere, the author's "Equivalent Generator Theorem" is used, which, as a replacement for Thévenin's theorem, permits calculation without consideration of the nature of the sources; they may be either dependent or independent. (The conventional Thévenin's theorem holds only for independent sources.) The important subject of transistor-connection transformations is then discussed in detail, employing the author's "floating" third-order matrix table, which employs built-in parameter formulas. This is generally the fastest known method for performing such transformations. Alternative methods are also described. The next subject dealt with is transistor amplifiers. Geared to the needs of the practicing engineer in the industry, this part of the book may be the one of greatest interest. The general approach to the solutions is nevertheless academic, contributing the necessary mathematical rigor, without which a book of this nature would lose its value. Empirical solutions are largely avoided. Everyday transistor problems are dealt with in order to make this section of greatest possible use to the reader.

The knowledge obtained in the previous chapters is then applied to problems on feedback amplifiers, employing internal as well as external feedback. Every effort has been made to familiarize the reader with the simple fundamental approaches to feedback problems and particularly to teach him many different kinds of stability criteria and how to employ them.

The subject matter now changes from transistors to tunnel diodes, and here both the series and the shunt amplifier are treated. A method of interpreting stimulance diodes as twoports is given, allowing the application of the Barkhausen-Nyquist stability criterion to diodes. The next and last chapter deals with nonlinear semiconductor networks, introducing the reader to the proper use of single-variable and double-variable Taylor series. The last chapter presents a collection of mixed problems. Throughout the transistor-problem solutions, the author has made frequent use of his "learning" or "model" transistors, which employ small and simple numbers as matrix elements and transistor parameters.

These "model" transistors make otherwise lengthy calculations rather brief and concise without much loss of educational value.

Although this book originated as a college text, it is hoped that many of its future readers will be engineers in industry, men who were never exposed to transistor technology, and men who wish to upgrade their acquaintance with transistor circuits. A reader having access to modern transistor textbooks should be able to digest this book without too much difficulty. Again, it is repeated that

The reader must attempt his own solutions before consulting those given in the text!

The learning acquired in this way will be at least ten times greater than that which would result from reading the book straight through.

In conclusion, I wish to thank my wife, Helen, for proof-reading the manuscript. I am also indebted to my brother, William, for his many helpful suggestions relating to the book's technical content.

Harry E. Stockman

Other books by the author of this volume include: *Transistor and Diode Experiments*, *The jω- or Symbolic Method*, *Introduction to Distributed Amplification*, *Time-Saving Network Calculations*, *Modern Television Techniques*.

List of Symbols

Y, y	admittance (in complex form, $\mathbf{Y} = G + jB$)
Y_c	admittance, characteristic
y_m	admittance, mutual (transadmittance)
$A(\omega)$	amplification, general
$A_I(\omega)$	amplification, current
$\alpha_{fb} = \alpha$, $\alpha_{fu} = \beta$, $\alpha_{fc} = \gamma$	amplification, current (closed 2-end, CB, CE, CC)
$A_V(\omega)$	amplification, voltage
μ_{fb}, μ_{fu}, μ_{fc}	amplification, voltage (open 2-end)
$A_i(\omega)$	amplification, inherent (feedback term)
$F(\omega)$	amplification, feedback loop
N	amplification in neper, decibel
ABP	amplification-bandwidth-product
ω	angular velocity
ω_o, ω_r	angular velocity, resonance
ω_D	angular velocity, driving generator
$\mathbf{s}$	angular velocity, complex (in general, $\mathbf{s} = \sigma + j\omega$)*
Ω	angular velocity, system self-behavior ($\Omega^2 = b^2 - a^2$, $\Omega^2 = b^2 - c^2$)
$(\sigma - j\Omega)$	angular velocity; negative-twin angular velocity
$(\sigma + j\Omega)$	angular velocity; positive-twin angular velocity
B, $\Delta\omega$, Δf	bandwidth
C, c	capacitance ($C = 1/S$)
$\mathbf{s}/2\pi$	complex frequency $[\mathbf{s}/2\pi = (\sigma/2\pi) + (j\omega/2\pi)]$
K, k, a, b, c	constants
G, g	conductance ($G = 1/R$)
$\mathbf{Z}^*$	conjugate of $\mathbf{Z}$, or Thévenin generator impedance
$\mathbf{Y}^*$	conjugate of $\mathbf{Y}$, or Norton generator admittance
$i(t)$, i	current, instantaneous
$\overline{I}$, $i(s)$	current, transform
I_o	current, initial
I, $\widehat{I}$	current, maximum or peak amplitude
I_{rms}	current, r.m.s. value
$\mathbf{I}_t$	current sinor, spinning (instantaneous complex quantity)

$\mathbf{I}$	current sinor, frozen (complex quantity)
σ	damping quantity in complex angular velocity (general symbol)
$a,\ c$	damping quantity in system self-behavior angular velocity
$K(s),\ D(s),\ d(s)$	denominator polynomial
Δ_y	determinant in y
Δ_{y1}	determinant in y, extended to include generator immittance
Δ_{y2}	determinant in y, extended to include load immittance
$\mathbf{s}_D = j\omega_D$	driving circle-generator complex angular velocity
$\mathbf{s}_D = \sigma_D + j\omega_D$	driving spiral-generator complex angular velocity
S	elastance ($S = 1/C$)
$Q,\ q$	electric charge
$E,\ \epsilon,\ W,\ w$	energy
$H(\omega)$	feedback transfer function
F_t	figure of merit
f	frequency ($\omega/2\pi$)
$G(\omega)$	gain (power gain)
$\mathbf{Y},\ \mathbf{y}$	immittance; impedance or admittance**
$Z,\ z$	impedance
$z_b,\ z_u,\ z_c$	impedance; base, emitter, collector
$L,\ l$	inductance; self-inductance
$M,\ m$	inductance, mutual
$\Gamma,\ \gamma$	inductance, reciprocal ($\Gamma = 1/L$**)
$J(\mathbf{K})$	j-part of $\mathbf{K}$
$z_{ij},\ y_{ij},\ \mathbf{y}_{ij}$	matrix elements (immittance matrix)
z_{ij1}	matrix element, extended to 1-end
z_{ij2}	matrix element, extended to 2-end
$h_{ij},\ k_{ij}$	matrix elements (hybrid matrix)
$a_{ij},\ b_{ij}$	matrix elements (transmission matrix)
b	mode response quantity in system self-behavior angular velocity
m	modulation factor; degree of modulation

$(\sigma - j\Omega)/2\pi$	negative-twin frequency
N, n	number of turns, constant
$N(s)$, $n(s)$	numerator polynomial
//	parallel with, in
α, β, γ, ϕ, Θ	phase angles
t_d	phase delay
t_{dd}	phase delay, differential
A^0	polynomial ratio multiplier
$(\sigma + j\Omega)/2\pi$	positive-twin frequency
P, p	power
Q	quality factor; operating point
X, x	reactance
Re(**K**)	real part of **K**
R, r	resistance ($R = 1/G$)
R_N, G_N	stimulance; negative resistance or conductance
B, b	susceptance
a, b, c	transistor quotients; CB, CE, CC
T, t	time
T	time constant
D	time derivative operator
n	turns ratio
V, v, E, e	voltage; electromotive force

*Many different symbols and terms are used to describe **s**-domain quantities, and many different names have been proposed in the literature for both the quantities and their units. The use of old and misleading terms, such as "imaginary" and "negative frequency," raises obstacles in the way of the logically thinking student. The latter term is particularly unfortunate inasmuch as there is no such thing as a negative frequency. See H. E. Stockman, "On Angular Velocity," *Proceedings of the IRE*, vol. 45, No. 3, March 1957, p 368 (correspondence). Also see J. Hollingworth: "The Symbolic Method," *Bull. Elec. Engr. Education*, England, No. 10, June 1953, pp 22-23.

**The author suggested this particular immittance symbol and the use of reciprocal inductance with the unit "yrneh" at Cruft Laboratory in 1942, but many other and perhaps better suggestions have been made. See H. E. Stockman, "On Reciprocal Inductance" *Proceedings of the IRE*, vol. 43, No. 3, March 1955 (correspondence). This reference credits Professor R. Rüdenberg of Harvard University as the originator of the excellent term "stimulance" for negative resistance and negative conductance.

Contents

1
Review of Network Calculations

The purpose of this chapter is to serve as a brief review course, bringing our knowledge of passive networks up to the required level. We will set up equations, carry out PI-TEE transformations, calculate transfer functions, determine port immittances and powers, and the like. We will make frequent use of the matrix tables in Appendix C in order to learn how to use these tables fast and accurately. The information in Appendices A and B will also be utilized, for example, in the application of the Output Immittance Theorem and in the writing of twoport equations and matrices. The reader is encouraged to use "spinning" and "frozen" sinors rigorously when employing the Symbolic Method and to learn how to distinguish between the two when writing equations. Although problems that employ the Laplace Transform Method of solution are also included, the reader is encouraged to solve periodic steady-state problems by means of the Symbolic Method as the first choice, and the Laplace Transform Method as the second choice, unless he can use with advantage some alternative approach, such as that of the D-operator Method—a method often overlooked by the practical engineer.

PROBLEM 1

Given is a bilateral, passive, linear network with numerous network elements, each one containing a number of CLR elements. The input port is designated $1,\underline{1}$ and the output port, $2,\underline{2}$. By the combination of network elements, the network has been brought down to the simple configuration in Fig. 1.1.

(A) Show by the application of Kirchhoff's Voltage-Sum Law that a solution can be obtained directly for any one of the currents. Show that the equation system reduces to only two equations, and write the equation pair in matrix form, indicating the component values in the logical network equivalent. Draw this equivalent.

(B) Show by application of Kirchhoff's Current-Sum Law that a solution can similarly be obtained for a specific voltage, and show that the equation system reduces to only two equations. Express this equation pair in matrix form, indicating the logical network equivalent. Draw this equivalent.

(C) For $\mathbf{Z}_1 = 0$, show by "long-hand" calculations how the z equation system can be obtained from the y equation system, and vice versa. Repeat the same transformations, using matrix algebra.

(D) For $\mathbf{Z}_1 = 0$, demonstrate that the PI and the TEE are equivalents of each other by performing PI-TEE and TEE-PI transformations. (Do not use handbook formulas.)

Solution

(A) Using the indicated mesh currents, we may formulate the equation system

$$\left.\begin{aligned} \mathbf{V}_1 &= \mathbf{Z}_a\mathbf{I}_1 - \mathbf{Z}_2\mathbf{I} \\ 0 &= -\mathbf{Z}_2\mathbf{I}_1 + \mathbf{Z}_b\mathbf{I} + \mathbf{Z}_4\mathbf{I}_2 \\ \mathbf{V}_2 &= \mathbf{Z}_4\mathbf{I} + \mathbf{Z}_4\mathbf{I}_2 \end{aligned}\right\} \quad (1.1)$$

The following convenient symbols are introduced:

$$\mathbf{Z}_a = \mathbf{Z}_1 + \mathbf{Z}_2; \quad \mathbf{Z}_b = \mathbf{Z}_2 + \mathbf{Z}_3 + \mathbf{Z}_4; \quad \mathbf{Z}_c = \mathbf{Z}_2 + \mathbf{Z}_3; \quad \mathbf{Z}_d = \mathbf{Z}_3 + \mathbf{Z}_4;$$

$$\mathbf{A} = 1/\mathbf{B} = \mathbf{Z}_1\mathbf{Z}_2 + \mathbf{Z}_1\mathbf{Z}_3 + \mathbf{Z}_2\mathbf{Z}_3$$

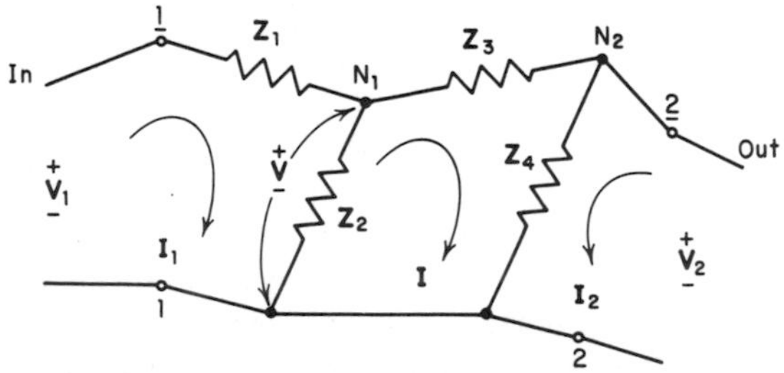

Fig. 1.1

Solving Equation system 1.1 for $\mathbf{I}_1$ by means of Cramer's Rule,

$$\mathbf{I}_1 = \frac{\Delta_{I_1}}{\Delta} = \begin{vmatrix} \mathbf{V}_1 & -\mathbf{Z}_2 & 0 \\ 0 & \mathbf{Z}_b & \mathbf{Z}_4 \\ \mathbf{V}_2 & \mathbf{Z}_4 & \mathbf{Z}_4 \end{vmatrix} \Bigg/ \begin{vmatrix} \mathbf{Z}_a & -\mathbf{Z}_2 & 0 \\ -\mathbf{Z}_2 & \mathbf{Z}_b & \mathbf{Z}_4 \\ 0 & \mathbf{Z}_4 & \mathbf{Z}_4 \end{vmatrix}$$

which we write

$$\mathbf{I}_1 = \mathbf{B}(\mathbf{Z}_c\mathbf{V}_1 - \mathbf{Z}_2\mathbf{V}_2) \tag{1.2}$$

Similarly, we obtain for the other two currents

$$\mathbf{I} = \mathbf{B}(\mathbf{Z}_2\mathbf{V}_1 - \mathbf{Z}_a\mathbf{V}_2) \tag{1.3}$$

$$\mathbf{I}_2 = -\mathbf{B}\mathbf{Z}_2\mathbf{V}_1 + (\mathbf{Y}_4 + \mathbf{B}\mathbf{Z}_a)\mathbf{V}_2 \tag{1.4}$$

Thus any one of the three currents may be singled out and calculated without reference to the other two. Eliminating $\mathbf{I}$ from Equation system 1.1, we obtain the equation system

$$\left.\begin{aligned} \mathbf{V}_1 &= \mathbf{Z}_a\mathbf{I}_1 - \mathbf{B}\mathbf{Z}_2(\mathbf{Z}_2\mathbf{V}_1 - \mathbf{Z}_a\mathbf{V}_2) \\ \mathbf{V}_2 &= \mathbf{B}\mathbf{Z}_4(\mathbf{Z}_2\mathbf{V}_1 - \mathbf{Z}_a\mathbf{V}_2) + \mathbf{Z}_4\mathbf{I}_2 \end{aligned}\right\} \tag{1.5}$$

Interpreted for a twoport, this equation system takes the form

$$\left.\begin{aligned} \mathbf{I}_1 &= \mathbf{y}_{11}\mathbf{V}_1 + \mathbf{y}_{12}\mathbf{V}_2 \\ \mathbf{I}_2 &= \mathbf{y}_{21}\mathbf{V}_1 + \mathbf{y}_{22}\mathbf{V}_2 \end{aligned}\right\} \tag{1.6}$$

which possesses the equality, $\mathbf{y}_{21} = \mathbf{y}_{12}$, signifying the bilateral characteristic of the network. The calculated parameter values are

$$\mathbf{y}_{11} = \mathbf{B}\mathbf{Z}_c \tag{1.7}$$

$$\mathbf{y}_{12} = \mathbf{y}_{21} = -\mathbf{B}\mathbf{Z}_2 \tag{1.8}$$

$$\mathbf{y}_{22} = \mathbf{Y}_4 + \mathbf{B}\mathbf{Z}_a \tag{1.9}$$

The matrix equation and the short-hand matrix equation corresponding to Equation system 1.6 are

$$\begin{vmatrix} \mathbf{I}_1 \\ \mathbf{I}_2 \end{vmatrix} = \begin{vmatrix} \mathbf{y}_{11} & \mathbf{y}_{12} \\ \mathbf{y}_{21} & \mathbf{y}_{22} \end{vmatrix} \begin{vmatrix} \mathbf{V}_1 \\ \mathbf{V}_2 \end{vmatrix} \tag{1.10}$$

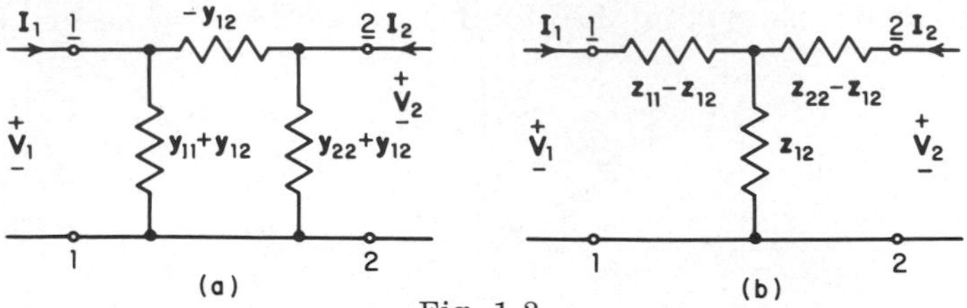

Fig. 1.2

$$|\mathbf{I}| = |\mathbf{y}|\,|\mathbf{V}| \tag{1.11}$$

Thus starting with mesh analysis, using voltage-sum equations, we end up with a node network, described by current-sum equations. We claim that the PI in Fig. 1.2a is the network equivalent read off from Equation system 1.6, but we may equally well claim that 1.6 is the equation system read off from the PI. It can easily be shown that this is the case, and the reader might carry out the pertinent calculations as an exercise. For $\mathbf{Z}_1 = 0$, the three network elements in the PI in Fig. 1.2a must be the elements in the given network in Fig. 1.1, and simple calculations show this to be true. We find that

$$\mathbf{y}_{11} + \mathbf{y}_{12}\Big|_{\mathbf{Z}_1=0} = 1/\mathbf{Z}_2$$

$$\mathbf{y}_{12} = \mathbf{y}_{21}\Big|_{\mathbf{Z}_1=0} = -1/\mathbf{Z}_3$$

$$\mathbf{y}_{22} + \mathbf{y}_{12}\Big|_{\mathbf{Z}_1=0} = 1/\mathbf{Z}_4$$

Looking back on Equation systems 1.5 and 1.6, we recall that the method used to find the y parameters was to reshuffle the equations in 1.5 to make them look like the equations in 1.6. There exists another, often more direct, method of obtaining the long-hand Equation system 1.6, and by means of it we read off the definitions for $\mathbf{y}_{11}$, $\mathbf{y}_{12}$, $\mathbf{y}_{21}$ and $\mathbf{y}_{22}$ from Equation system 1.6 and apply these definitions to the given network in Fig. 1.1. In accordance with this method, $\mathbf{y}_{11}$ is more or less directly obtained when the 2-end is closed, and it then constitutes the input admittance, $\mathbf{I}_1/\mathbf{V}_1$. We are here using the Network Element Combination Method, obtaining

$$\mathbf{y}_{11} = 1/(\mathbf{Z}_1 + \mathbf{Z}_2/\!/\mathbf{Z}_3) = \mathbf{B}\mathbf{Z}_C$$

To determine $\mathbf{y}_{12} = \mathbf{y}_{21}$ we close the 1-end of the network, drive it from the 2-end, and write the following equation in accordance with the Current Proportioning Method:

$$\mathbf{I}_1 = -\left(\frac{\mathbf{Z}_2}{\mathbf{Z}_1 + \mathbf{Z}_2} \times \frac{\mathbf{V}_2}{\mathbf{Z}_3 + \mathbf{Z}_1\mathbf{Z}_2/(\mathbf{Z}_1 + \mathbf{Z}_2)}\right) = -\mathbf{B}\mathbf{Z}_2\mathbf{V}_2 \qquad (1.12)$$

from which

$$\mathbf{y}_{12} = \mathbf{y}_{21} = \mathbf{I}_1/\mathbf{V}_2 = -\mathbf{B}\mathbf{Z}_2 \qquad (1.13)$$

Again for $\mathbf{y}_{22}$ we use the Network Element Combination Method and obtain upon inspection

$$\mathbf{y}_{22} = 1/[\mathbf{Z}_4 /\!/ (\mathbf{Z}_3 + \mathbf{Z}_1 /\!/ \mathbf{Z}_2)] = \mathbf{Y}_4 + \mathbf{B}\mathbf{Z}_a \qquad (1.14)$$

These results agree with those previously obtained. For further exercise on the use of this method, we shall now proceed to obtain the z parameters in the same manner, first writing the equation system

$$\left.\begin{aligned} \mathbf{V}_1 &= \mathbf{z}_{11}\mathbf{I}_1 + \mathbf{z}_{12}\mathbf{I}_2 \\ \mathbf{V}_2 &= \mathbf{z}_{21}\mathbf{I}_1 + \mathbf{z}_{22}\mathbf{I}_2 \end{aligned}\right\} \qquad (1.15)$$

To determine $\mathbf{z}_{11}$, we leave the 2-end open and inspect the network. The final result is

$$\mathbf{z}_{11} = \mathbf{Z}_1 + \mathbf{Z}_2\mathbf{Z}_d/\mathbf{Z}_b \qquad (1.16)$$

$$\mathbf{z}_{12} = \mathbf{z}_{21} = \mathbf{Z}_2\mathbf{Z}_4/\mathbf{Z}_b \qquad (1.17)$$

$$\mathbf{z}_{22} = \mathbf{Z}_4\mathbf{Z}_c/\mathbf{Z}_b \qquad (1.18)$$

The network representation of Equation system 1.15 is the network equivalent in Fig. 1.2b. We may check the results in Equation systems 1.16, 1.17, and 1.18 by setting $\mathbf{Z}_4$ equal to infinity. The network element values in the TEE must then be the same as the ones appearing in the given network, Fig. 1.1, and we thus obtain

$$(\mathbf{z}_{11} - \mathbf{z}_{12})\Big|_{\mathbf{Z}_4=\infty} = \mathbf{Z}_1$$

$$\mathbf{z}_{12} = \mathbf{z}_{21}\Big|_{\mathbf{Z}_4=\infty} = \mathbf{Z}_2$$

$$(\mathbf{z}_{22} - \mathbf{z}_{12})\Big|_{\mathbf{Z}_4=\infty} = \mathbf{Z}_3$$

(B) The given network has three meshes and two nodes in addition to the reference node. If $\mathbf{I}_1$ and $\mathbf{I}_2$ are used as variables on the left-hand side, and if $\mathbf{V}$ and $\mathbf{V}_2$ are now used as voltage variables rather than $\mathbf{V}_1$ and $\mathbf{V}_2$, $\mathbf{Z}_1$ will not appear in the equation system, which becomes

$$\left.\begin{aligned} \mathbf{I}_1 &= (\mathbf{Y}_2 + \mathbf{Y}_3)\mathbf{V} - \mathbf{Y}_3\mathbf{V}_2 = \bar{\mathbf{y}}_{11}\mathbf{V} + \bar{\mathbf{y}}_{12}\mathbf{V}_2 \\ \mathbf{I}_2 &= -\mathbf{Y}_3\mathbf{V} + (\mathbf{Y}_3 + \mathbf{Y}_4)\mathbf{V}_2 = \bar{\mathbf{y}}_{21}\mathbf{V} + \bar{\mathbf{y}}_{22}\mathbf{V}_2 \end{aligned}\right\} \tag{1.19}$$

Inserting the conditions of $\mathbf{Z}_1 = 0$ in Equation systems 1.12, 1.13, and 1.14, we find that full agreement exists. The twoport equation system in Equation system 1.19 represents the form in which we should aim to read off equation systems. In using this form, we are automatically employing Maxwell's Cyclic Voltages, just as in mesh analysis we similarly employ Maxwell's Cyclic Currents. Our writing is also in agreement with the use of the Superposition Theorem. First considering node N_1, we set $\mathbf{V}_2 = 0$ obtaining the first term in the first equation in 1.19. Then we set $\mathbf{V} = 0$ and obtain the second term in the first equation. The second equation in 1.19 is obtained in the same fashion. Using Cramer's Rule we can then determine either $\mathbf{V}$ or $\mathbf{V}_2$.

The matrix equation and short-hand matrix equation corresponding to the equations in 1.19 are

$$\begin{vmatrix} \mathbf{I}_1 \\ \mathbf{I}_2 \end{vmatrix} = \begin{vmatrix} \bar{\mathbf{y}}_{11} & \bar{\mathbf{y}}_{12} \\ \bar{\mathbf{y}}_{21} & \bar{\mathbf{y}}_{22} \end{vmatrix} \begin{vmatrix} \mathbf{V} \\ \mathbf{V}_2 \end{vmatrix} \tag{1.20}$$

$$|\mathbf{I}| = |\bar{\mathbf{y}}|\,|\mathbf{V}| \tag{1.21}$$

The equivalent PI is the one shown in Fig. 1.2a, although with $\bar{\mathbf{y}}$ rather than $\mathbf{y}$ parameters.

We previously chose to select $\mathbf{V}$ and $\mathbf{V}_2$ as voltage variables. By using the substitution $\mathbf{V} = \mathbf{V}_1 - \mathbf{Z}_1\mathbf{I}_1$ we can change Equation system 1.19 to the voltage variables $\mathbf{V}_1$ and $\mathbf{V}_2$, and the reader may do this as an exercise, obtaining Equation system 1.6 as end result.

(C) For a comparison between long-hand equation methods and matrix equation methods, let us use the first alternative to proceed from Equation system 1.15 to Equation system 1.6. We begin by rewriting Equation system 1.15 with the currents on the left-hand side, obtaining

$$\begin{aligned} \mathbf{I}_1 &= \mathbf{z}_{22}\mathbf{V}_1/\Delta_z - \mathbf{z}_{12}\mathbf{V}_2/\Delta_z \\ \mathbf{I}_2 &= -\mathbf{z}_{12}\mathbf{V}_1/\Delta_z + \mathbf{z}_{11}\mathbf{V}_2/\Delta_z \end{aligned} \qquad \Delta_z = \mathbf{z}_{11}\mathbf{z}_{22} - \mathbf{z}_{12}^2 \tag{1.22}$$

A comparison with Equation system 1.6 then yields

$$\begin{aligned} \mathbf{y}_{11} &= \mathbf{z}_{22}/\Delta_z \\ \mathbf{y}_{12} &= \mathbf{y}_{21} = -\mathbf{z}_{12}/\Delta_z \\ \mathbf{y}_{22} &= \mathbf{z}_{11}/\Delta_z \end{aligned} \tag{1.23}$$

Using the quicker matrix method, we follow the rule of dividing all elements in the z matrix by the z determinant Δ_z, interchanging the matrix elements along the principal diagonal, and changing the signs in front of the elements along the secondary diagonal. Thus we obtain, starting from the z matrix,

$$\begin{vmatrix} \mathbf{z}_{11} & \mathbf{z}_{12} \\ \mathbf{z}_{21} & \mathbf{z}_{22} \end{vmatrix} \rightarrow \begin{vmatrix} \dfrac{\mathbf{z}_{11}}{\Delta_z} & \dfrac{\mathbf{z}_{12}}{\Delta_z} \\ \dfrac{\mathbf{z}_{21}}{\Delta_z} & \dfrac{\mathbf{z}_{22}}{\Delta_z} \end{vmatrix} \rightarrow \begin{vmatrix} \dfrac{\mathbf{z}_{22}}{\Delta_z} & -\dfrac{\mathbf{z}_{12}}{\Delta_z} \\ -\dfrac{\mathbf{z}_{21}}{\Delta_z} & \dfrac{\mathbf{z}_{11}}{\Delta_z} \end{vmatrix} = \begin{vmatrix} \mathbf{y}_{11} & \mathbf{y}_{12} \\ \mathbf{y}_{21} & \mathbf{y}_{22} \end{vmatrix} \tag{1.24}$$

The same technique is used when we transform from the y to the z matrix. Rather than following the sequence implied by the expressions in 1.24, we can obtain the desired result much quicker by using Table I, Appendix C.

(D) Alternatively we may take the step from a PI to a TEE, which conventionally means from y to z parameters, or go in the opposite direction, by employing PI-TEE transformation. Appendix A shows a method for doing this that makes the reader independent of handbook formulas. The "all" quantity is $\mathbf{Z}_{all} = \mathbf{Z}_2 + \mathbf{Z}_3 + \mathbf{Z}_4 = \mathbf{Z}_b$, so that for the simple case of $\mathbf{Z}_1 = 0$, the arms in the produced TEE become

$$\mathbf{Z}_1' = \mathbf{Z}_2\mathbf{Z}_3/\mathbf{Z}_b; \quad \mathbf{Z}_2' = \mathbf{Z}_2\mathbf{Z}_4/\mathbf{Z}_b; \quad \mathbf{Z}_3' = \mathbf{Z}_3\mathbf{Z}_4/\mathbf{Z}_b \tag{1.25}$$

This agrees with the results in 1.16, 1.17, and 1.18, which is evident if we carry out the indicated subtractions, such as $\mathbf{z}_{11} - \mathbf{z}_{12}$.

Conclusions to this solution

We have learned that in whatever way we write the initial equation-pair system for the network in Fig. 1.1, either a z equation system or a y equation system can be produced. As a regular procedure we formulate one of these equation systems and then determine its four parameters by first reading off their definitions from the equation system. We introduce open-end considerations, if z parameters are what we want, and closed-end considerations, if y parameters are what we want. While one may go from one equation system to the other by long-hand calculations, we find it much faster to write down the matrix equations and then use matrix transformation. One can do this as is indicated by 1.24, but here still another time-saver appears in form of the matrix tables in Appendix C. We have become familiar with the idea that the matrix equation is the mathematical description, and the equivalent network the diagram description, of one and the same thing. One can be read off from the other; if we know one, we generally know the other.

In this problem, and in the following, the same vertical bars have been used to designate both a determinant and a matrix. The text usually indicates which one is intended, and no difficulty should occur.

PROBLEM 2

A physical network that is passive and reasonably linear is simulated in the laboratory by the equivalent TEE and PI shown in Fig. 2.1. The driving-generator resistance equals the input resistance and the load resistance: $R_D = R_{\text{in}} = R_L = R$.

(A) Derive expressions for the transfer functions, $A_V(\omega)_T = V_2/V_1$ and $G(\omega)_T = P_2/P_1$, using the equivalent TEE in Fig. 2.1a.

(B) Derive expressions for the same, employing the equivalent PI in Fig. 2.1b, obtaining $A_V(\omega)_P$ and $G(\omega)_P$.

(C) Express R_1 and R_3 of the equivalent TEE in terms of $A_V(\omega)_T$ and R.

(D) Express R' and R''' of the equivalent PI in terms of $A_V(\omega)_P$ and R.

(E) By TEE/PI transformation, show that the values R_1 and R_3 substantiate the values R' and R'''.

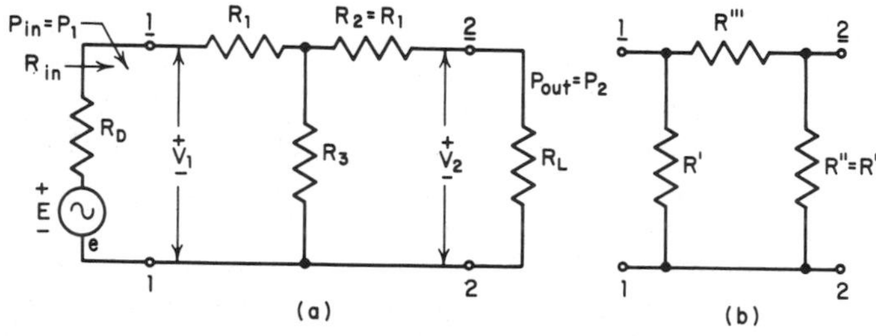

Fig. 2.1

(F) Using the equivalent TEE, design an attenuator for 20-db attenuation when $R = 100$ ohm and determine the input and output powers, P_1 and P_2, when $v_1(t) = 10\sqrt{2}\ \cos(2\pi 10^3 t + 30°)$.

Solution

(A) Using the Voltage Proportioning Method, we write directly

$$V_2 = V_1 \frac{R}{R_1 + R} \times \frac{R_3 /\!/ (R_1 + R)}{R_1 + R_3 /\!/ (R_1 + R)}$$

from which

$$A_V(\omega)_T = V_2/V_1 = RR_3/(R_1R_3 + R_1R_4 + R_3R_4) \qquad (2.1)$$

where $R_4 = (R_1 + R)$. Because of the common impedance level, $R_{in} = R_L = R$, we may write the decibel formula

$$N(\omega)_T = 20\ log\ V_2/V_1 = 20\ log\ A_V(\omega)_T\ db \qquad (2.2)$$

The voltage amplification is less than one, andthe decibel figure is accordingly negative. The (power) gain is

$$G(\omega)_T = \frac{P_2}{P_1} = \frac{V_2^2}{R} \times \frac{R}{V_1^2} = \left(\frac{V_2}{V_1}\right)^2 = A_V^2(\omega)_T \qquad (2.3)$$

The decibel formula now takes the form

$$N(\omega)_T = 10\ log\ P_2/P_1 = 20\ log\ A_V(\omega)_T\ db \qquad (2.2a)$$

which agrees with Eq. 2.2.

(B) Again using the Voltage Proportioning formula, we write

$$V_2 = V_1 \times R' /\!/ R/(R''' + R' /\!/ R)$$

from which

$$A_V(\omega)_P = A_V(\omega)_T = V_2/V_1 = R'R/(R'R + R'R''' + RR''') \qquad (2.4)$$

The decibel expression is the same as in Eq. 2.2 with subscript P replacing T.

(C) We begin by writing a formula for the input resistance,

$$R_{in} = R = R_1 + R_3 /\!/ (R_1 + R) = (R_1R_3 + R_1R_4 + R_3R_4 / (R_3 + R_4) \quad (2.5)$$

Using the simplified notation $A_V(\omega)_T = A_V(\omega)_P = A$ and eliminating R_3 from the combination of Eqs. 2.1 and 2.5, we obtain an expression for R_1. Then determining R_3, we write the two equations

$$R_1 = R(1 - A)/(1 + A) \quad (2.6)$$

$$R_3 = 2AR/(1 - A^2) \quad (2.7)$$

(D) The same procedure applied to the PI network in Fig. 2.1b yields

$$R_{in} = R = R' /\!/ (R''' + R' /\!/ R) = R' \frac{RR' + RR''' + R'R'''}{(R')^2 + R'R''' + 2RR' + RR'''} \quad (2.8)$$

Combining equations, we obtain

$$R' = R(1 + A)/(1 - A) \quad (2.9)$$

$$R''' = R(1 - A^2)/2A \quad (2.10)$$

(E) Going in the direction from the PI to the TEE we find the "all" resistance in the PI to be $R_{all} = 2R' + R'''$. Using the method described in Appendix A, we write directly

$$R_1 = R'R'''/R_{all} \quad (2.11)$$

$$R_3 = R'^2/R_{all} \quad (2.12)$$

Expressing R' and R''' in terms of A with the aid of Eqs. 2.9 and 2.10, we find that

$$R_1 = R(1 - A)/(1 + A) \quad (2.13)$$

$$R_3 = 2AR/(1 - A^2) \quad (2.14)$$

which agree with Eqs. 2.6 and 2.7. It is easily verified that we obtain substantiating results also when going in the opposite direction—from a TEE to a PI.

(F) Inserting values in Eq. 2.2, we obtain directly

$$-20 = 20 \log A; \; A = 0.1 \quad (2.15)$$

The values of R_1 and R_3 are now, from Eqs. 2.6 and 2.7,

$$R_1 = 100(1 - 0.1)/(1 + 0.1) = 82\Omega \tag{2.16}$$

$$R_3 = 2 \times 0.1 \times 100/(1 - 0.1^2) = 20\Omega \tag{2.17}$$

These are the values in the desired TEE attenuator. For the given value of the applied voltage, it follows that the rms value is 10 volt. V_2, in rms value, is then $V_2 = AV_1 = 0.1 \times 10 = 1$ volt. The two powers are, accordingly,

$$P_1 = V_1^2/R_{in} = V_1^2/R = 10^2/100 = 1 \text{ watt} \tag{2.18}$$

$$P_2 = V_2^2/R_L = V_2^2/R = 1/100 = 0.01 \text{ watt} \tag{2.19}$$

For checking purposes, we may sum up all the individual powers developed in the system, and the result should equal the applied power. The input current is $V_1/R_{in} = 10/100 = 0.1$ ampere, and the power developed in R_1 is therefore 0.82 watt. The output current is $V_2/R_L = 1/100 = 0.01$ ampere, so that the power developed in R_2 becomes 0.008 watt. Finally, the current in the mid-branch is $0.1 - 0.01 = 0.09$ ampere and the dissipated power is $20\ (0.09)^2 = 0.162$ watt. Summing up, we obtain $0.82 + 0.008 + 0.162 + 0.01 = 1$ watt. This is the value of P_1, proving that our result is right. The source E must deliver 2 watt, since matching exists between the generator and the network.

(F) Hyperbolic-function solution—Since a common impedance level is employed in this problem, we may treat the network in a simple fashion by means of hyperbolic functions. Such functions are treated in textbooks on filters and attenuators. The neper attenuation is obtained from

$$V_1/V_2 = 10 = e^{\gamma} \tag{2.20}$$

$$\gamma = 2.3 \text{ neper} \tag{2.21}$$

The formulas for R_1 and R_3 in the TEE are

$$R_1 = R\ tanh\ \gamma/2 \tag{2.22}$$

$$R_3 = R/sinh\ \gamma \tag{2.23}$$

With the aid of a table of hyperbolic functions, we then write

$$R_1 = 100 \times 0.82 = 82\Omega \tag{2.24}$$

$$R_3 = 100/4.94 = 20\Omega \tag{2.25}$$

which are the correct results (see Eqs. 2.16 and 2.17).

Conclusions to this solution

This solution gives us further experience with the use of the Proportioning Method, indicating its attractive features in comparison with other methods.[1] Although we calculate decibels as in Eq. 2.2, using a voltage ratio, it should be noted that we have here the special case of a common immittance level. The use of current and voltage ratios in decibel calculations often leads to errors, since one may forget to pay attention to impedance levels. As a rule with few exceptions, we should therefore use power ratios in connection with decibels. Another way out is to use some specially provided unit, such as the "decilog" unit, which can be applied to anything and everything. In part (E) we note the advantage of using the handbook-formula-free PI-TEE transformation formula. In part (F) the availability of two different methods for determining the requested power should be noted—one using the power ratio for the system and the other summing up the individual powers. In most problems, one method can be used as a check on the other. Finally, we have an example of the use of hyperbolic functions. A further study of the attenuator discussed in this problem reveals that the component values cannot be given arbitrary values, and as an example, R_1 cannot be larger than R for a positive value of R_3. (NOTE: The singular form, not the plural form, must always be used for such units as ampere, volt, and watt. We say 2 ampere, not 2 amperes.)

PROBLEM 3

A network is represented by the following matrix

$$|r| = \begin{vmatrix} 4 & 2 \\ 2 & 4 \end{vmatrix}$$

(A) Draw the network equivalent of the corresponding twoport and discuss it with regard to the fact that the matrix shows double diagonal symmetry. Calculate the determinant.

[1]Stockman, H. E., "The Potentiometer Idea in Network Calculations," *Proceedings of the IRE* (correspondence), vol. 31, No. 2, Feb. 1943.

(B) Transform from r to k parameters and show side by side the r and k parameter equation systems.

(C) With the 2-end of the twoport closed, derive an expression for the input resistance R_{in}: (1) from the produced network, and (2) from each equation system. Compare the results.

(D) Verify that the fundamental relationship, $k_{11}k_{22} + k_{12}^2 = 1$, holds.

Solution

(A) The given matrix indicates the following twoport parameters:

$$r_{11} = 4 \text{ ohm} \qquad r_{12} = 2 \text{ ohm}$$
$$r_{21} = 2 \text{ ohm} \qquad r_{22} = 4 \text{ ohm} \tag{3.1}$$

The network equivalent is therefore the one shown in Fig. 3.1. The passive nature of the twoport is indicated by the symmetry around the main diagonal: $r_{21} = r_{12}$. The symmetry around the opposite diagonal implies equal arm resistance: $r_{22} = r_{11}$. The determinant is

$$\Delta_r = r_{11}r_{22} - r_{12}r_{21} = 4 \times 4 - 2 \times 2 = 12 \text{ohm}^2 \tag{3.2}$$

(B) The most direct transformation is obtained with the aid of Table 1, Appendix C, from which:

$$k_{11} = \frac{1}{r_{11}} = \frac{1}{4}\,℧ \qquad k_{12} = \frac{-r_{12}}{r_{11}} = -\frac{1}{2}$$
$$k_{21} = r_{21}/r_{11} = 1/2 \qquad k_{22} = \Delta_r/r_{11} = 3\Omega \tag{3.3}$$

The required equation systems are (from Table 3, Appendix C):

$$V_1 = r_{11}I_1 + r_{12}I_2 = 4I_1 + 2I_2 \tag{3.4}$$
$$V_2 = r_{21}I_1 + r_{22}I_2 = 2I_1 + 4I_2 \tag{3.5}$$

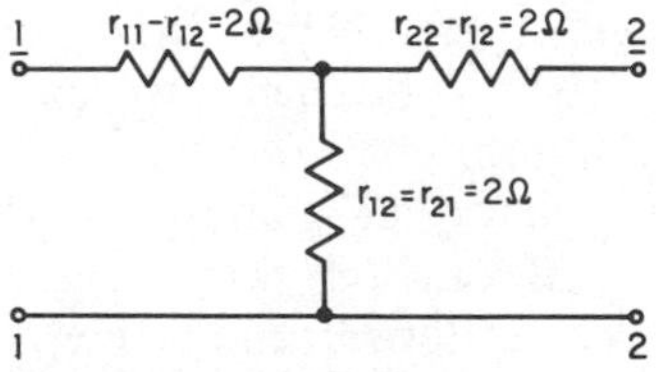

Fig. 3.1

$$\left.\begin{aligned} I_1 &= k_{11}V_1 + k_{12}I_2 = \tfrac{1}{4}V_1 - \tfrac{1}{2}I_2 \\ V_2 &= k_{21}V_1 + k_{22}I_2 = \tfrac{1}{2}V_1 + 3I_2 \end{aligned}\right\} \qquad (3.6)\ (3.7)$$

(C) Applying the Network Element Combination Method to the network in Fig. 3.1 with the 2-end closed, we obtain

$$\begin{aligned} R_{\text{in}} &= r_{11} - r_{12} + \frac{r_{12}(r_{22} - r_{12})}{r_{22}} \\ &= \Delta r/r_{22} = 12/4 = 3 \text{ ohm} \end{aligned} \qquad (3.8)$$

Using next the r parameter equation system in (3.4) (3.5), we write, with $V_2 = 0$,

$$R_{\text{in}} = V_1/I_1 = r_{11} - r_{12}r_{21}/r_{22} = \Delta r/r_{22} = 3 \text{ ohm} \qquad (3.9)$$

Finally using the k parameter equation system in (3.6) (3.7),

$$R_{\text{in}} = V_1/I_1 = k_{22}/\Delta_k = 3 \text{ ohm} \qquad (3.10)$$

Thus all results agree.

(D) The k parameter determinant is $\Delta_k = k_{11}k_{22} - k_{12}k_{21}$. If the r parameter bilateral condition $r_{21} = r_{12}$ is expressed by means of k parameters, it takes the form $k_{21} = -k_{12}$. Accordingly, the determinant becomes $\Delta_k = k_{11}k_{22} + k_{12}^2$. For a bilateral network with opposite diagonal symmetry this becomes unity, since Table 2, Appendix C, states that $\Delta_k = z_{22}/z_{11} = z_{22}/z_{22} = 1$. In numbers we obtain

$$\Delta_k = (1/4)(3) + (-1/2)^2 = 1 \qquad (3.11)$$

Thus we have verified that the quoted relationship holds.

Conclusions to this solution

We note from the solution in (A) how every twoport is determined by its matrix, and how main diagonal symmetry or lack of symmetry immediately discloses by $r_{21} = r_{12}$ or $r_{21} \neq r_{12}$ whether the twoport is passive or active, and whether it has function sources or not. From (B) we learn how we can transform any one of the six basic matrices into any one of the others, using Table 1, Appendix C, and how the corresponding equation systems may be written on inspection. From (C) we learn that although port and transfer functions can be determined from an available network equivalent, they are usually more rapidly obtained from equations and equation systems. Finally in (D) we find the given relationship to describe the determinant (from Table 2, Appendix C).

The following statement applies not only to this problem but to a large number of the following ones. When we deal with transistor network calculations in linear network theory, we like to center our thinking around the matrix. The matrix has everything that concerns the transistor in it; extended to include port external immittances, it describes the total system completely. By matrix techniques we usually solve problems faster, more concisely, and in a manner that facilitates back-checking.

PROBLEM 4

Given is the PI twoport with attached generator and load shown in Fig. 4.1 and the relationships $R_1 = R_2 = R$ and $C_1 = C_2 = C$. Calculate the output current $\mathbf{I}_2$:

(A) Using mesh currents and determinants.

(B) Using the Voltage Proportioning Method.

Solution

(A) Generalizing and introducing mesh currents, we obtain the network in Fig. 4.2, from which we read off the equation system:

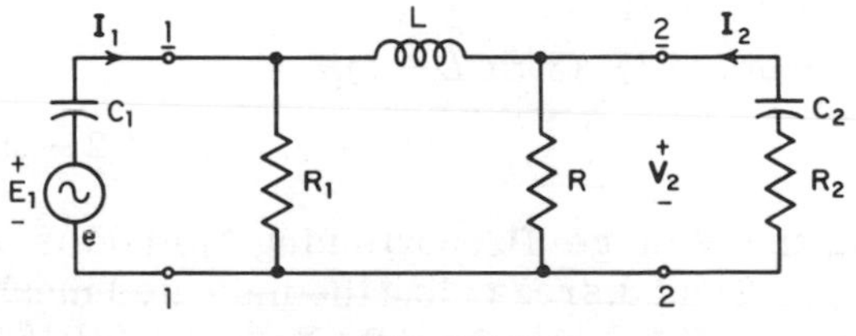

Fig. 4.1

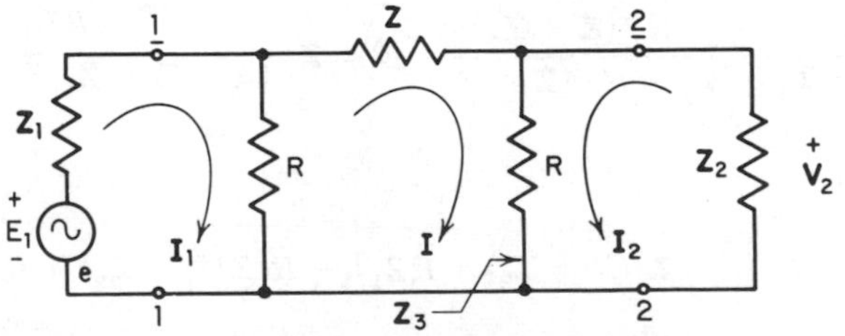

$\mathbf{Z}_1 = 1/j\omega C$, $\mathbf{Z} = j\omega L$, $\mathbf{Z}_2 = R + 1/j\omega C$, $\mathbf{z}_{11} = R + \mathbf{Z}_1$, $\mathbf{z}_{22} = 2R + \mathbf{Z}$, $\mathbf{z}_{33} = R + \mathbf{Z}_2$

Fig. 4.2

$$\left.\begin{aligned} E_1 &= \mathbf{z}_{11}\mathbf{I}_1 - R\mathbf{I} \\ 0 &= -R\mathbf{I}_1 + \mathbf{z}_{22}\mathbf{I} + R\mathbf{I}_2 \\ 0 &= \qquad\quad R\mathbf{I} + \mathbf{z}_{33}\mathbf{I}_2 \end{aligned}\right\} \tag{4.1}$$

With the aid of Cramer's Rule the output current is then computed to be

$$\mathbf{I}_2 = \frac{\Delta_{I_2}}{\Delta} = \begin{vmatrix} \mathbf{z}_{11} & -R & E_1 \\ -R & \mathbf{z}_{22} & 0 \\ 0 & R & 0 \end{vmatrix} \Bigg/ \begin{vmatrix} \mathbf{z}_{11} & -R & 0 \\ -R & \mathbf{z}_{22} & R \\ 0 & R & \mathbf{z}_{33} \end{vmatrix} \tag{4.2}$$

or with proper quantities inserted from the legend in Fig. 4.2

$$\mathbf{I}_2 = -R^2E_1/\{R^2(\mathbf{Z} + \mathbf{Z}_1 + \mathbf{Z}_2) + R[\mathbf{Z}\mathbf{Z}_2 + \mathbf{Z}_1(\mathbf{Z} + 2\mathbf{Z}_2)] + \mathbf{Z}\mathbf{Z}_1\mathbf{Z}_2\} \tag{4.3}$$

Inserting remaining quantities, we write

$$\begin{aligned} (\mathbf{Z} + \mathbf{Z}_1 + \mathbf{Z}_2) &= [\omega CR + j(\omega^2 CL - 2)]/\omega C \\ \mathbf{Z}\mathbf{Z}_2 &= L(1 + j\omega CR)/C \\ (\mathbf{Z} + 2\mathbf{Z}_2) &= [2\omega CR + j(\omega^2 CL - 2)]/\omega C \\ \mathbf{Z}\mathbf{Z}_1\mathbf{Z}_2 &= L(\omega CR - j)/\omega C^2 \end{aligned} \tag{4.4}$$

The final answer is therefore

$$\mathbf{I}_2 = \omega^2C^2R^2E_1/\{-\omega^2C^2R^3 - (3\omega^2CL - 2)R + j\omega[L + 2CR^2(2 - \omega^2CL)]\} \tag{4.5}$$

(B) Using the Voltage Proportioning Method as applied to the network in Fig. 4.2 and disregarding the indicated mesh currents, we obtain, with $\mathbf{V}_2 = -\mathbf{Z}_2\mathbf{I}_2$ and $\mathbf{Z}_3 = \mathbf{R}/\!/\mathbf{Z}_2 = R\mathbf{Z}_2/(R + \mathbf{Z}_2)$,

$$-\mathbf{Z}_2\mathbf{I}_2 = \frac{\mathbf{Z}_3}{\mathbf{Z} + \mathbf{Z}_3} \times \frac{R/\!/(\mathbf{Z} + \mathbf{Z}_3)}{\mathbf{Z}_1 + R/\!/(\mathbf{Z} + \mathbf{Z}_3)} E_1 = \mathbf{Z}_3 \frac{RE_1}{(R + \mathbf{Z} + \mathbf{Z}_3)\mathbf{Z}_1 + R(\mathbf{Z} + \mathbf{Z}_3)}$$

from which

$$\mathbf{I}_2 = -R^2E_1/\{\mathbf{Z}_1[(R + \mathbf{Z})(R + \mathbf{Z}_2) + R\mathbf{Z}_2] + R[\mathbf{Z}(R + \mathbf{Z}_2) + R\mathbf{Z}_2]\} \tag{4.6}$$

This result agrees with that in Eq. 4.3. From this point on the solutions are very similar.

Conclusions to this solution

In simple problems of this kind, the Voltage and Current Proportioning Methods usually give a quicker solution than even Cramer's Rule, employing determinants. In addition, the Proportioning Methods offer the great advantage that a smaller number of variables are required, and no confusion regarding the signs of additional variables can occur since no additional variables are introduced. The following rule is frequently applicable: When output voltage is required, do not involve currents, and when output current is required, do not involve voltages.

PROBLEM 5

For the twoport shown in Fig. 5.1, calculate:

(A) The transfer admittance, $\mathbf{Y}_{tr} = \mathbf{I}_2/E_1$, using the Thévenin-Norton theorem.

(B) The input impedance, $\mathbf{Z}_{in}$.

(C) The output admittance, $\mathbf{Y}_{out}$, using more than one method.

Solution

(A) In the corresponding Thévenin generator in Fig. 5.2:

$$E^* = \mathbf{Y}_1 E_1/(\mathbf{Y}_1 + \mathbf{Y}_2) \qquad \mathbf{Z}^* = 1/\mathbf{Y}^* = 1/(\mathbf{Y}_1 + \mathbf{Y}_2) \tag{5.1}$$

where

$$\mathbf{Y}_1 = G + j\omega C \qquad \mathbf{Y}_2 = j\omega K \qquad \mathbf{Z}_L = R + j\omega L \tag{5.2}$$

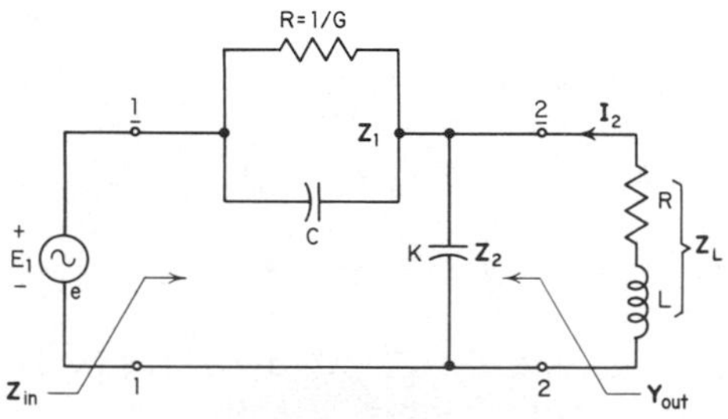

Fig. 5.1

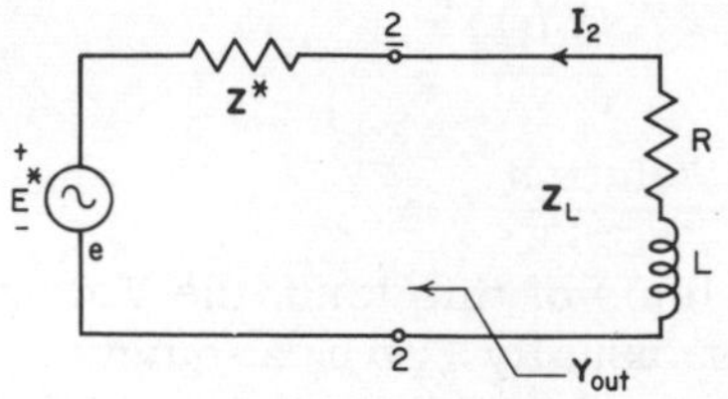

Fig. 5.2

Note that $\mathbf{Z}^*$ here means Thévenin generator impedance, not the conjugate of $\mathbf{Z}$. The current $\mathbf{I}_2$ is

$$\mathbf{I}_2 = -\mathbf{Y}_1 E_1/[1 + \mathbf{Z}_L(\mathbf{Y}_1 + \mathbf{Y}_2)]$$

and

$$\mathbf{Y}_{tr} = \frac{\mathbf{I}_2}{E_1} = \frac{-\mathbf{Y}_1}{1 + \mathbf{Z}_L(\mathbf{Y}_1 + \mathbf{Y}_2)} \tag{5.3}$$

in which we may insert the quantities given in 5.2.

(B) The input impedance is

$$\mathbf{Z}_{in} = \mathbf{Z}_1 + 1/(\mathbf{Y}_2 + \mathbf{Y}_L) \tag{5.4}$$

in which expression we may insert previously given quantities.

(C1) The quickest method by far to determine the output admittance is to apply the Output Immittance Theorem to Eq. 5.3:

$$\mathbf{Y}_{out} = \mathbf{Y}_1 + \mathbf{Y}_2 \tag{5.5}$$

(C2) Inspecting the network in Fig. 5.2, we note that E^* is an independent source, and the generator is therefore a Thévenin generator. Accordingly,

$$\mathbf{Y}_{out} = \mathbf{Y}^* = \mathbf{Y}_1 + \mathbf{Y}_2 \tag{5.5a}$$

(C3) Inspecting the network in Fig. 5.1, we note that E_1 is an independent source. We may therefore apply the Network Element Combination Method, writing

$$\mathbf{Y}_{out} = \mathbf{Y}_1 + \mathbf{Y}_2 \tag{5.5b}$$

(C4) We may also use the Applied Source Method, but since E_1 in Fig. 5.1 is an independent source, this method turns into the one described in (C3).

The current in $\mathbf{Y}_2$ is $\mathbf{Y}_2\mathbf{V}_2$, and in accordance with the Current Proportioning Method we can write directly

$$\mathbf{Y}_2\mathbf{V}_2 = \frac{gE\mathbf{Z}_1}{\mathbf{Z}_1 + \mathbf{Z} + \mathbf{Z}_2} = \frac{gE\mathbf{Y}_2}{\mathbf{Y}_1 + \mathbf{Y}_2 + \mathbf{Z}\mathbf{Y}_1\mathbf{Y}_2} \tag{6.4}$$

rom which

$$\mathbf{A} = \mathbf{V}_2/E = g/(\mathbf{Y}_1 + \mathbf{Y}_2 + \mathbf{Z}\mathbf{Y}_1\mathbf{Y}_2) \tag{6.5}$$

serting here the expressions in Eqs. 6.1, 6.2, and 6.3, we obtain

$$= g/\{G_1 + G_2 - \omega^2 L(C_1G_2 + C_2G_1) + j\omega[C_1 + C_2 + L(G_1G_2 - \omega^2 C_1C_2)]\} \tag{6.6}$$

with given approximations

$$= g/\{G_1 - \omega^2 L(C_1G_2 + C_2G_1) + j\omega[C_1 + L(G_1G_2 - \omega^2 C_1C_2)]\} \tag{6.7}$$

(B1) Using the Network Element Combination Method, we leave input port open, writing

$$\mathbf{Y}_{out} = \mathbf{Y}_2 + 1/(\mathbf{Z}_1 + \mathbf{Z}) \tag{6.8}$$

form in which this can be written with the aid of Eqs. 6.1, 6.2, 6.3 and with given approximations is the following:

$$\doteq G_2 \frac{R_2 - \omega^2 L(C_1R_1 + C_2R_2) + j\omega L(1 + C_1R_1R_2/L - \omega^2 C_1C_2R_1R_2)}{R_1(1 - \omega^2 C_1 L) + j\omega L} \tag{6.9}$$

(B2) To show that the Output Immittance Theorem can be ied even in cases where no load admittance exists, we shall the theorem here. To do this we assume that a load admittance, is shunted across $\mathbf{Y}_2$. Extending $\mathbf{Y}_2$ by $\mathbf{Y}_L$ in Eq. 6.5, we read e denominator

$$\mathbf{Y}_1 + \mathbf{Y}_2 + \mathbf{Y}_L + \mathbf{Z}\mathbf{Y}_1(\mathbf{Y}_2 + \mathbf{Y}_L)$$

which we obtain Eq. 6.8 by isolating $\mathbf{Y}_L$ and allowing it to . The two results agree.

sions to this solution

e learned from this solution that the Proportioning Method a much quicker result than the method of writing a formal

Conclusion to this solution

We note the advantage of mixing **Z** and **Y** symbols,
the one that gives the simplest solution and the
looking answer. We should learn to switch back and f
quantity and its inverse all the time, and in this way
times able to avoid fractions altogether. In accor
terminology, the equivalent network in Fig. 5.2 alw
a series-form generator. However, this series-fo
only a Thévenin generator when the specific req
filled that the voltage source is an independent so
adhere to this definition, we may encounter d

PROBLEM 6

Given the network illustrated in Fig. 6.1—i
nected transistor is used to convert the volta
current source gE, feeding the indicated PI

(A) The transfer function $\mathbf{A} = \mathbf{V}_2/E$, and giv
the approximations $G_1 \gg G_2$ and $C_1 \gg C_2$.

(B) The output admittance $\mathbf{Y}_{out}$ by more
introducing the approximations used in (A).

Solution

(A) The immittances constituting the PI

$$\mathbf{Y}_1 = G_1 + j\omega C_1$$

$$\mathbf{Y}_2 = G_2 + j\omega C_2$$

$$\mathbf{Z} = j\omega L$$

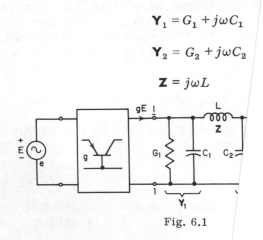

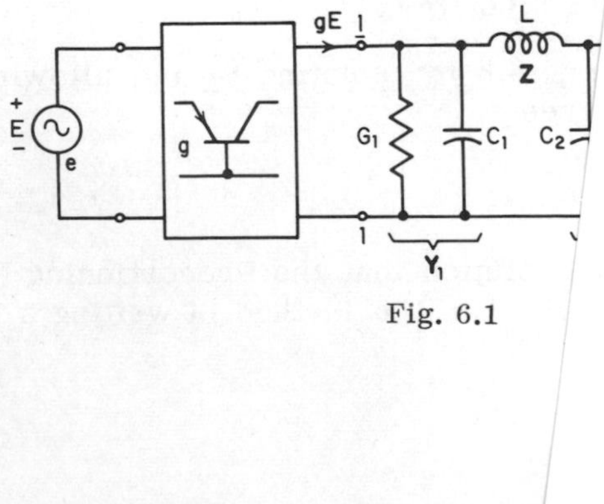

Fig. 6.1

equation system and a subsequent follow-up with determinants. In fact, a Proportioning Method solution is almost always quicker than a determinant solution, and determinants should therefore be avoided in problems of this type unless they are desirable for a particular reason. (For example, we may employ a matrix solution, yielding the determinants directly.) All the time we are switching between a quantity and its inverse—a good habit to acquire. To demonstrate this, we write Eq. 6.9 as a mixture of R and C symbols—an advantage when we wish to introduce CR time constants. Finally, we learned how to apply the Output Immittance Theorem when the network is not terminated in a load admittance.

PROBLEM 7

Given the twoport shown in Fig. 7.1—it is driven by the applied instantaneous voltage $e(t)$—determine the steady-state output voltage $v(t)$ employing the following methods (note that the dotted mesh-currents are part of the solution under A):

(A) By means of the D-Operator Method.[1]

(B) By means of the Symbolic Method, making use of the Voltage Proportioning Method.[1]

(C) By means of the Laplace Transform Method,[1] employing the inverse transform ($T = 1/2a$):

$$\frac{1}{(s^2 + \omega^2)(s^2 + s/T + \omega_0^2)} \rightarrow \frac{1/\omega}{\sqrt{(\omega_0^2 - \omega^2)^2 + \omega^2/T^2}} \sin\left(\omega t - \tan^{-1}\frac{\omega/T}{\omega_0^2 - \omega^2}\right)$$

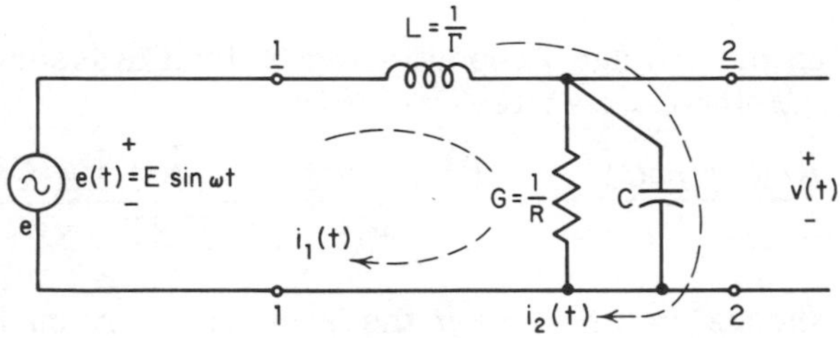

Fig. 7.1

[1]These three methods are described in the author's textbooks, *The jω-or Symbolic Method* (1956) and *Introduction to Distributed Amplification* (1956), available in libraries. The methods are also described in many comprehensive mathematical textbooks.

Solution

(A) For simplicity, we shall drop the time designation, t, when writing instantaneous values. The two mesh-currents are $i_1 = v/R$ and $i_2 = Cdv/dt = CDv$, where D is the operator ($D = d/dt$ and $D^2 = -\omega^2$). Kirchhoff's Voltage-Sum Law yields the equation

$$e = LD(i_1 + i_2) + v \tag{7.1}$$

or

$$RE \sin \omega t = LD(v + CRDv) + Rv \tag{7.2}$$

Solving with $A = R(1 - \omega^2 CL)$, we obtain the following expression for the output voltage

$$v = RE \sin \omega t/[R(1 - \omega^2 CL) + LD] = RE \sin \omega t/(A + LD) \tag{7.3}$$

Multiplying numerator and denominator by $(A - LD)$ and allowing D to operate on $\sin \omega t$, we obtain

$$v = RE\ (A \sin \omega t - \omega L \cos \omega t)/(A^2 + \omega^2 L^2) \tag{7.4}$$

which is the answer in two-term form. Using the proper transform formulas (see reference in preceding footnote), we obtain

$$v = RE \sin (\omega t - \tan^{-1} \omega L/A)/\sqrt{A^2 + \omega^2 L^2}$$

or

$$v = RE \frac{\sin \left(\omega t - \tan^{-1} \dfrac{\omega L}{R(1 - \omega^2 CL)}\right)}{\sqrt{R^2(1 - \omega^2 CL)^2 + \omega^2 L^2}} \tag{7.5}$$

(B) Using the Voltage Proportioning Method in association with the Symbolic Method, we write

$$\mathbf{V} = \frac{E/(G + j\omega C)}{1/(G + j\omega C) + j\omega L} = \frac{RE \underline{|\, - \tan^{-1} \omega L/R(1 - \omega^2 CL)}}{\sqrt{R^2(1 - \omega^2 CL)^2 + \omega^2 L^2}} \tag{7.6}$$

The instantaneous value is then the expression given by Eq. 7.5 above. This method is much faster than the D-Operator Method, unless we want the answer in two-term form.

We should here avoid the classical equation-writing methods and always use the Proportioning Method for voltage or for current. This results in a faster solution, and errors are less likely to occur. If, however, we insist that the problem be solved without this time-saving rule, the following is an example of how the solution may proceed. We may write

$$\Gamma \int (e - v)dt = C\,dv/dt + Gv$$

or

$$(-\Gamma E/\omega)\cos \omega t = C\,dv/dt + Gv + \Gamma \int v\,dt \qquad (7.7)$$

In symbolic notation this becomes

$$-\Gamma E/\omega = (j\omega C + G + \Gamma/j\omega)\mathbf{V} \qquad (7.8)$$

or after multiplication on both sides with $-j\omega$, setting $(\Gamma - \omega^2 C) = A_1$.

$$\mathbf{V} = -j\Gamma E/(A_1 + j\omega G) = \Gamma E \underline{\left|-\tan^{-1}\omega G/A_1 - \pi/2\right.}/\sqrt{A_1{}^2 + \omega^2 G^2} \qquad (7.9)$$

The instantaneous value is therefore

$$v = \Gamma E \cos\,(\omega t - \tan^{-1}\,\omega G/A_1 - \pi/2)/\sqrt{A_1{}^2 + \omega^2 G^2}$$

which we may write

$$v = \Gamma E\,\frac{\sin\left(\omega t - \tan^{-1}\dfrac{\omega G}{\Gamma - \omega^2 C}\right)}{\sqrt{(\Gamma - \omega^2 C)^2 + \omega^2 G^2}} \qquad (7.10)$$

Although different notations are used, it can be seen that this result agrees with that in Eq. 7.5.

(C) We noticed above that using the Proportioning Method greatly simplifies the application of the Symbolic Method. It offers the same simplification to the application of the Laplace Transform Method, which is evident if we first redraw the network in Fig. 7.1 as is shown in Fig. 7.2. (In practical engineering, it is not always

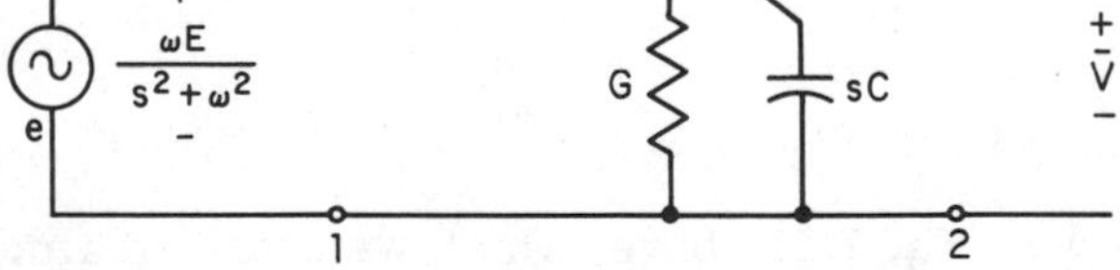

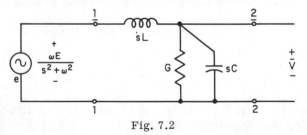

Fig. 7.2

necessary to redraw networks this way.) We note that in Fig. 7.2 the driving instantaneous voltage has been replaced by the driving transform voltage obtained from a transform-pair table and that the symbol $v(s)$ in the output has been superseded by the symbol $\overline{V}$. Occasionally, we do not have time to write the (s) type symbols, and we then prefer the super-bar symbols, which also give a more concise presentation. The Voltage Proportioning Method now yields, with $\omega_0^2 = 1/CL$,

$$\overline{V} = \frac{\omega E}{s^2 + \omega^2} \times \frac{1/(G + sC)}{sL + 1/(G + sC)} = \omega\omega_0^2 E \frac{1}{(s^2 + \omega^2)(s^2 + sG/C + \omega_0^2)} \tag{7.11}$$

With $C/G = T$ we can now make use of the given transformation formula, writing

$$\begin{aligned} v &= \frac{\omega\omega_0^2 E(1/\omega)\, sin\left(\omega t - tan^{-1} \dfrac{\omega/T}{\omega_0^2 - \omega^2}\right)}{\sqrt{(\omega_0^2 - \omega^2)^2 + \omega^2/T^2}} \\ &= \frac{E\, sin\left(\omega t - tan^{-1} \dfrac{\omega GL}{1 - \omega^2 CL}\right)}{\sqrt{(1 - \omega^2 CL)^2 + \omega^2 G^2 L^2}} \end{aligned} \tag{7.12}$$

This result agrees with that in Eq. 7.5. This is the way simple engineering problems should be solved with the aid of the Laplace Transform Method. For the one who insists on solving the problem in an academic fashion, the following procedure may be used. We may start out from the integro-differential equation in Eq. 7.7:

$$(-\Gamma E/\omega)\, cos\ \omega t = C\, dv/dt + Gv + \Gamma \int v\, dt$$

Differentiating, we obtain

$$\Gamma E\, sin\ \omega t = Cd^2v/dt^2 + Gdv/dt + \Gamma v$$

Here we insert the direct Laplace Transforms, writing

$$\omega\Gamma E/(s^2 + \omega^2) = (Cs^2 + Gs + \Gamma)v(s)$$

from which

$$v(s) = \omega\omega_0^2 E/(s^2 + \omega^2)(s^2 + s/T + \omega_0^2)$$

This agrees with Eq. 7.11 above, which we obtained almost directly by employing the Proportioning Method.

Conclusions to this solution

This was the first problem in which we encountered the D-Operator Method. This method deserves much greater attention than it is receiving from students and engineers. As an extra method for checking purposes, it is sometimes invaluable. Also, when the answer is desired as a two-term answer, the method occasionally proves to be the quickest one. This is also the first time we encounter the Laplace Transform Method, which for periodic steady-state problems is overrated by most students. With reference to simple and conventional engineering problems, we should, if possible, avoid the academic application of the method and instead attempt to write the answer directly by the application of the Proportioning Method. Finally, we used the Symbolic Method, which proved to be the fastest one. In the periodic steady state, it is almost always superior to the Laplace Transform Method, which in addition requires tables. The Laplace Transform Method should generally be avoided in the periodic steady state.

NOTE: The symbol s is complex. In reality, we should use boldface type and reproduce it as **s.** Since relaxation of this stricture does not cause any difficulty, the symbol s is used in this text.

PROBLEM 8

A physical inductor—L, R—is at time $t = 0$ connected to a capacitor C and charged to the voltage V_0 (see Fig. 8.1). Derive a mathematical expression for the time variation of the capacitor charge, $q(t)$, from the time $t = 0$.

Solution

First solution. We begin by drawing the transform network shown in Fig. 8.2 where V_0 appears as the step voltage V_0/s. The transform equation for current takes the form

$$I = (V_0/s)[1/(sL + R + 1/sC)] = V_0/L(s^2 + s2a + b^2) \qquad (8.1)$$

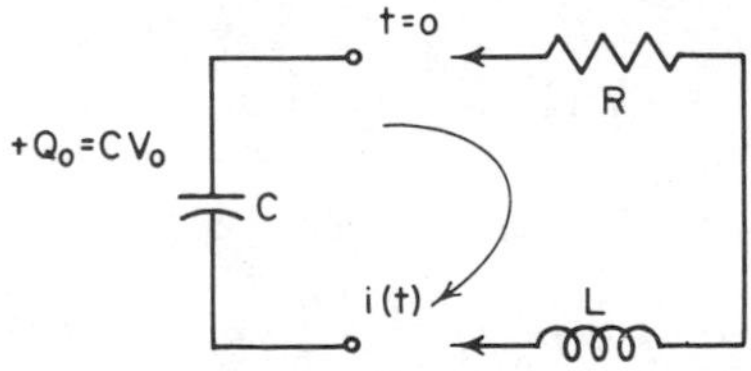

Fig. 8.1

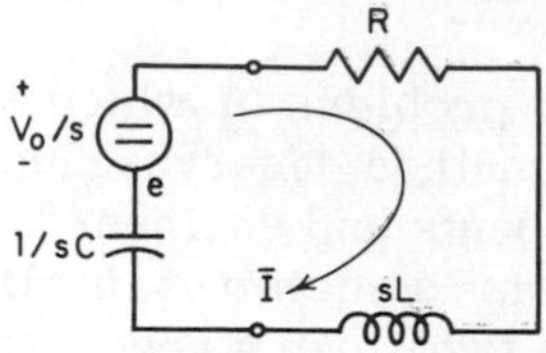

Fig. 8.2

where $a = R/2L$ and $b^2 = 1/CL$. We may now extend the denominator to contain a full square, writing

$$\bar{I} = V_0/L\,[(s+a)^2 + \Omega^2] \tag{8.2}$$

where $\Omega^2 = b^2 - a^2$. The desired quantity is charge, and for a current that is building up charge in a capacitor, the transform equation is $\bar{Q} = \bar{I}/s$. For a capacitor losing charge, the transform equation is $\bar{Q} = -\bar{I}/s$, and the charge in the capacitor which we are drawing on is $Q_0 = CV_0$. This charge appears suddenly at $t = 0$ and must therefore be introduced with its voltage in the form of a step-voltage, so that V_0 becomes V_0/s and CV_0 becomes CV_0/s. Accordingly,

$$\bar{Q} = -\bar{I}/s + CV_0/s = -V_0/sL[(s+a)^2 + \Omega^2] + CV_0/s \tag{8.3}$$

For the last term the inverse transform is CV_0. For the first term we use the transform-pair formula given below, with $\Omega^2 = b^2 - a^2$,

$$\frac{1}{s[(s+a)^2 + \Omega^2]} \rightarrow \frac{1}{a^2+\Omega^2} - e^{-at}\,\frac{sin[\Omega t + tan^{-1}\Omega/a]}{\Omega\sqrt{a^2+\Omega^2}} \tag{8.4}$$

Therefore,

$$q(t) = -V_0/Lb^2 + (V_0 e^{-at}/Lb\Omega)\,sin\,[\Omega t + tan^{-1}\Omega/a] + CV_0 \tag{8.5}$$

where the first and the last terms cancel. Accordingly,

$$q(t) = (V_0 e^{-at}/bL\Omega)\,sin\,[\Omega t + tan^{-1}\Omega/a] \tag{8.6}$$

where, as before, $a = R/2L$, $b = 1/\sqrt{CL}$, and $\Omega = \sqrt{b^2 - a^2}$

Second solution. We write Eq. 8.1 in the following form:

$$\bar{I} = V_0/L(s+s_1)(s+s_2) \tag{8.7}$$

so that

$$\bar{Q} = -\bar{I}/s + CV_0/s = -V_0/sL(s+s_1)(s+s_2) + CV_0/s \qquad (8.8)$$

where the roots are $-a \pm \sqrt{a^2 - b^2}$. Thus,

$$\left.\begin{matrix} s_1 \\ s_2 \end{matrix}\right\} = a \mp \sqrt{a^2 - b^2} = a \mp j\Omega \qquad (8.9)$$

We now make use of the following transform-pair formula:

$$\frac{1}{s(s+s_1)(s+s_2)} \to \frac{1}{s_1 s_2} + \frac{1}{s_2 - s_1}\left(\frac{1}{s_2}e^{-s_2 t} - \frac{1}{s_1}e^{-s_1 t}\right) \qquad (8.10)$$

Accordingly,

$$q(t) = -\frac{V_0}{L}\left\{\frac{1}{a^2+\Omega^2} + \frac{1}{j2\Omega}\left[\frac{e^{-(a+j\Omega)t}}{a+j\Omega} - \frac{e^{-(a-j\Omega)t}}{a-j\Omega}\right]\right\} + CV_0$$

$$= -CV_0 - \frac{CV_0 e^{-at}}{j^2\Omega}\left[-j2\Omega\,\frac{e^{j\Omega t} + e^{-j\Omega t}}{2} - j2a\,\frac{e^{j\Omega t} - e^{-j\Omega t}}{j2}\right] + CV_0 \qquad (8.11)$$

$$q(t) = CV_0 e^{-at}[\cos \Omega t + (a/\Omega)\sin \Omega t] \qquad (8.12)$$

That this answer agrees with that in Eq. 8.6 can be shown by the use of the trigonometric transformation formula [1]

$$H\cos x + K\sin x = \sqrt{H^2 + K^2}\,\sin(x + \tan^{-1} H/K) \qquad (8.13)$$

from which

$$\cos \Omega t + \frac{a}{\Omega}\sin \Omega t = \sqrt{1 + a^2/\Omega^2}\,\sin(\Omega t + \tan^{-1}\Omega/a)$$

Thus

$$q(t) = (bCV_0 e^{-at}/\Omega)\sin(\Omega t + \tan^{-1}\Omega/a)$$

which agrees with Eq. 8.6, since $bC = 1/bL$.

Third solution. Using as an alternative the Heuristic Method and for simplicity leaving out the designation t in $i(t)$ and $q(t)$, we write the integro-differential equation, making use of the relation $i = dq/dt$, obtaining

[1]This is Formula D105 in the author's textbook, *The jω- or Symbolic Method*.

$$0 = L\,di/dt + Ri + 1/C \int i\,dt = \frac{d^2q}{dt^2} + 2a\frac{dq}{dt} + b^2q \tag{8.14}$$

Guessing at the solution, $q = q_0e^{kt}$, we write the corresponding characteristic equation and its roots, obtaining

$$0 = k^2 + 2ak + b^2 \qquad (K_1, K_2) = -a \pm \sqrt{a^2 - b^2} = -a \pm j\Omega \tag{8.15}$$

The instantaneous value of the charge is therefore

$$q = q_{01}e^{K_1t} + q_{02}e^{K_2t} = e^{-at}\,(q_{01}e^{j\Omega t} + q_{02}e^{-j\Omega t}) \tag{8.16}$$

We must now determine the constants, q_{01} and q_{02}. For $t = 0$, we note that $q = Q_0$ and $i(t) = 0$. Upon differentiation of Eq. 8.16, we therefore write

$$Q_0 = q_{01} + q_{02} \qquad 0 = K_1q_{01} + K_2q_{02} \tag{8.17}$$

$$q_{01} = Q_0\frac{\Omega - ja}{2\Omega} \qquad q_{02} = Q_0\frac{\Omega + ja}{2\Omega} \tag{8.18}$$

Inserting these expressions in Eq. 8.16, we finally obtain

$$q(t) = Q_0e^{-at}[\cos \Omega t + (a/\Omega) \sin \Omega t] \tag{8.19}$$

which agrees with Eq. 8.12, since $Q_0 = CV_0$.

Conclusions to this solution

It is a good idea to redraw the network as a transform network whenever the system is energized (see Fig. 8.2). This allows us to write Ohm's Law directly, employing transform notation. Note that we write $\bar{I}$, not $i(s)$. From this point on, the procedure is to formulate an s-combine that we are likely to find in a transform-pair table. Over one hundred transform tables are presently available, but few are suitable for use by students. Many tables are made for special purposes, such as for use in servomechanism calculations. The amount of labor involved in the solution of such a problem depends greatly upon whether or not the student can find his own s-combine in the table at his disposal. Each reader is advised to make up his own transform-pair table as he goes along. The two solutions given above are very common so far as the produced type of s-combine is concerned. In the first type, we complete the square, and this is usually the faster method. In the second type, we determine the roots, and although this is generally a longer solution, it is preferable if we are dealing with roots anyhow, as in stability problems.

The third, non-Laplace solution is of great interest here, since we can make a direct comparison between this solution and the Laplace solutions. It may seem at first that the third solution is faster than the preceding ones, but in reality it is not. The reason why the third solution may seem quicker is that it is presented more concisely and that it utilizes already introduced quantities, such as a and Ω. In a very simple problem like this one, there is not much difference in time and labor between the solutions, but in a more intricate problem, the third solution will be the longest one, primarily because of all the labor involved in the determination of constants (see Eq. 8.17). In the general use of the Laplace Transform Method, we acknowledge the constants right away. In addition, this method fits in very nicely with modern ways of solving network problems, employing the Variable Proportioning Method, equivalent networks, s-plane considerations, the treatment of an ensuing periodic steady-state solution by means of the Symbolic Method, and so on. Nevertheless, many teachers and engineers of the "old school" are so skilled in the use of the classical integro-differential equation method that apparently they solve many problems just as fast, or faster, than we do, using the Laplace method. Occasionally, they will state that a person using the classical method knows what he is doing all the time, whereas "Laplacers" carry through "mechanical" manipulations, which they do not always understand. There is something to this, since many students not only use the Laplace Transform Method "mechanically," and thus invite errors, but also employ the method excessively, as some sort of a cure-all.

PROBLEM 9

Given is the twoport shown in Fig. 9.1, utilizing mutual inductance as the coupling element and driven by the applied instantaneous voltage, $v_1(t)$. It is assumed that the physical inductors have high Q.

(A) Using the D-Operator Method, derive an expression for the secondary steady-state instantaneous current $i_2(t)$.

(B) Derive an expression for the same current, using the Symbolic Method.

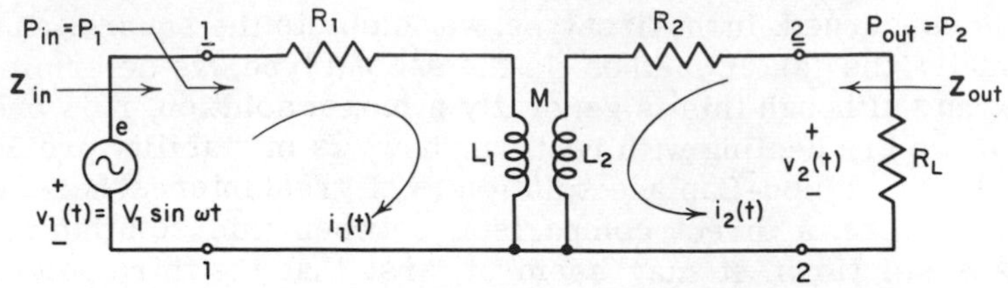

Fig. 9.1

(C) Proceeding with the Symbolic Method, derive an expression for the input impedance, $\mathbf{Z}_{in}$, and discuss its terms.

(D) Same question, but derive the output impedance $\mathbf{Z}_{out}$.

(E) Maintaining the input port, transform the two-mesh network to a one-mesh network and draw the network equivalent.

(F) Maintaining the output port, transform the two-mesh network to a one-mesh network and draw the network equivalent.

(G) Calculate the voltage transfer function, $\mathbf{A}_V(\omega) = \mathbf{V}_2/V_1$ and determine the output impedance using the Denominator Output Immittance Theorem.

(H) Calculate the maximum gain, $(P_2/P_a)_{max}$ and determine the value $R_{L\ opt}'$ of R_L at which this maximum gain occurs.

(I) Calculate the maximum output power, $P_{2\ max}$, and determine the value $R_{L\ opt}''$ of R_L at which this maximum power occurs.

Solution

(A) No indication is given with respect to the winding direction of the inductors, L_1 and L_2. We shall therefore proceed with the reservation that we may insert a minus sign in the answer to cover the possibility of the opposite sign of M. The time designations, (t), will be left out in most of the following calculations.

We shall begin by reading off the twoport equation system directly from Fig. 9.1. For $D = d/dt$, $D^2 = -\omega^2$, $R_2 + R_L = r$, $R_1 + L_1 D = a$, and $r + L_2 D = b$, we write

$$\left.\begin{aligned} v_1 &= a i_1 + M D i_2 \\ 0 &= M D i_1 + b\, i_2 \end{aligned}\right\} \qquad \begin{matrix}(9.1)\\(9.2)\end{matrix}$$

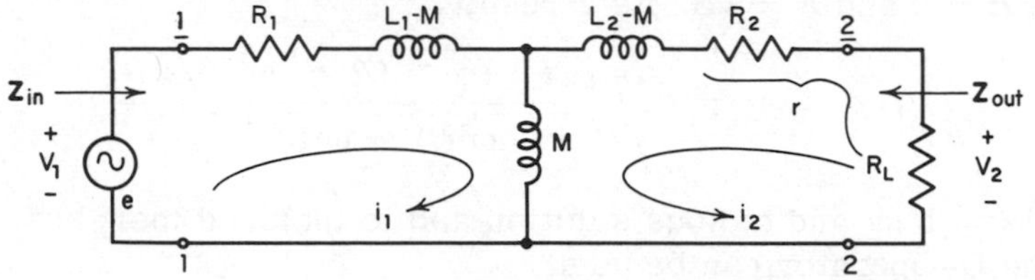

Fig. 9.2

As an alternative we may introduce the equivalent TEE for the coupled inductors, constituting a transformer (see Fig. 9.2). The equation system we read off is precisely the same as in (9.1) (9.2). Proceeding by applying Cramer's Rule, we obtain

$$i_2 = \begin{vmatrix} a & v_1 \\ MD & 0 \end{vmatrix} \Big/ \begin{vmatrix} a & MD \\ MD & b \end{vmatrix} = \frac{-MDv_1}{ab + \omega^2 M^2}$$

$$= -MDv_1 / [(R_1 + L_1 D)(r + L_2 D) + \omega^2 M^2] = -MDv_1 / (A + BD) \quad (9.3)$$

where

$$A = R_1 r - \omega^2 (L_1 L_2 - M^2) \quad (9.4)$$

$$B = L_1 r + L_2 R_1 \quad (9.5)$$

Applying the D-Operator Method, we now proceed as follows:

$$i_2 = \frac{-MV_1 (A - BD) D \sin \omega t}{A^2 - B^2 D^2} = -MV_1 \frac{A\omega \cos \omega t + \omega^2 B \sin \omega t}{A^2 + \omega^2 B^2}$$

Inserting proper quantities, we obtain

$$i_2 = -\omega M V_1 \frac{(R_1 r - \omega^2 C) \cos \omega t + \omega B \sin \omega t}{(R_1 r - \omega^2 C)^2 + \omega^2 B^2} \quad (9.6)$$

where

$$C = (L_1 L_2 - M^2) \quad (9.7)$$

This is the final answer in the two-term form. To obtain the more practical single-term form, we use the transformation formula[1]:

$$H \cos x + K \sin x = \sqrt{H^2 + K^2} \sin (x + \tan^{-1} H/K) \quad (9.8)$$

[1]Formula D105 in *The jω-or Symbolic Method.*

where $H = A$ and $K = \omega B$. As a result,

$$i_2(t) = -\omega M V_1 \frac{sin\,[\omega t + tan^{-1}(R_1 r - \omega^2 C)/\omega B]}{\sqrt{(R_1 r - \omega^2 C)^2 + \omega^2 B^2}} \tag{9.9}$$

This is a long and tedious solution and is included merely to show that the D-Operator can be used.

(B) In twoport notation, the following z parameters appear

$$\begin{aligned} \mathbf{z}_{11} &= r_{11} + jx_{11} = R_1 + jx_1 = R_1 + j\omega L_1 \\ \mathbf{z}_{12} &= jx_{12} = j\omega M \qquad (9.10) \\ \overline{\mathbf{z}}_{22} &= \overline{r}_{22} + jx_{22} = r + jx_2 = r + j\omega L_2 \end{aligned}$$

The matrix equation and the long-hand equation system are

$$\begin{vmatrix} V_1 \\ 0 \end{vmatrix} = \begin{vmatrix} \mathbf{z}_{11} & \mathbf{z}_{12} \\ \mathbf{z}_{21} = \mathbf{z}_{12} & \overline{\mathbf{z}}_{22} \end{vmatrix} \begin{vmatrix} \mathbf{I}_1 \\ \mathbf{I}_2 \end{vmatrix} \tag{9.11}$$

$$\overline{\Delta}_z = \mathbf{z}_{11}\overline{\mathbf{z}}_{22} - \mathbf{z}_{12}^{\,2} \tag{9.12}$$

$$\left.\begin{aligned} V_1 &= \mathbf{z}_{11}\mathbf{I}_1 + \mathbf{z}_{12}\mathbf{I}_2 \qquad (9.13) \\ 0 &= \mathbf{z}_{12}\mathbf{I}_1 + \overline{\mathbf{z}}_{22}\mathbf{I}_2 \qquad (9.14) \end{aligned}\right\}$$

Then, in accordance with Cramer's Rule

$$\mathbf{I}_2 = \begin{vmatrix} \mathbf{z}_{11} & V_1 \\ \mathbf{z}_{12} & 0 \end{vmatrix} \Big/ \ \overline{\Delta}_z = \frac{-\mathbf{z}_{12}V_1}{\mathbf{z}_{11}\overline{\mathbf{z}}_{22} - \mathbf{z}_{12}^{\,2}} \tag{9.15}$$

which is the concise answer in the $j\omega$-domain. Inserting proper quantities, we may write

$$\mathbf{I}_2 = -j\omega M V_1 / [(R_1 + jx_1)(r + jx_2) + \omega^2 M^2] \tag{9.16}$$

To return this to the time domain, we multiply by exponent $j\omega t$ on both sides, thus obtaining

$$\mathbf{I}_{2t} = \mathbf{I}_2 e^{j\omega t} = -\omega M V_1 e^{j\omega t} / [\omega B - j(R_1 r - \omega^2 C)] \qquad 9.17)$$

Since the applied voltage is a sine wave, we select the quadrature component and thus obtain the answer given by Eq. 9.9. This is the engineer's way of solving the problem. Not only is the method much quicker than the D-Operator Method, but we obtain the in-between frozen-sinor answer very quickly, and finally we obtain the answer in the desirable single-term form.

(C1) We may easily obtain the input impedance by solving for $\mathbf{I}_1$ rather than $\mathbf{I}_2$ by means of Cramer's Rule, writing

$$\mathbf{I}_1 = \begin{vmatrix} V_1 & \mathbf{z}_{12} \\ 0 & \bar{\mathbf{z}}_{22} \end{vmatrix} \Big/ \bar{\Delta}_z = \frac{\bar{\mathbf{z}}_{22} V_1}{\mathbf{z}_{11}\bar{\mathbf{z}}_{22} - \mathbf{z}_{12}^2} \qquad (9.18)$$

from which

$$\mathbf{Z}_{\text{in}} = V_1/\mathbf{I}_1 = \mathbf{z}_{11} - \mathbf{z}_{12}^2/\bar{\mathbf{z}}_{22} \qquad (9.19)$$

Inserting proper quantities, we obtain

$$\mathbf{Z}_{\text{in}} = R_1 + jx_1 + \omega^2 M^2/(r + jx_2) \qquad (9.20)$$

or

$$\begin{aligned} \mathbf{Z}_{\text{in}} &= R_{\text{in}} + jX_{\text{in}} = R_1 + R_2' + j\omega(L_1 - L_2') \\ &= R_1 + \frac{\omega^2 M^2 r}{r^2 + \omega^2 L_2^2} + j\omega\left(L_1 - \frac{\omega^2 M^2 L_2}{r^2 + \omega^2 L_2^2}\right) \end{aligned} \qquad (9.21)$$

It is seen that the input impedance first of all consists of the quantities already present in the first mesh: R_1 and $j\omega L_1$. The next term to be considered is the damping term, R_2', injected from the second mesh, increasing the input resistance to the total value $(R_1 + R_2')$. The last term is the reactance term $j\omega L_2'$, injected from the second mesh, which reduces the input inductance to the value $(L_1 - L_2')$. Summarizing the effect of coupling a secondary mesh to a primary mesh, we increase the resistance and decrease the inductance of the primary mesh. This is true whatever the sign of the mutual inductance, M.

(C2) As an alternative for calculating the input impedance, we may use the Network Element Combination Method, writing

$$\mathbf{Z}_{\text{in}} = \mathbf{z}_{11} - \mathbf{z}_{12} + \mathbf{z}_{12} /\!/ (\bar{\mathbf{z}}_{22} - \mathbf{z}_{12}) \qquad (9.22)$$

which yields the result in Eq. 9.19 and thus agrees with the previous solution.

(D1) A quick way of obtaining $\mathbf{Z}_{out}$ is to use Eq. 9.19 with interchanged subscripts, meaning that we are flipping around the twoport between its terminations, or merely interchanging the meshes. Accordingly, with $\mathbf{z}_{22} = R_2 + j\omega L_2 \neq \bar{\mathbf{z}}_{22}$,

$$\mathbf{Z}_{out} = \mathbf{z}_{22} - \mathbf{z}_{12}^2/\mathbf{z}_{11} \tag{9.23}$$

Inserting proper quantities, we write

$$\mathbf{Z}_{out} = R_2 + jX_2 + \omega^2 M^2/(R_1 + jX_1) \tag{9.24}$$

or

$$\mathbf{Z}_{out} = R_{out} + jX_{out} = R_2 + R_1' + j\omega(L_2 - L_1')$$

$$= R_2 + \frac{\omega^2 M^2 R_1}{R_1^2 + \omega^2 L_1^2} + j\omega\left(L_2 - \frac{\omega^2 M^2 L_1}{R_1^2 + \omega^2 L_1^2}\right) \tag{9.25}$$

(D2) As an alternative, we may use the Applied Source Method, writing Eqs. 9.13 and 9.14 with $V_1 = 0$ and $\mathbf{V}_2 \neq 0$, setting $\mathbf{V}_2 = \mathbf{V}_{20}$ and $\mathbf{I}_2 = \mathbf{I}_{20}$. The equation system and the desired ratio then take the form

$$0 = \mathbf{z}_{11}\mathbf{I}_{10} + \mathbf{z}_{12}\mathbf{I}_{20} \tag{9.26}$$

$$\mathbf{V}_{20} = \mathbf{z}_{12}\mathbf{I}_{10} + \mathbf{z}_{22}\mathbf{I}_{20} \tag{9.27}$$

$$\mathbf{Z}_{out} = \frac{\mathbf{V}_{20}}{\mathbf{I}_{20}} = \mathbf{z}_{22} - \mathbf{z}_{12}^2/\mathbf{z}_{11} \tag{9.23a}$$

which agrees with Eq. 9.23. We find that the output impedance first of all consists of the second-mesh impedance $(R_2 + j\omega L_2)$. In addition, the first mesh injects the damping term, R_{11}', and the reactance term, $-j\omega L_1'$.

(E) This question is already answered by Eq. 9.21, and the equivalent network is shown in Fig. 9.3. Another way of obtaining this equivalent is to apply the Network Element Combination Method to the network in Fig. 9.2.

(F) This question is already answered by Eq. 9.25, and the equivalent network is shown in Fig. 9.4. Another way of obtaining this equivalent is to apply the Network Element Combination Method to the network in Fig. 9.2. Figure 9.4 shows the corresponding Thévenin generator.

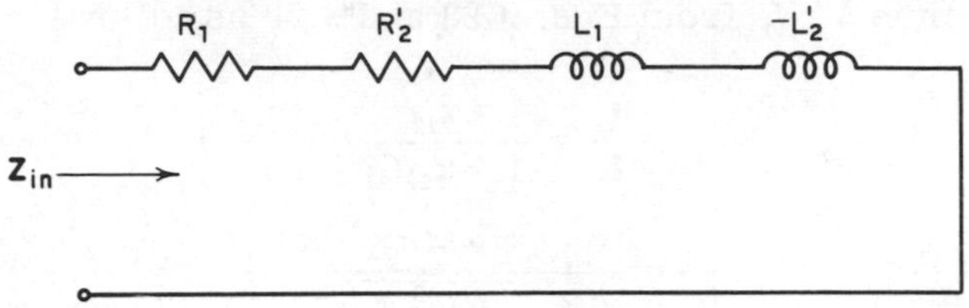

Fig. 9.3

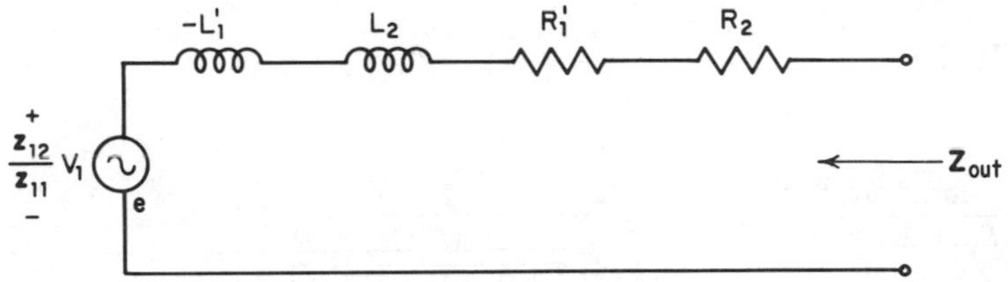

Fig. 9.4

(G) For this purpose we write the equation system in the form

$$\left.\begin{aligned} V_1 &= \mathbf{z}_{11}\mathbf{I}_1 + \mathbf{z}_{12}\mathbf{I}_2 \\ \mathbf{V}_2 &= \mathbf{z}_{21}\mathbf{I}_1 + \mathbf{z}_{22}\mathbf{I}_2 \end{aligned}\right\} \qquad \begin{aligned} (9.28) \\ (9.29) \end{aligned}$$

With

$$\mathbf{\Delta}_z = \mathbf{z}_{11}\mathbf{z}_{22} - \mathbf{z}_{12}^2 \qquad (9.30)$$

the voltage amplification takes the form

$$\mathbf{A}_V(\omega) = \frac{\mathbf{V}_2}{\mathbf{V}_1} = \frac{\mathbf{z}_{12}}{\mathbf{z}_{11} + \mathbf{\Delta}_z G_L} \qquad (9.31)$$

Upon inspection, the denominator yields the output impedance as $(\mathbf{z}_{22} - \mathbf{z}_{12}^2/\mathbf{z}_{11})$, which agrees with Eq. 9.23.

(H) To determine the maximum gain, we must first calculate the two powers, P_1 and P_2, and then maximize their ratio. We shall consider R_L as a variable resistance that can be set to any value—one specific value, $R_{L\,\mathrm{opt}}$, giving the desired maximum gain. The gain is

$$G = \frac{P_2}{P_1} = \frac{V_2^2/R_L}{I_1^2 R_{\mathrm{in}}} = \left(\frac{V_2}{I_1}\right)^2 \times \frac{1}{R_{\mathrm{in}} R_L} \qquad (9.32)$$

We determine V_2/I_1 from Eqs. 9.28 and 9.29 as follows

$$\frac{\mathbf{V}_2}{\mathbf{I}_1} = \frac{\mathbf{z}_{12}}{1 + \mathbf{z}_{22}G_L} \tag{9.33}$$

$$\frac{V_2}{I_1} = \frac{\omega M R_L}{\sqrt{(R_2 + R_L)^2 + \omega^2 L_2^2}} \tag{9.34}$$

Using the expression for R_{in} given by Eq. 9.21, we write

$$G = \left(\frac{V_2}{I_1}\right)^2 \times \frac{1}{R_{\text{in}} R_L}$$

$$= \frac{\omega^2 M^2 R_L^2}{(R_2 + R_L)^2 + \omega^2 L_2^2} \times \frac{1}{\left(R_1 + \dfrac{\omega^2 M^2 (R_2 + R_L)}{(R_2 + R_L)^2 + \omega^2 L_2^2}\right) R_L}$$

$$= \frac{\omega^2 M^2}{G_L [R_1 (R_2 + R_L)^2 + \omega^2 (L_2^2 R_1 + M^2 R_2) + \omega^2 M^2 R_L]} = \frac{\omega^2 M^2}{u} \tag{9.35}$$

Here only the denominator u contains the variable R_L. We therefore seek the minimum of u rather than the maximum of G. Leaving-out constants, we write

$$\frac{du}{dR_L} = \frac{d}{dR_L}\{R_1 R_L + [R_1 R_2^2 + \omega^2 (L_2^2 R_1 + M^2 R_2)]/R_L\}$$

$$= R_1 - \frac{R_1 R_2^2 + \omega^2 (L_2^2 R_1 + M^2 R_2)}{(R_L'{}_{\text{opt}})^2} = 0 \tag{9.36}$$

from which

$$R_L'{}_{\text{opt}} = \sqrt{R_2^2 + \omega^2 (L_2^2 + M^2 R_2/R_1)} \tag{9.37}$$

Inserting this value in Eq. 9.35 we obtain

$$G_{\max} = \frac{\omega^2 M^2 R_L'{}_{\text{opt}}}{R_1 (R_2 + R_L'{}_{\text{opt}})^2 + \omega^2 (L_2^2 R_1 + M^2 R_2) + \omega^2 M^2 R_L'{}_{\text{opt}}} \tag{9.38}$$

which can be further developed.

(I) The output power is $P_2 = V_2^2/2R_L$. From Eq. 9.31 we obtain, using the magnitude of $\mathbf{V}_2$,

$$P_2 = \frac{V_2^2}{2R_L} = \frac{1}{2R_L}\left|\frac{\mathbf{z}_{12} V_1}{\mathbf{z}_{11} + \mathbf{\Delta}_z G_L}\right|^2$$

$$= \frac{1}{2R_L}\left| \frac{jx_{12}V_1}{r_{11} + jx_{11} + [(r_{11}+jx_{11})(r_{22}+jx_{22}) - (jx_{12})^2]G_L} \right|^2$$

$$= \frac{1}{R_L} \times \frac{(x_{12}^2/2)V_1^2}{|r_{11} + A_1G_L + j(x_{11}+A_2G_L)|^2} = \frac{(x_{12}^2/2)V_1^2}{R_L[(r_{11}+A_1G_L)^2 + (x_{11}+A_2G_L)^2]}$$

$$= \frac{(x_{12}^2/2)V_1^2}{z_{11}^2R_L + 2r_{11}A_1 + 2x_{11}A_2 + (A_1^2 + A_2^2)G_L} = \frac{(x_{12}^2/2)V_1^2}{u_1} \quad (9.39)$$

We note that only the denominator, here designated u_1, contains the load immittance. Rather than seek the maximum of the entire expression, we seek the minimum of the denominator, writing

$$u_1 = z_{11}^2R_L + (A_1^2 + A_2^2)G_L \quad (9.40)$$

$$\frac{du_1}{dR_L} = z_{11}^2 - (A_1^2 + A_2^2)/(R_L{}''_{opt})^2 = 0 \quad (9.41)$$

thus obtaining

$$R_L{}''_{opt} = (1/z_{11})\sqrt{A_1^2 + A_2^2} \quad (9.42)$$

where

$$A_1 = r_{11}r_{22} - x_{11}x_{22} + x_{12}^2 \quad (9.43)$$

$$A_2 = x_{11}r_{22} + x_{22}r_{11} \quad (9.44)$$

We know from the Maximum Power Transfer Theorem that maximum output power $P_{2\,max}$ is obtained for $R_L{}''_{opt} = |\mathbf{Z}_{out}| = Z_{out}$. Therefore, from Eq. 9.23

$$R_L{}''_{opt} = (1/z_{11})\sqrt{A_1^2 + A_2^2} = Z_{out} = |\mathbf{z}_{22} - \mathbf{z}_{12}^2/\mathbf{z}_{11}| \quad (9.45)$$

Carrying out this calculation, we find that full agreement exists.

To find $P_{2\,max}$ we merely insert $R_L{}''_{opt}$ from Eq. 9.42 into Eq. 9.39, obtaining

$$P_{2\,max} = x_{12}^2V_1^2/4(r_{11}A_1 + x_{11}A_2 + z_{11}\sqrt{A_1^2 + A_2^2}) \quad (9.46)$$

As an alternative, if we start out from $R_L{}''_{opt} = Z_{out}$ as a given fact, we obtain $P_{2\,max}$ as follows, again employing Eq. 9.39,

$$P_{2\,\max} = \frac{z_{11}}{2\sqrt{A_1^2 + A_2^2}} \times \frac{x^2_{12} V_1^2}{\left| r_{11} + jx_{11} + (A_1 + jA_2) \dfrac{z_{11}}{\sqrt{A_1^2 + A_2^2}} \right|^2} \qquad (9.47)$$

Carrying out the implied calculations, we obtain the answer given by Eq. 9.46. It follows from the quite different looking formulas for $R_L{}'_{\text{opt}}$ in Eq. 9.37 and $R_L{}''_{\text{opt}}$ in Eq. 9.42 that the gain maximum and P_2 maximum may occur at very different values of R_L.

Conclusions to this solution

This has been our longest problem so far. Quite a lot of elementary computation labor was involved. This brings up the necessity for the reader to possess thorough training in calculating fast without errors. A certain prowess in speed - calculation is required, but speed-calculation does not consist merely of fast addition, multiplication, and the like, but more important, fast and accurate sizing up of the meaning of problem formulations, and, in addition, proper choice of solution techniques and mathematical tools. It is more important for the student to know the first third of the mathematics course thoroughly than to know the entire course vaguely! Considering the assignments in this problem, we found that the Symbolic Method, as expected, gives the fastest solution and also provides the very desirable single-term answer. We again found the Output Immittance Theorem to give the output impedance fast and directly. In various calculations we used both the determinant $\boldsymbol{\Delta}_z$ not involving R_L, and the determinant $\bar{\boldsymbol{\Delta}}_z$ involving R_L; we should always use the one that fits in best. In seeking a maximum, we found it simpler to seek a minimum for the denominator, provided it fully describes the influence of the variable— in this case, R_L. Since the R_L value for maximum gain is not the same as that for maximum output power, keep the two strictly apart.

PROBLEM 10

A step voltage $\rfloor E_1$ is at time $t = 0$ applied to the primary winding of the coupling transformer shown in Fig. 10.1. Determine the transient current $i_2(t)$ in the secondary mesh.

Solution

As usual, we begin by drawing the transform network (see Fig. 10.2). The twoport equation system is

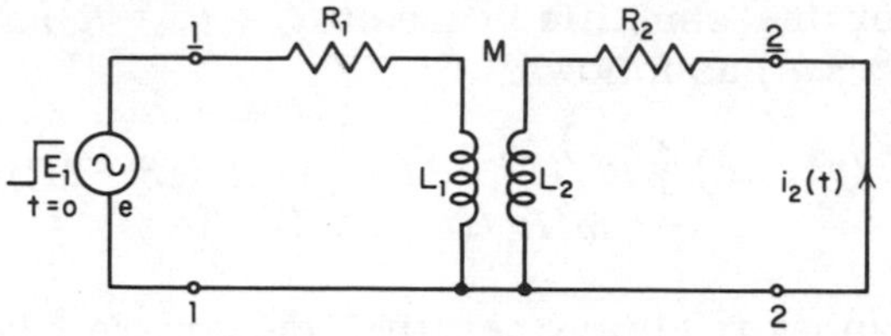

Fig. 10.1

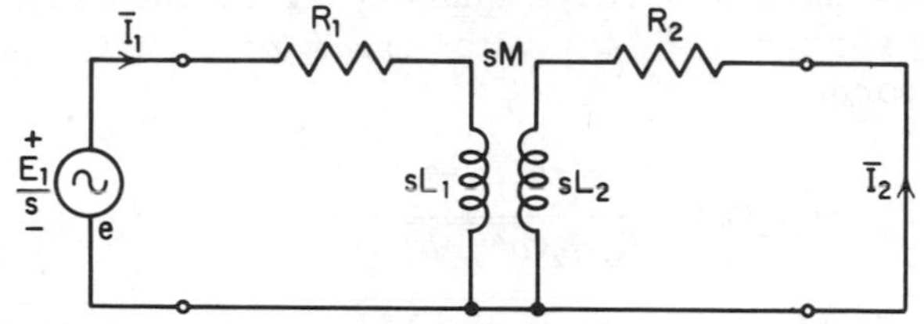

Fig. 10.2

$$\frac{E_1}{s} = (sL_1 + R_1)\bar{I}_1 + sM\bar{I}_2 \qquad (10.1)$$

$$0 = sM\bar{I}_1 + (sL_2 + R_2)\bar{I}_2 \qquad (10.2)$$

Solving for $\bar{I}_2$, we obtain

$$\bar{I}_2 = -E_1M/[s^2A + sB + R_1R_2] \qquad (10.3)$$

where $A = (L_1L_2 - M^2)$ and $B = (L_1R_2 + L_2R_1)$. We next rewrite Eq. 10.3 as follows, completing the square,

$$\bar{I}_2 = -E_1M/A(s^2 + s2a + b^2) = -(E_1M/A)/[(s+a)^2 + \Omega^2] \qquad (10.4)$$

where $a = B/2A$, $b^2 = R_1R_2/A$, and $\Omega^2 = b^2 - a^2$. Making use of the transform formula,

$$\frac{1}{(s+a)^2 + \Omega^2} \rightarrow \frac{e^{-at}}{\Omega} \sin \Omega t \qquad (10.5)$$

we now write

$$i_2(t) = -\frac{E_1 b^2 M \; e^{-at}}{R_1R_2\sqrt{b^2 - a^2}} \sin \sqrt{b^2 - a^2}\, t \qquad (10.6)$$

While this answer is correct, it does not properly describe what happens when we apply a step voltage to the transformer. Since no capacitance is involved, a damped sine wave should not be expected, and we therefore change the answer to appear in terms of a hyperbolic function. It may be sufficient if we carry out the following discussion for the simplified case of $R_1 = R_2 = R$ and $L_1 = L_2 = L$, evaluating $(b^2 - a^2)$ as follows:

$$\begin{aligned}(b^2 - a^2) &= R^2/(L^2 - M^2) - |LR/(L^2 - M^2)|^2 \\ &= -M^2R^2/(L^2 - M^2)^2 \qquad (10.7)\end{aligned}$$

Since this quantity is always negative, the square root will produce a j unless we interchange b^2 and a^2, giving us the assurance that we shall now have a positive quantity under the radical sign. We replace $-j\ sin\ j(a^2 - b^2)^{\frac{1}{2}}t$ with $sin\,h\ (a^2 - b^2)^{\frac{1}{2}}t$, writing Eq. 10.6 in the form

$$i_2(t) = \frac{-E_1b^2Me^{-at}}{R_1R_2\sqrt{a^2 - b^2}}\ sin\,h\sqrt{a^2 - b^2}\ t \qquad (10.8)$$

This is the final answer as it should be given by an engineer. The observant student may have noted, however, that no information was given in the problem formulation about the sign of M, or the winding directions of L_1 and L_2. In the industry, such information is sometimes missing, and the error of giving just one answer is then easily made. In school it is an absolute necessity that two answers be given, one for $+M$ as above, and one for $-M$, reversing the direction of the current $i_2(t)$ in Eq. 10.8.

Conclusions to this solution

We may distinguish between the following steps: (a) drawing the transform network; (b) writing the transform equation system and solving for the unknown; (c) rewriting this unknown in terms of a suitable s-combine; (d) looking up the corresponding time-domain expression in a transform-pair table; and (e) writing out the final answer. This is the sequence we follow in almost all the problems. In this case we went further to write the response in the form of the surge it really is. It is a good habit to go still further and plot the response, and the reader is encouraged to do so in all problems. The practice has not been followed here because of the extra space requirements. Again we note the necessity of introducing proper abbreviating symbols at the beginning of a problem so as not to have to drag long expressions through all the computations. This practice of using short-hand symbols is worth gold when it comes to checking back on the accuracy of a solution. Attention is called to the direct solutions which can often be obtained if students get used to the method of "completing the square" in the s-combine. In most cases, the Laplace-Transform Method is used by engineers as a shop method, just like the Symbolic Method, and it is so simple that it can even be used by radio technicians. We do not any longer write several equations in the time-domain before the Laplace symbol appears for the first time, or determine constants by falling back on the classical method, or use partial fractions or integration in the complex plane, at least not as a first way out. The mentioned mathematical tools are extremely useful, but should not be considered for immediate use in simple problems like the one above.

PROBLEM 11

The delayed pulse shown in Fig. 11.1 is applied to the indicated energized network. Find the current $i(t)$ for $t > 0$.

Solution

We begin by drawing the transform network shown in Fig. 11.2. Here the capacitor voltage, V_0, provides the initial-condition source, V_0/s, in series with the capacitor, since at $t = 0$ it appears as a step voltage. The source transform is obtained from a transform-pair table. Ohm's law applied to the network in Fig. 11.2 now yields the transform equation

$$\begin{aligned}\bar{I} &= [(E/s)(e^{-st_1} - e^{-st_2}) - V_0/s] \times 1/(R + 1/sC) \\ &= (E/R)(e^{-st_1} - e^{-st_2})/(s + s_1) - (V_0/R)/(s + s_1)\end{aligned} \tag{11.1}$$

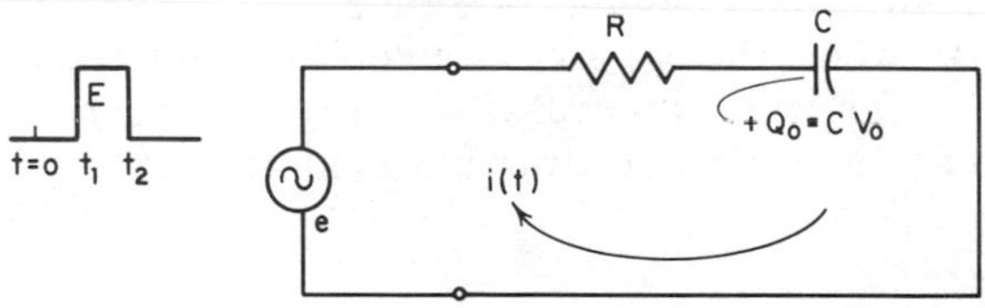

Fig. 11.1

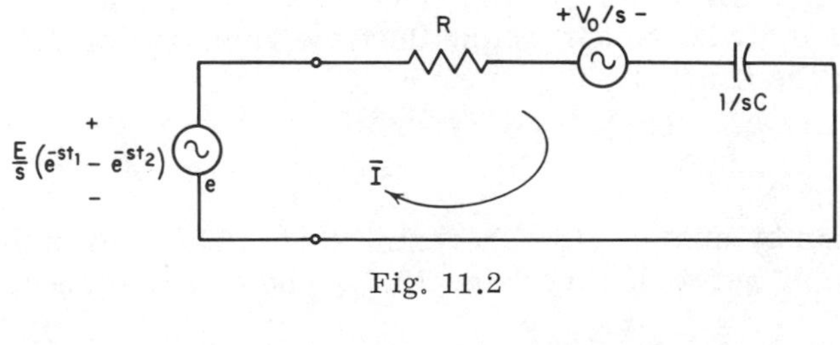

Fig. 11.2

where $s_1 = 1/CR$. For $t < t_1$ the first term vanishes, and for $t < t_2$ the second part of the first term vanishes. Making use of the transform formulas

$$1/(s + s_1) \rightarrow e^{-s_1 t} \tag{11.2}$$

$$e^{-st_1}/(s + s_1) \rightarrow e^{-s_1(t-t_1)} \ (for\ t > t_1) \tag{11.3}$$

$$(e^{-st_1} - e^{-st_2})/(s + s_1) \rightarrow e^{-s_1(t-t_1)} - e^{-s_1(t-t_2)} \quad (for\ t > t_2) \tag{11.4}$$

we obtain for

$$0 < t < t_1: \quad i(t) = -\frac{V_0}{R} e^{-t/CR}$$

$$t_1 < t < t_2: \quad i(t) = -\frac{V_0}{R} e^{-t/CR} + \frac{E}{R} e^{-(t-t_1)/CR} \tag{11.5}$$

$$t > t_2: \quad i(t) = -\frac{V_0}{R} e^{-t/CR} + \frac{E}{R}\left(e^{-(t-t_1)/CR} - e^{-(t-t_2)/CR}\right)$$

which is the complete answer to the problem.

Conclusions to this solution

We are in this solution again reminded of the beaten track we must follow in the application of the Laplace Transform Method: One begins by drawing the transform network with inserted initial-condition sources. We must have a good reason each time we deviate from this scheme. Another thing we learned in this solution is that when the applied source implies the existence of several consecutive time intervals, we may with advantage split up the answer so as to cover one time interval at a time.

PROBLEM 12

Apply the Thévenin-Norton Theorem to the network shown in Fig. 12.1 in order to determine the time variation of the voltage, $v(t)$, from the time, $t = 0$.

Solution

We begin by applying the Thévenin-Norton Theorem and drawing the transform network (see Fig. 12.2). The characteristics of the

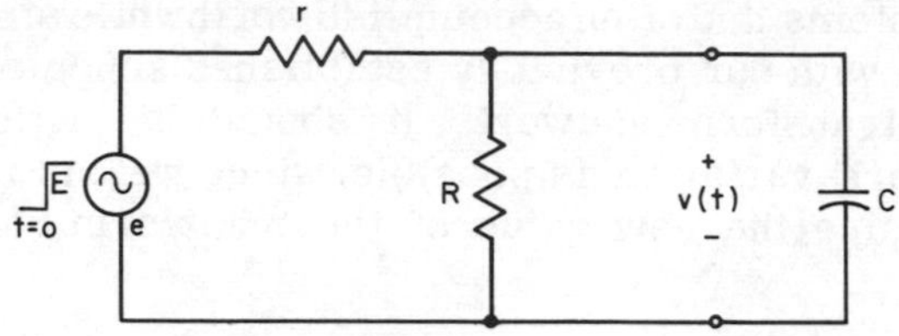

Fig. 12.1

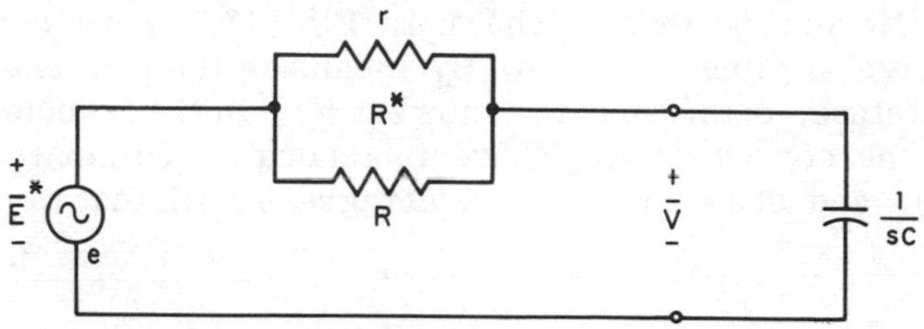

Fig. 12.2

Thévenin generator are

$$\bar{E}* = \frac{E}{s} \times \frac{R}{r+R} \qquad R* = \frac{rR}{r+R} \tag{12.1}$$

Using the Voltage Proportioning Method we write

$$\bar{V} = \bar{E}^* \frac{1/sC}{R* + 1/sC} = RE/s(sCrR + r + R) = (E/Cr)/s(s + s_1) \tag{12.2}$$

where $s_1 = (r + R)/CrR$. Using the transform-pair formula

$$\frac{1}{s(s+s_1)} \rightarrow \frac{1}{s_1}(1 - e^{-s_1 t}) \tag{12.3}$$

we write

$$v(t) = \frac{ER}{r+R}(1 - e^{-[(r+R)/CrR]t}) \tag{12.4}$$

which is the final answer.

<u>Conclusions to this solution</u>

This problem is included merely to remind us that the conventional network theorems for linear networks are also valid for transient problems and often accomplish worthwhile simplifications. In accordance with our previously established scheme, we begin by drawing the transform network. It should be noticed that still another network variation is possible, since we can reverse r and R and determine the new value of the transform voltage source.

PROBLEM 13

The Norton generator shown in Fig. 13.1 has a source that comes alive at time $t = 0$. (A) By means of the Current Proportioning Method, determine the current $i(t)$ in the inductor L. (B) Produce the corresponding Thévenin generator, calculate the current, $i(t)$, and show that the result agrees with that in (A).

Solution

(A) We begin as usual by drawing the transform network (see Fig. 13.2). The transform voltage is obtained from a transform-pair table. Applying the Current Proportioning Method, we write

$$\bar{I} = \frac{1}{(s+a)^2} \times \frac{1}{sL+R} = \frac{1}{L} \times \frac{1}{(s+a)^2(s+s_1)} \qquad (13.1)$$

where $s_1 = R/L$. We next make use of the transform-pair formula

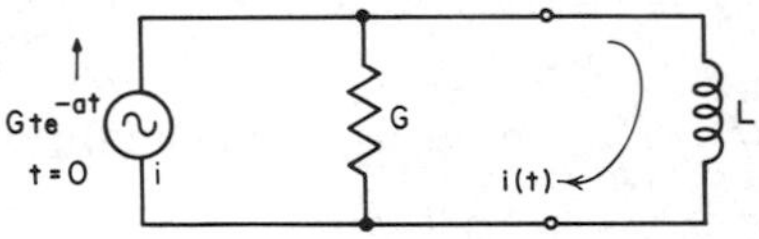

Fig. 13.1

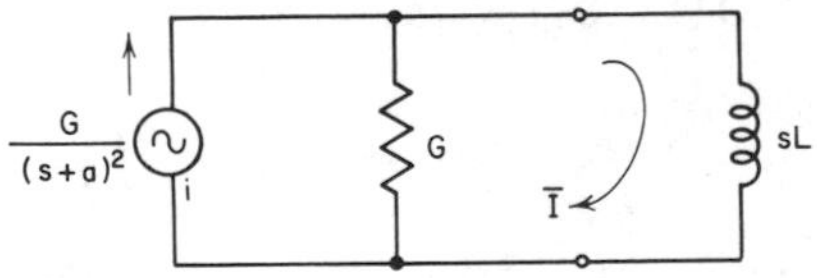

Fig. 13.2

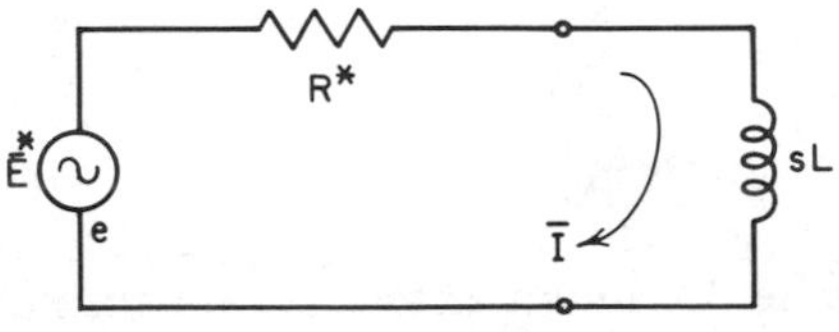

Fig. 13.3

$$\frac{1}{(s+a)^2(s+s_1)} \rightarrow \frac{e^{-s_1 t}}{(s_1-a)^2} + \frac{(s_1-a)t-1}{(s_1-a)^2}\, e^{-at} \tag{13.2}$$

from which we obtain the final answer in the time domain

$$i(t) = \frac{L}{(R-aL)^2}\left[e^{-(Rt/L)} + \left(\frac{R-aL}{L}\, t - 1\right) e^{-at}\right] \tag{13.3}$$

(B) The required Thévenin generator, shown in Fig. 13.3, has the characteristics

$$\bar{E}^* = 1/(s+a)^2 \qquad R^* = 1/G^* = 1/G \tag{13.4}$$

In accordance with Ohm's Law, therefore,

$$\bar{I} = \bar{E}^*/(sL + R^*) = 1/L\ [(s+a)^2(s+s_1)] \tag{13.5}$$

which agrees with Eq. 13.1. The balance of the solution is the same as above.

Conclusions to this solution

We are again reminded of the routine procedure of starting our solution by drawing a transform network. We are also reminded of the procedure of looking up the transform of the driving function in a table instead of deriving it each time. Engineers should not have to derive anything; everything should be available in a matter of seconds from tables. Unfortunately, no transform-pair tables especially written for students exist, and as a result the student occasionally is forced to derive things or to put together things from information in different tables. Again, the reader is advised to make up his own transform-pair table as he goes along.

SOME FINAL THOUGHTS

As an additional exercise, the reader may review the problem conclusions, trying to find similarities and differences in solution techniques. There are a dozen, or so, little rules and procedures that may help the reader in his solution work. There also exist about as many major rules and procedures that provide enormous help in problem solving. Attention to these rules and procedures makes all the difference between a fast and direct solution and a slow and roundabout one. Naturally, when we solve problems more than one way, as we always should when time permits, some solutions will prove to be short and elegant and others, long and tedious. This is all right; this is how we learn to distinguish a fast solution from a slow one.

Here are a few rules that will help the reader to gain greater speed and accuracy in his solution work:[1]

1. Never start calculation work without a clear-cut idea of the problem formulation. Read it carefully, and then read it again!
2. Visualize a line of approach—an open path through the problem—before you rush headlong into calculations.
3. Consider other possible ideas for solutions before you select one as the most suitable. Keep the remaining ideas "on ice."
4. Use proper mathematical tools; do not try to kill a fly with a sledge hammer or an elephant with a pebble.
5. Use all the short-cuts provided by network rules and theorems.
6. Use clear-cut and logical symbols, easily distinguishable from one another; employ a suitable sign convention.
7. To achieve conciseness, lump individual symbols into groups and give each group a simple designation. Dissolve the group at the end of the problem, if necessary.
8. Draw simple block and network diagrams to support your thinking.
9. Use all available engineering aids, such as table and desk computers.
10. Always consider using laboratory measurements as possible substitutes for awkward computations as well as difficult theory.
11. Set up your own study system with practical filing facilities.

All these rules do not work all the time, but most of them work most of the time.

[1]These rules are elaborated upon in greater detail in the author's *Time-Saving Network Calculations*, available in libraries.

2
Treatment of Function Sources

In this chapter we shall discuss a subject of the very greatest importance: the subject of function sources, such as **kI** and **kV**, where **k** is a complex constant, **I** is the current, and **V** is the voltage. There are few subjects as surrounded by superstition as the subject of function sources; one wonders what can be and what cannot be done with these sources, whether or not a certain theorem holds for them, and the like. Briefly, function sources fall into two categories: function sources with *independent* variable and function sources with *dependent* variable. A certain confusion exists because a source may be independent in one part of a problem and dependent in another. The difference may be caused by our disregard of a generator immittance. Mathematically, an independent source **kI** is no more difficult to handle than the independent current, **I**. Our close attention is required the moment **I** becomes dependent so that **kI** becomes a dependent source, which we occasionally may refer to as a "genuine function source."

It is true that all problems can be solved by brute application of Kirchhoff's laws, but sometimes this procedure leads to lengthy calculations. Whatever short-cuts we master for independent-source networks, we should be ready to apply to dependent-source networks. Particularly in problems requesting an equivalent generator as answer, we should be able to produce one directly, whether the network has dependent sources or not. The original Thévenin theorem fails us when dependent sources appear in the network. A new theorem, the Equivalent Generator Theorem, has been formulated, which enables us to handle all networks in the same fashion. Ample exercises on function sources have been given in the following problem solutions.

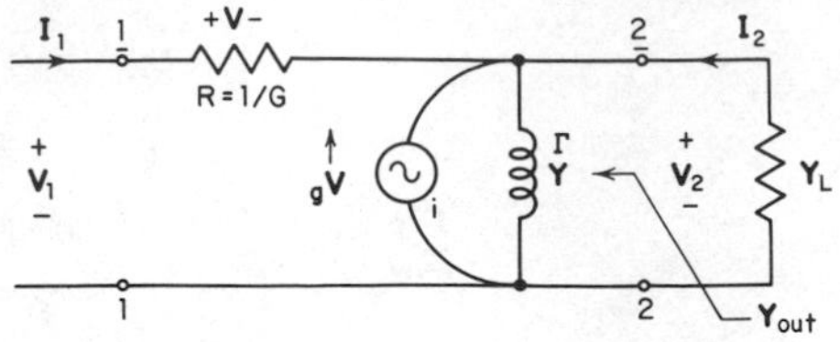

Fig. 1.1

PROBLEM 1

The function-source network shown in Fig. 1.1 may to a first approximation be simulated by means of a semiconductor device and an inductor, $L = 1/\Gamma$.

(A) Without the aid of twoport theory and by direct application of Kirchhoff's laws, determine the voltage- and current- transfer functions, $\mathbf{A}_V(\omega) = \mathbf{V}_2/\mathbf{V}_1$ and $\mathbf{A}_I(\omega) = \mathbf{I}_2/\mathbf{I}_1$.

(B) Calculate the output admittance $\mathbf{Y}_{\text{out}}$ by various methods.

(C) Using the twoport y matrix, write the network matrix in terms of network elements, draw the equivalent network, and calculate $\mathbf{A}_V(\omega)$, $\mathbf{A}_I(\omega)$, and $\mathbf{Y}_{\text{out}}$ with the aid of the y parameters.

(D) By the proper use of matrix algebra, transform the y matrix into a z matrix, and draw the equivalent network.

(E) Determine $\mathbf{A}_V(\omega)$, $\mathbf{A}_I(\omega)$, and $\mathbf{Y}_{\text{out}}$ from the network equivalent derived in (D), and check against previous formulas.

(F) Determine the output voltage, $\mathbf{V}_2$, with the aid of the Superposition Theorem to verify that we can truly open- and short-circuit function sources.

(G) Derive a shunt-form generator equivalent, and discuss the validity of open- and short-circuiting function sources.

Solution

(A) As $\mathbf{I}_1 = G\mathbf{V}$ and $\mathbf{I}_2 = -\mathbf{Y}_L\mathbf{V}_2$, we may formulate the system:

$$\left.\begin{aligned} \mathbf{V} &= \mathbf{V}_1 - \mathbf{V}_2 \qquad (1.1)\\ g\mathbf{V} + G\mathbf{V} - (\mathbf{Y} + \mathbf{Y}_L)\mathbf{V}_2 &= 0 \qquad (1.2)\end{aligned}\right\}$$

Solving for $\mathbf{V}_2/\mathbf{V}_1$, we obtain

$$\mathbf{A}_V(\omega) = \frac{\mathbf{V}_2}{\mathbf{V}_1} = \frac{g + G}{g + G + \mathbf{Y} + \mathbf{Y}_L} \tag{1.3}$$

Introducing $\mathbf{Y} = jB = 1/j\omega L = -j\Gamma/\omega$ we may write this for the special case of $\mathbf{Y}_L = G_L$:

$$\mathbf{A}_V(\omega) = \frac{\mathbf{V}_2}{\mathbf{V}_1} = \frac{g + G}{g + G + G_L - j\Gamma/\omega} \tag{1.4}$$

Solving for $\mathbf{I}_2/\mathbf{I}_1$ instead, we obtain

$$\mathbf{A}_I(\omega) = \frac{\mathbf{I}_2}{\mathbf{I}_1} = -\frac{g + G}{G(1 + \mathbf{Y}\mathbf{Z}_L)} \tag{1.5}$$

(B1) Our first choice in determining the output immittance is to make use of the Output Immittance Theorem, applicable whenever the proper transfer function is known.[1] While either $\mathbf{V}_1$ or $\mathbf{I}_1$ could be an applied constant quantity, we shall here consider $\mathbf{V}_1$ constant. Selecting the transfer function in Eq. 1.3, we write its denominator $(g + G + \mathbf{Y} + \mathbf{Y}_L)$. The output admittance then accords with

$$\mathbf{Y}_{\text{out}\,V} = g + G + \mathbf{Y} = g + G - j\Gamma/\omega \tag{1.6}$$

(B2) Next we shall use the Matched Condition Output Immittance Theorem, in accordance with which, from Eq. 1.3,

$$\frac{g + G}{g + G + \mathbf{Y} + \mathbf{Y}_{\text{out}}} = \frac{1}{2} \times \frac{g + G}{g + G + \mathbf{Y} + 0}$$

This is the same answer we obtained in Eq. 1.6 above.

(B3) Finally, using the Applied Source Method, we write the original equation system 1.1, 1.2 with $\mathbf{V}_{20}$, $\mathbf{I}_{20}$ replacing $\mathbf{V}_2$, $\mathbf{I}_2$; then with $\mathbf{V}_{10} = 0$, we solve for $\mathbf{V}_{20}/\mathbf{I}_{20}$, thus obtaining the same result as in Eq. 1.6 above. If we instead make the assumption that $\mathbf{I}_1$ is constant, the result is that the series resistance, R, becomes insignificant, while the voltage, V, across it remains to appear in the function source. If we apply the Output Immittance Theorem to Eq.

[1]This theorem was described by the author in 1956. See "Three Output Immittance Theorems," *Electronic Industries*, Jan. 1958. Also see "A New Tool for Easier Network Synthesis," *Electronic Design*, Feb. 1, 1965, and continued discussion in *Electronic Design*, April 12, 1965.

1.5, the result becomes

$$\mathbf{Y}_{\text{out}\,I} = \mathbf{Y} \tag{1.7}$$

The same result is obtained with other methods.

(C) We write the twoport y equation system from Table 3, Appendix C, and then turn Eqs. 1.1 and 1.2 into a similar equation system, obtaining

$$\left.\begin{aligned} \mathbf{I}_1 &= \mathbf{y}_{11}\mathbf{V}_1 + \mathbf{y}_{12}\mathbf{V}_2 \\ \mathbf{I}_2 &= \mathbf{y}_{21}\mathbf{V}_1 + \mathbf{y}_{22}\mathbf{V}_2 \end{aligned}\right\} \qquad \begin{aligned} &(1.8) \\ &(1.9) \end{aligned}$$

$$\left.\begin{aligned} \mathbf{I}_1 &= G\mathbf{V}_1 - G\mathbf{V}_2 \\ \mathbf{I}_2 &= -g'\mathbf{V}_1 + \mathbf{Y}'\mathbf{V}_2 \end{aligned}\right\} \qquad \begin{aligned} &(1.8a) \\ &(1.9a) \end{aligned}$$

where $g' = (g + G)$ and $\mathbf{Y}' = (g + G + \mathbf{Y})$. The y matrix therefore takes the form

$$|\mathbf{y}| = \begin{vmatrix} \mathbf{y}_{11} & \mathbf{y}_{12} \\ \mathbf{y}_{21} & \mathbf{y}_{22} \end{vmatrix} = \begin{vmatrix} G & -G \\ -g' & \mathbf{Y}' \end{vmatrix} \tag{1.10}$$

The more direct method consists in opening or short-circuiting the twoport, in this case, short-circuiting it. The resulting parameters are:

$$\begin{aligned} \mathbf{y}_{11} &= \left.\frac{\mathbf{I}_1}{\mathbf{V}_1}\right|_{V_2=0} = g & \mathbf{y}_{12} &= \left.\frac{\mathbf{I}_1}{\mathbf{V}_2}\right|_{V_1=0} = -G \\ \mathbf{y}_{21} &= \left.\frac{\mathbf{I}_2}{\mathbf{V}_1}\right|_{V_2=0} = -(g+G) = -g' & \mathbf{y}_{22} &= \left.\frac{\mathbf{I}_2}{\mathbf{V}_2}\right|_{V_1=0} = g + G + \mathbf{Y} = \mathbf{Y}' \end{aligned} \tag{1.11}$$

It is seen that these results agree with those previously obtained. The network determinant is

$$\Delta_y = \mathbf{y}_{11}\mathbf{y}_{22} - \mathbf{y}_{12}\mathbf{y}_{21} = G\mathbf{Y} \tag{1.12}$$

Attempting to obtain a PI equivalent, we note that Fig. 1.1 already depicts a PI equivalent, although the first leg in the PI is missing. We may nevertheless formally derive the PI implied by the y parameters, its general form being (from Eq. 1.9)

$$\mathbf{I}_2 = \mathbf{y}_{12}\mathbf{V}_1 + \mathbf{y}_{22}\mathbf{V}_2 + \mathbf{y}_{21}\mathbf{V}_1 - \mathbf{y}_{12}\mathbf{V}_1$$
$$= \mathbf{y}_{12}\mathbf{V}_1 + \mathbf{y}_{22}\mathbf{V}_2 + \mathbf{y}_m\mathbf{V}_1 \tag{1.13}$$

where $\mathbf{y}_m$ is the mutual admittance

$$\mathbf{y}_m = \mathbf{y}_{21} - \mathbf{y}_{12} = -g \tag{1.14}$$

Fig. 1.2 shows the formal result of this procedure, with the missing first leg of the PI included. The balance of the PI does not appear to agree with that in Fig. 1.1, however. By transferring the shunt conductance, g, to the function source, we quickly arrive at full agreement.

The desired expressions for $\mathbf{A}_V(\omega)$, $\mathbf{A}_I(\omega)$, and $\mathbf{Y}_{out}$ can be derived from the network equivalent in Fig. 1.2, but it is more expedient to obtain them from Equation systems 1.8 and 1.9. Thus we find that

$$\mathbf{A}_V(\omega) = \frac{\mathbf{V}_2}{\mathbf{V}_1} = \frac{-\mathbf{y}_{21}}{\mathbf{y}_{22} + \mathbf{Y}_L} = \frac{g + G}{g + G + \mathbf{Y} + \mathbf{Y}_L} \tag{1.3a}$$

$$\mathbf{A}_I(\omega) = \frac{\mathbf{I}_2}{\mathbf{I}_1} = \frac{\mathbf{y}_{21}}{\mathbf{y}_{11} + \Delta_y \mathbf{Z}_L} = -\frac{g + G}{G(1 + \mathbf{Y}\mathbf{Z}_L)} \tag{1.5a}$$

The output admittance is read off from Eq. 1.3a by means of the Output Immittance Theorem.

(D) We can quickly transfer from y to z parameters using Table 1, Appendix C, and also Table 2, which states that $\Delta_y = 1/\Delta_z = G\mathbf{Y}$. The z parameters are as follows:

$$\mathbf{z}_{11} = \frac{\mathbf{y}_{22}}{\Delta_y} = \frac{\mathbf{Y}'}{G\mathbf{Y}} \qquad \mathbf{z}_{12} = \frac{-\mathbf{y}_{12}}{\Delta_y} = \frac{1}{\mathbf{Y}}$$
$$\mathbf{z}_{21} = \frac{-\mathbf{y}_{21}}{\Delta_y} = \frac{g'}{G\mathbf{Y}} \qquad \mathbf{z}_{22} = \frac{\mathbf{y}_{11}}{\Delta_y} = \frac{1}{\mathbf{Y}} \tag{1.15}$$

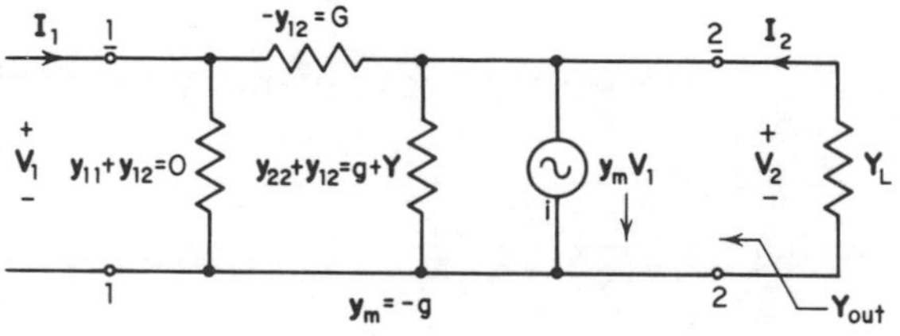

Fig. 1.2

The z matrix is therefore

$$|\mathbf{z}| = \begin{vmatrix} \mathbf{z}_{11} & \mathbf{z}_{12} \\ \mathbf{z}_{21} & \mathbf{z}_{22} \end{vmatrix} = \begin{vmatrix} \mathbf{Y}'/G\mathbf{Y} & 1/\mathbf{Y} \\ g'/G\mathbf{Y} & 1/\mathbf{Y} \end{vmatrix} \tag{1.16}$$

and the corresponding equation system is

$$\mathbf{V}_1 = \mathbf{z}_{11}\mathbf{I}_1 + \mathbf{z}_{12}\mathbf{I}_2 = (\mathbf{Y}'/G\mathbf{Y})\mathbf{I}_1 + (1/\mathbf{Y})\mathbf{I}_2 \tag{1.17}$$

$$\mathbf{V}_2 = \mathbf{z}_{21}\mathbf{I}_1 + \mathbf{z}_{22}\mathbf{I}_2 = (g'/G\mathbf{Y})\mathbf{I}_1 + (1/\mathbf{Y})\mathbf{I}_2 \tag{1.18}$$

We shall next proceed to draw the TEE equivalent. Manipulating in the same manner as in Eqs. 1.13 and 1.14, we obtain

$$\mathbf{V}_2 = \mathbf{z}_{12}\mathbf{I}_1 + \mathbf{z}_{22}\mathbf{I}_2 + \mathbf{z}_{21}\mathbf{I}_1 - \mathbf{z}_{12}\mathbf{I}_1 \tag{1.19}$$

$$\mathbf{V}_2 = \mathbf{z}_{12}\mathbf{I}_1 + \mathbf{z}_{22}\mathbf{I}_2 + \mathbf{z}_m\mathbf{I}_1 \tag{1.20}$$

$$\mathbf{z}_m = \mathbf{z}_{21} - \mathbf{z}_{12} = g/G\mathbf{Y} \tag{1.21}$$

where $\mathbf{z}_m$ is the mutual impedance. Fig. 1.3 shows the desired TEE equivalent. Note that the output arm contains no series impedance.

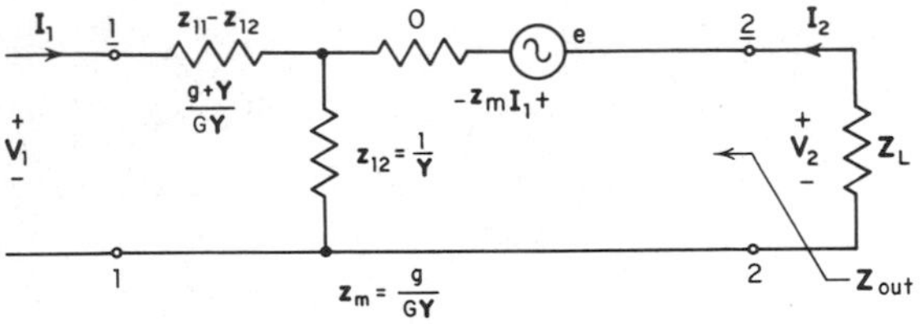

Fig. 1.3

(E) Using the equation system (1.17) (1.18) rather than the equivalent TEE, we obtain

$$\mathbf{A}_V(\omega) = \frac{\mathbf{V}_2}{\mathbf{V}_1} = \frac{-\mathbf{z}_{21}\mathbf{Z}_L}{\Delta_z'} = \frac{-g'}{G\mathbf{Y}\mathbf{Y}_L\Delta_z'} \tag{1.22}$$

where $\Delta_z' = \mathbf{z}_{11}\mathbf{z}_{22}' - \mathbf{z}_{12}\mathbf{z}_{21}$, with $\mathbf{z}_{22}' = \mathbf{z}_{22} + \mathbf{Z}_L$. Thus $\Delta_z' = \Delta_z + \mathbf{z}_{11}\mathbf{Z}_L$. Accordingly,

$$\mathbf{A}_V(\omega) = \frac{(g + G)\mathbf{Z}_L}{G\mathbf{Y}(\Delta_z + \mathbf{z}_{11}\mathbf{Z}_L)} = \frac{g + G}{g + G + \mathbf{Y} + \mathbf{Y}_L} \tag{1.3b}$$

which agrees with Eq. 1.3. Similarly,

$$\mathbf{A}_I(\omega) = \frac{-\mathbf{z}_{21}}{\mathbf{z}_{22}} = -\frac{g + G}{G(1 + \mathbf{YZ}_L)} \tag{1.5b}$$

which agrees with Eq. 1.5. The output admittance is determined as before.

(F) In the expression, $g\mathbf{V} = g\mathbf{V}_1 - g\mathbf{V}_2$, $g\mathbf{V}_1$ is the independent source, while $g\mathbf{V}_2$ is the dependent source. Conventionally, we avoid open- and short-circuit function sources since this requires careful consideration and other solution methods exist, for example, the method of elimination of the function source (see G). If we consider the sources only as they appear in the undisturbed network, there is no distinction between independent and dependent sources, since we do not change anything. We can therefore apply the Superposition Theorem.

In a d-c network, to take an example, *all* sources would temporarily be replaced by batteries. As a consequence of this, a zero value of one source, such as $\mathbf{V}_1$, does not mean that another source $g_m\mathbf{V}_1$ is also zero, while in most all other solution techniques $\mathbf{V}_1 = 0$ automatically means that $g_m\mathbf{V}_1$ is also zero. Accepting this line of thought, we can apply the Superposition Theorem, writing with $G + \mathbf{Y} + \mathbf{Y}_L = \mathbf{Y}_3$,

$$\text{For } \mathbf{V}_1 \text{ on and } g\mathbf{V} \text{ open-circuited:} \quad \mathbf{V}_2' = G\mathbf{V}_1/\mathbf{Y}_3 \tag{1.23}$$

$$\text{For } g\mathbf{V} \text{ on and } \mathbf{V}_1 \text{ short-circuited:} \quad \mathbf{V}_2'' = g\mathbf{V}/\mathbf{Y}_3 \tag{1.24}$$

The total voltage is then

$$\mathbf{V}_2 = \mathbf{V}_2' + \mathbf{V}_2'' = (G\mathbf{V}_1 + g\mathbf{V})/\mathbf{Y}_3 \tag{1.25}$$

from which, with $\mathbf{V} = \mathbf{V}_1 - \mathbf{V}_2$,

$$\mathbf{A}_V(\omega) = \frac{g + G}{g + \mathbf{Y}_3} = \frac{g + G}{g + G + \mathbf{Y} + \mathbf{Y}_L} \tag{1.3c}$$

This result agrees with that in Eq. 1.3. Thus we have found in this example that under certain conditions dependent sources may be open-circuited and short-circuited just like conventional independent sources.

(G) One way of treating networks with function sources is to eliminate the function sources. To do this here, we split up the function source $g\mathbf{V}$ in Fig. 1.1 into the two sources, $g\mathbf{V}_1$ and $-g\mathbf{V}_2$. The source, $g\mathbf{V}_1$, is independent and is left in the network. The other one represents the genuine function source, $g\mathbf{V}_2$, directed downwards. Applying the Compensation Theorem to this source, we turn it into the conductance, g, lumped together with the admittance, $\mathbf{Y}$. We have in this manner produced the network shown in Fig. 1.4a, which is free from dependent sources. Using the Thévenin-Norton Theorem to determine the equivalent Norton generator, we passivate the network in Fig. 1.4a and obtain the output admittance as

$$\mathbf{Y}_{\text{out } V} = \mathbf{Y}^* = g + G + \mathbf{Y} \tag{1.6a}$$

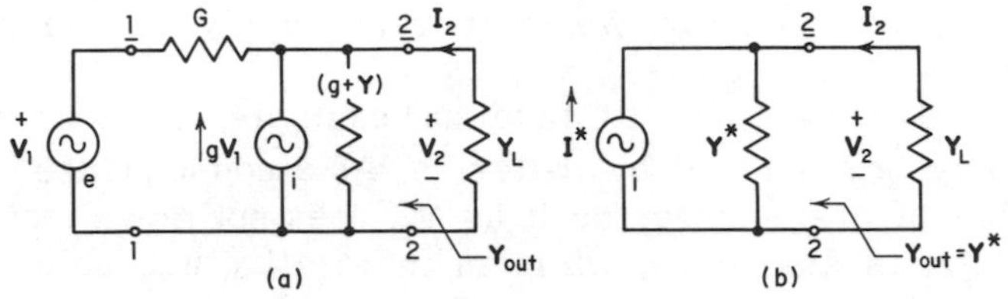

Fig. 1.4

This is the generator admittance in the Norton generator shown in Fig. 1.4b. To determine its source, we merely short-circuit the port 2,2 in Fig. 1.4a by setting $\mathbf{Y}_L$ = infinity. Accordingly we obtain

$$\mathbf{I}^* = (g + G)\mathbf{V}_1 \tag{1.26}$$

which is the desired source, acting in the indicated direction. We can now use the created Norton generator to calculate both the output admittance, which is $\mathbf{Y}^*$ since the source is independent, and $\mathbf{A}_V(\omega)$. As an alternative, we may equally well use the Thévenin-Norton Theorem to obtain the corresponding Thévenin generator, shown in Fig. 1.5a, and we can similarly use the Thévenin generator to calculate $\mathbf{Z}_{\text{out}} = 1/\mathbf{Y}_{\text{out}}$ and $\mathbf{A}_V(\omega)$.

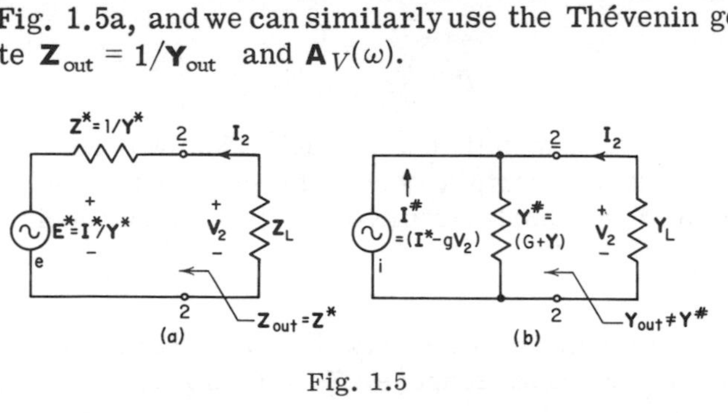

Fig. 1.5

Let us again examine the procedure by means of which we obtained the Norton generator in Fig. 1.4b and the Thévenin generator in Fig. 1.5a. By applying the Compensation Theorem to the given network in Fig. 1.1, we manipulated the dependent source so as to make it vanish, obtaining the network in Fig. 1.4a, which is free of dependent sources and therefore allows us to apply the Thevénin-Norton Theorem. This is a roundabout solution. We could have combined the Thévenin and the Norton Theorems in the fashion of the Generator-Transformation Theorem, Appendix A, part 7, and obtained the generator immittance as the specified current-voltage or voltage-current ratio. A more direct procedure results from the application of the new Equivalent Generator Theorem, Appendix A, part 11. The voltage transfer function is already available in Eq. 1.3. Upon inspection, we read off directly, for $\mathbf{Y}_L = 0$, and for $\mathbf{Y}_L$ vanishing in the denominator,

$$\mathrm{E}^* = \frac{g + G}{g + G + \mathbf{Y}}\mathbf{V}_1 \qquad \mathbf{Z}^* = \frac{1}{g + G + \mathbf{Y}} \tag{1.27}$$

which are the characteristics of the Thévenin generator in Fig. 1.5a. To obtain the Norton generator, we could go on and make use of the Generator Transformation Theorem, or we could return to the Equivalent Generator Theorem. Noting that $\mathbf{V}_2 = -\mathbf{I}_2/\mathbf{Y}_L$ in Eq. 1.3, we write upon inspection, for $\mathbf{Y}_L = \infty$, and for $\mathbf{Y}_L$ vanishing in the denominator,

$$\mathbf{I}^* = (g + G)\mathbf{V}_1 \qquad \mathbf{Y}^* = g + G + \mathbf{Y} \tag{1.28}$$

which are the characteristics of the Norton generator in Fig. 4b. Thus the Equivalent Generator Theorem will suffice to give us both the Thévenin and the Norton generators and in a rather direct fashion. It does so without the need of any preliminary checking on the nature of the sources, since the new theorem, in contrast to the original Thévenin and Norton Theorems, is valid for all sources.

Whereas Fig. 1.4b shows one logical equivalent generator of shunt form, Fig. 1.5b shows another. The first one has the output admittance, $\mathbf{Y}^*$, as generator admittance, whereas the second one has the looking-in admittance with *all* sources removed as generator admittance. Both generators yield the correct expressions for $\mathbf{V}_2/\mathbf{V}_1$ and $\mathbf{Y}_{out}$, but naturally the generator in Fig. 1.4b is more generally useful. Since the two generator admittances are different, it is evident that the two sources also must be different, and actually, the generator source difference is specified by the generator immittance difference. This can be shown as follows. We note that the admittance, $\mathbf{Y}^{\#}$, is g smaller than the admittance $\mathbf{Y}^{*}$. Thus the admittance g must show up in the current source in the form of an added current source, which in accordance with Ohm's law is $-g\mathbf{V}_2$. This procedure illustrates one method of deriving the network in Fig. 1.5b.

Conclusions to this solution

We found in Problem (A) that function sources are handled without difficulty, and in an automatic fashion, in the direct application of Kirchhoff's laws. In Problem (B) we found that the Output Immittance Theorem provides the fastest method for determining the output admittance. Problem (C) reminds us how to analyze a twoport in an engineering fashion by making up the equation system pattern in advance to determine the parameters that fit into the four "pigeon holes."

Fig. 1.3 provides a significant example of how to produce the conventional TEE equivalent and then label it in parameters which are not z parameters. We express the z TEE as a y TEE by means of Table 1, Appendix C. In the same manner we can label the TEE in h, k, a, or b parameters. In Problem (E) we are reminded of the fact that equations are generally faster than network equivalents for the determination of port immittances and transfer functions. Thus in calculating the requested transfer function, we prefer to go back to the existing equation system rather than to obtain the transfer function from an analysis of the network equivalent.

In (F) we determine the output voltage $\mathbf{V}_2$ by means of the Superposition Theorem and find that the correct result is obtained if the function source variables are given the values appearing in the undisturbed network. This is logical, since, for the Superposition Theorem to apply, all function sources must temporarily appear in the disguise of independent sources. Although a widespread opinion exists that function sources cannot be open-circuited and short-circuited, we learn that this can be done if it is done right.

In (G) we are concerned with ways and means of producing the Thévenin and Norton generators as equivalents of the given network. We find here that the Equivalent Generator Theorem is self-sufficient, and that there is no need of consulting any other theorem. It yields both the required generators merely upon inspection of the proper transfer function. Actually, it replaces the conventionally used theorems, not only for the type of network discussed here, but for all types of networks previously handled (in the manner indicated) by the Compensation Theorem, the Thévenin Theorem, the Norton Theorem, and the Thévenin-Norton Theorem. In (G) we are also confronted with the fact that two shunt-form generators exist; these provide equivalence to each other and to the given network in Fig. 1.1. The more important generator of the two has the output admittance as generator admittance and an independent source, and therefore becomes the Norton generator. The somewhat less important generator of the two has the passivated network admittance (all sources removed) as generator admittance, and as a result, its generator admittance does not equal the output admittance, nor is the source independent. It has been shown how we can go from the first generator to the second one by shuffling part of the generator admittance into the source, and vice versa. (See the last reference in Footnote 1.)

PROBLEM 2

A particular semiconductor device, utilizing a special biasing scheme is represented by the equivalent network in Fig. 2.1 employing two function sources. Determine the voltage amplification, $A_V(\omega) = V_2/V_1$, and the output admittance, G_{out}:

(A) By a conventional solution not using the Superposition Theorem.

(B) By using the Superposition Theorem.

(C) By producing the four equivalent networks for a linear system:

(C1) A shunt-form generator with $G_{out} = 1/R_{out}$ as shunt element.

(C2) A series-form generator with $R_{out} = 1/G_{out}$ as series element.

(C3) A shunt-form generator with the passivated network conductance, $G^{\#} = 1/R^{\#}$, as shunt element.

(C4) A series-form generator with the generator resistance unequal to the output resistance.

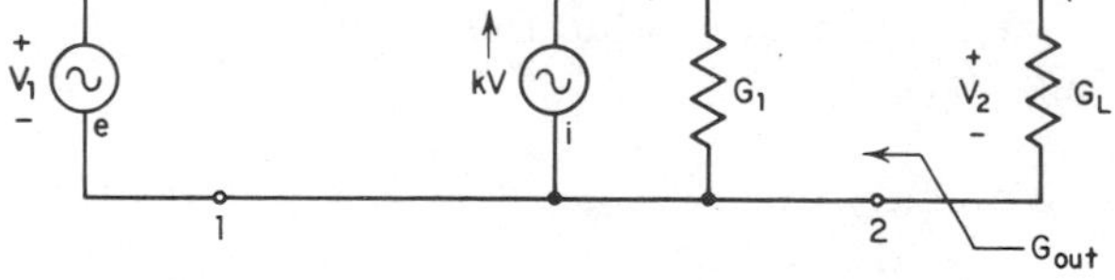

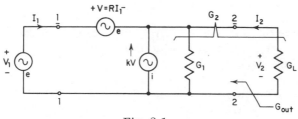

Fig. 2.1

(D) Turn the shunt-form generator, kV, G_1, that appears inside the given network into a series-form generator, and then determine $A_V(\omega)$ and G_{out} by any convenient method.

(E) Describe the easiest method of turning the given network in Fig. 2.1 into an active PI.

(F) Determine by any suitable method the current transfer function, $A_I(\omega) = I_2/I_1$.

(G) Obtain the Thévenin equivalent generator by direct application of the Equivalent Generator Theorem.

Solution

(A) The simplest solution is obtained if we turn the source V into a resistance, R, by means of the Compensation Theorem. If we wish, however, to solve the problem without employing this theorem, we write

$$I_1 + kRI_1 - G_2 V_2 = o \tag{2.1}$$

Noting that $V_1 - V_2 = V = RI_1$, we obtain

$$A_V(\omega) = \frac{V_2}{V_1} = \frac{k + G}{k + G + G_1 + G_L} \tag{2.2}$$

The output conductance is most easily obtained with the aid of the Output Immittance Theorem from Eq. 2.2

$$G_{out} = k + G + G_1 \tag{2.3}$$

As an alternative method, we may use the Applied Source Method, setting $V_2 = V_{20}$ and $I_2 = I_{20}$. The inverse ratio of these quantities yields the result in Eq. 2.3.

(B) Involving all sources in the operation, we make one source appear at a time with the value the source has in the undisturbed network. Thus we write:

For only V_1 alive: $V_2' = V_1$
For only V alive: $V_2'' = -V = -RI_1$
For only kV alive: $V_2''' = 0$

The total output voltage is then

$$V_2 = V_2' + V_2'' + V_2''' = V_1 - RI_1 + o \tag{2.4}$$

where I_1 has the value given by Eq. 2.1. Solving for V_2/V_1, we obtain the results in Eq. 2.2. The output conductance G_{out} is obtained as in Problem (A).

(C) One way of solving network problems involving function sources is to *first eliminate all function sources*. This can be done in several ways. One method would be to interpret the network as an ELL-section. Since in formulating a transfer function we automatically eliminate all function sources, none can appear in the new network (see Fig. 2.2a). The equivalent Norton generator is therefore obtained in a straight-forward manner (see Fig.2.2b). The Norton generator has the characteristics

$$G* = G_{out} = k + G + G_1 \tag{2.3a}$$

$$I* = (k + G)V_1 \tag{2.5}$$

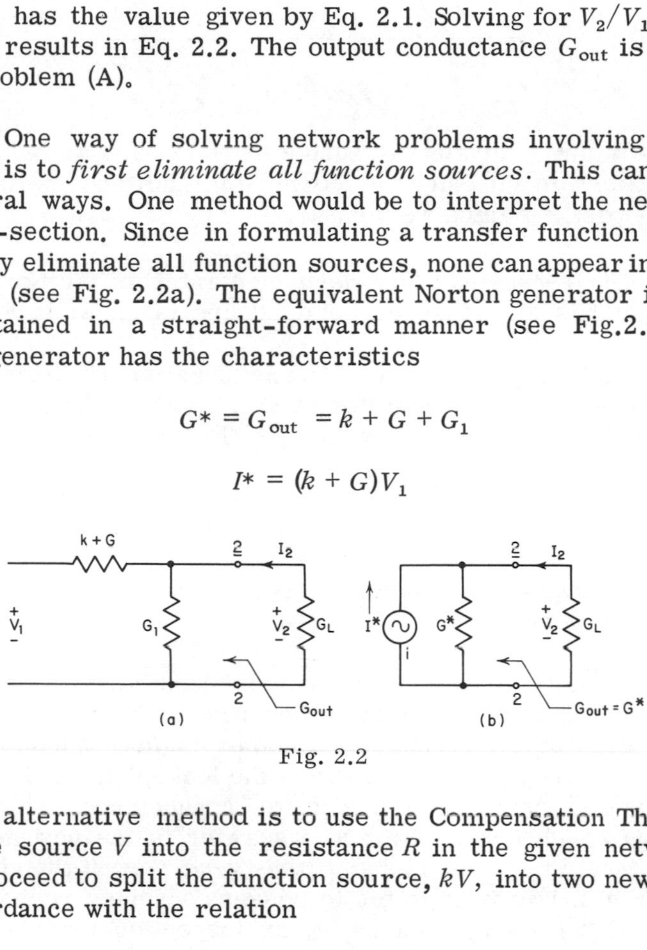

Fig. 2.2

An alternative method is to use the Compensation Theorem to turn the source V into the resistance R in the given network. We then proceed to split the function source, kV, into two new sources in accordance with the relation

$$kV = kV_1 - kV_2 \tag{2.6}$$

Here kV_1 is an independent source since V_1 is constant. The second source is a dependent source. Noting that the voltage across it is V_2, we may use the Compensation Theorem to turn it into the conductance, k. Thus we obtain the network in Fig. 2.3, which, like the one in Fig. 2.2, is free from dependent sources. Calculating $A_V(\omega)$ and G_{out} from the new network equivalent, we obtain the results stated in Eqs. 2.2 and 2.3. Note that whenever we encounter a linear

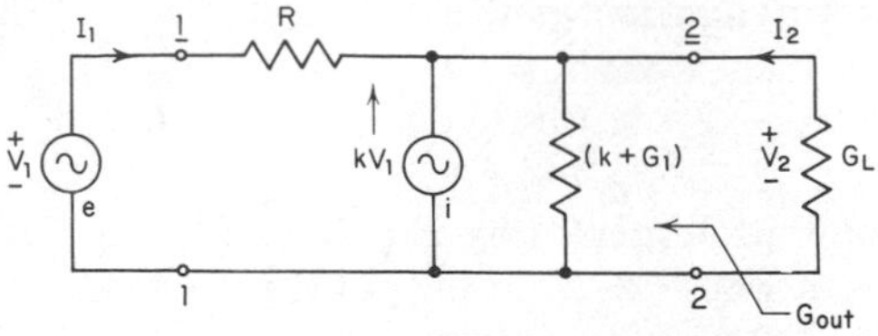

Fig. 2.3

network—or any equivalent of such a network—and we bring it into the laboratory to measure the looking-in immittance pertaining to the output port, the thing we measure is G_{out} or R_{out}.

(C1) The requested shunt-form generator is the Norton generator that has already been obtained and is shown in Fig. 2.2b.

(C2) Applying the Generator Transformation Theorem, we turn the shunt-form Norton generator in Fig. 2.2b into the series-form generator shown in Fig. 2.4a, which is a Thévenin generator. Here,

$$E^* = R^*I^* = V_1 \frac{k + G}{k + G + G_1} \tag{2.7}$$

Using this generator to calculate $A_V(\omega)$ and G_{out}, we again obtain the results in Eqs. 2.2 and 2.3.

(C3) We have already developed one shunt-form generator: the Norton generator in Fig. 2.2b, which has the output conductance, G_{out}, as generator conductance. Another logical shunt-form generator is obtained if we instead use the looking-in conductance of the passivated network as generator conductance. This is the *passivated conductance*, $G^{\#}$, and we refer to the new generator obtained (see Fig. 2.4b) as a *fictitious generator*. If the given network in Fig. 2.1 is interpreted to possess a series resistance, R, in place of the voltage source, V, an inspection reveals that the passivated conductance is $G^{\#} = (G + G_1)$, since V_1 and kV are the

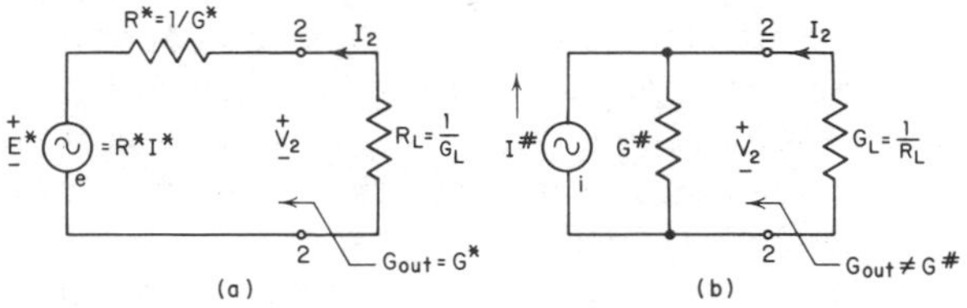

Fig. 2.4

sources which vanish when we passivate the network. Our immediate question is how the source $I^\#$ of the new generator is determined. One way of obtaining $I^\#$ presents itself if we split G^* in the Norton generator in Fig. 2.2b into two parts, one of which is $G^\#$. Thus $G^* = G^\# + k$, where k is transferred to the current generator, $-kV_2$, by means of the Compensation Theorem. Adding this current component to I^*, we obtain as characteristics for the fictitious new generator in Fig. 2.4b, from Eq. 2.5,

$$I^\# = (k + G)V_1 - kV_2 \tag{2.8}$$

$$G^\# = (G + G_1) \tag{2.9}$$

Another way in which we may obtain $I^\#$ is to apply the Superposition Theorem with the sources alive just as they appear in the given, undisturbed network. This means that V_2 has a certain finite value, although $V_2 = 0$ when the output port 2,2 is closed. We write:

For V_1 on, kV open-circuited:	$I_2'' = -GV_1$
For kV on, V_1 short-circuited:	$I_2'' = -kV$

The total negative short-circuit current is then

$$I^\# = -(I_2' + I_2'') = GV_1 + kV = (k + G)V_1 - kV_2 \tag{2.8a}$$

which agrees with Eq. 2.8. This is a direct method by means of which we can derive the fictitious generator by the application of the Superposition Theorem. If the generator in Fig. 2.4b is used for the calculation of $A_V(\omega)$ and G_{out}, we obtain the results stated in Eqs. 2.2 and 2.3.

(C4) A fictitious series-form generator would be one which, like the fictitious generator in Fig. 2.4b, employs the passivated conductance as generator conductance, appearing as a series resistance. Accordingly, $R^\# = 1/G^\#$ (see the equivalent generator in Fig. 2.5a). We wish to establish some direct method for determining the source $E^\#$ in this new generator. Guided by a comparison with the Thêvenin generator in Fig. 2.4a, we proceed to split up the series resistance, R^*, into two parts, one of which must be $R^\#$:

$$R^* = R^\# + \left(\frac{1}{k + G + G_1} - \frac{1}{G + G_1}\right) \tag{2.10}$$

We now must insert the extra resistance into the source E^*, and

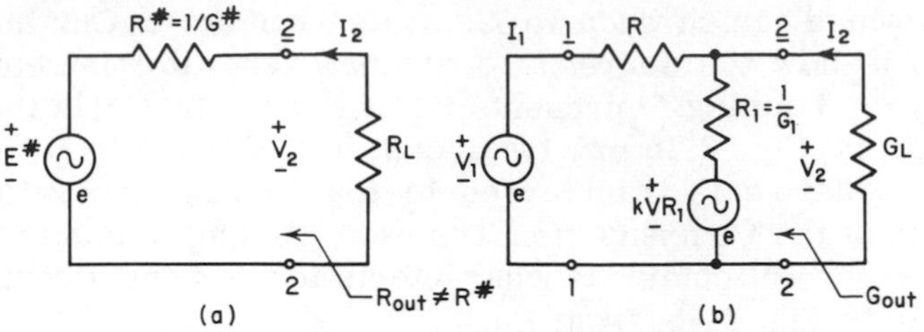

Fig. 2.5

accordingly, we obtain, using the Compensation Theorem, and with the aid of Eqs. 2.3, 2.5, and 2.10

$$E^{\#} = V_1 \frac{k + G}{k + G + G_1} - I_2 \frac{k}{(k + G + G_1)(G + G_1)} \tag{2.11}$$

Calculating $A_V(\omega)$ and G_{out} using the fictitious generator in Fig. 2.5a, we again obtain the results given by Eqs. 2.2 and 2.3. The use of this generator makes for longer calculations, however, and the method has been included merely for completeness of presentation.

(D) The network with the requested series-form generator is shown in Fig. 2.5b. One way of analyzing the network is to write the equation system

$$\left.\begin{aligned} (1 - kR_1)V_1 + kR_1V_2 &= (R + R_1)I_1 + R_1I_2 \\ -kR_1V_1 + kR_1V_2 &= R_1\,I_1 + (R_1 + R_L)I_2 \end{aligned}\right\} \quad \begin{aligned}(2.12)\\(2.13)\end{aligned}$$

which we may solve for V_2/V_1, obtaining the result in Eq. 2.2. Thus function sources, just like other sources, may be employed in generator transformations. Accordingly G_{out} is given by Eq. 2.3 in accordance with the Output Immittance Theorem.

(E) The given network already has the form of an active PI if we consider the existence of a first shunt-leg of zero conductance.

(F) To determine the current transfer function $A_I(\omega) = I_2/I_1$, we merely solve Eq. 2.1 for I_2/I_1, obtaining

$$I_2/I_1 = -(1 + kR)/(1 + G_1R_L) \tag{2.14}$$

Since the Norton generator in Fig. 2.2b is an equivalent, we can also calculate I_2/I_1 from this generator, but in accordance with Eq. 2.5 this will involve V_1 instead of I_1. Thus an extra calculation of V_1/I_1

becomes necessary, and from the initially given equations we obtain,

$$\begin{aligned} V_1 - V_2 = V &= RI_1 \\ V_1 &= RI_1 - R_L I_2 \end{aligned} \tag{2.15}$$

I_2/I_1 can now be calculated, and the answer agrees with that in Eq. 2.14. Similarly, we can calculate I_2/I_1 by means of the Thévenin generator shown in Fig. 2.4a. We also have two fictitious generators, the one in Fig. 2.4b and the one in Fig. 2.5a. Since they also are equivalents to the given network, we can use them to calculate I_2/I_1, although the calculations become somewhat longer than the ones above. Looking into the remaining networks, the one in Fig. 2.5b readily gives the relation in Eq. 2.14. Similarly we can use the network in Fig. 2.3, employing Eq. 2.15 to turn V_1 into I_1. The only network not yet discussed is that in Fig. 2.2 but this network is not a general equivalent of the given network and only represents an interpretation of the voltage ratio given by Eq. 2.2. Thus it is not intended for current-ratio calculations.

(G) Following the formulation of the Equivalent Generator Theorem word by word, we first study the transfer function, which is given by Eq. 2.2. Making the load admittance vanish, we obtain G_{out} as given by Eq. 2.3. The open-port voltage is obtained from Eq. 2.2 and given by Eq. 2.7. Thus the resulting equivalent Thévenin generator is the generator shown in Fig. 2.4a, and we obtained it in a most direct fashion with the Equivalent Generator Theorem.

Conclusions to this solution

This solution brought up some new material. We verified again that the Superposition Theorem can be used for the setting up of the basic equations for the given network, with its function sources, provided we introduce the function sources with their "live" values from the undisturbed network. We obtained one solution by employing the method of eliminating all dependent sources before we began the solution. In part (C) we produced the four equivalents of a linear network. Here the two fictitious generators are not of the same interest as the Norton and Thévenin generators, but represent a case that might occur, namely when a function source (by means of a transistor or tunnel diode) is added to an already existing network of known output immittance. Otherwise, the fictitious generators are merely included to widen the scope of the network-theory approach. The solution shows how we can at our leisure change immittance to a source, and vice versa, and a method has been developed by means of which the fictitious shunt-form generator can be obtained directly by employing the Superposition Theorem. We also made use of the author's Equivalent Generator Theorem. Finally, we have calculated the current transfer function, I_2/I_1, and found that it can be calculated from every network which is an equivalent of the given network, but naturally not from networks of limited validity, representing only a specific formula for a specific purpose.

PROBLEM 3

A special CE-connected transistor amplifier is investigated experimentally in the laboratory. It is concluded that it has the network equivalent shown in Fig. 3.1.

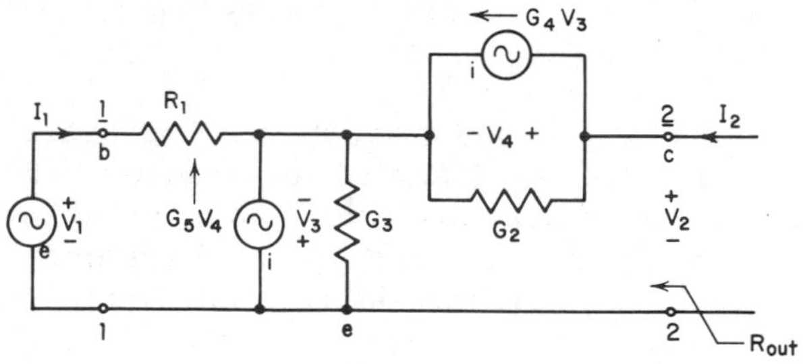

Fig. 3.1

(A) Find the h matrix, representing the total network, by applying the parameter definitions directly to the given network. (Prime notation may be dispensed with since the CE-connection is the only connection used.)

(B) Determine the voltage amplification, $A_V(\omega) = V_2/V_1$, when a load resistance R_L is attached to the output port, and also determine the output resistance R_{out}.

(C) By means of the Compensation Theorem, replace both function sources by immittances, draw the obtained network, and use it to determine again $A_V(\omega)$ and R_{out}.

Solution

(A) We employ the following definitions:

$$h_{11} = (V_1/I_1)_{2\ \mathrm{cl}} \qquad h_{21} = (I_2/I_1)_{2\ \mathrm{cl}}$$
$$h_{12} = (V_{10}/V_{20})_{1\ \mathrm{op}} \qquad h_{22} = (I_{20}/V_{20})_{1\ \mathrm{op}} \tag{3.1}$$

Starting with h_{11} and setting $V_3 = V_4$ and $V_3 = R_1 I_1 - V_1$, we write

$$I_1 + G(R_1 I_1 - V_1) = 0 \qquad G = 1/R = G_5 + G_2 + G_3 + G_4 \tag{3.2}$$

from which

$$h_{11} = (R_1 + R) \tag{3.3}$$

For h_{12} we note that $V_{10} = -V_{30}$ and $V_{40} = V_{20} - V_{10}$, thus

$$-(G_3 + G_4)V_{10} + (G_2 + G_5)(V_{20} - V_{10}) = 0 \tag{3.4}$$

from which

$$h_{12} = R(G_2 + G_5) \tag{3.5}$$

For h_{21} we note that $V_3 = V_4$, thus

$$I_1 + (G_3 + G_5)V_3 + I_2 = 0 \qquad I_2 = (G_2 + G_4)V_3 \tag{3.6}$$

from which

$$h_{21} = -R(G_2 + G_4) \tag{3.7}$$

In determining h_{22} we note that $I_{20} = (G_4 V_{30} + G_2 V_{40})$ and that $V_{20} = V_{40} - V_{30}$. Thus we write

$$G_5 V_{40} + G_3 V_{30} + I_{20} = 0 \tag{3.8}$$

from which

$$h_{22} = R(G_2 G_3 - G_4 G_5) \tag{3.9}$$

These four elements constitute the desired h matrix.

(B) The voltage amplification formulas derived from the two-port equation system take the form

$$A_V(\omega) = V_2/V_1 = -h_{21}/(\Delta_h + h_{11} G_L) \tag{3.10}$$

Inserting proper quantities, we obtain

$$\Delta_h = R[R_1(G_2G_3 - G_4G_5) + G_2] \tag{3.11}$$

and

$$A_V(\omega) = G_1(G_2 + G_4)/[G_1G_2 + G_2G_3 - G_4G_5 + (G + G_1)G_L] \tag{3.12}$$

From the Output Immittance Theorem

$$R_{\text{out}} = (G + G_1)/(G_1G_2 + G_2G_3 - G_4G_5) \tag{3.13}$$

(C) Replacing G_5V_4 by the conductance G_5V_4/V_3 and G_4V_3 by the conductance G_4V_3/V_4, we obtain the new network shown in Fig. 3.2. Setting $V_4 = (V_2 + V_3)$ and $V_3 = (-V_1 + R_1I_1)$, we can write the following equation system:

$$\left.\begin{aligned} I_1 - G_LV_2 - (G_3 + G_5)(V_1 - R_1I_1) + G_5V_2 &= 0 \\ G_LV_2 - (G_2 + G_4)(V_1 - R_1I_1) + G_2V_2 &= 0 \end{aligned}\right\} \tag{3.14}$$

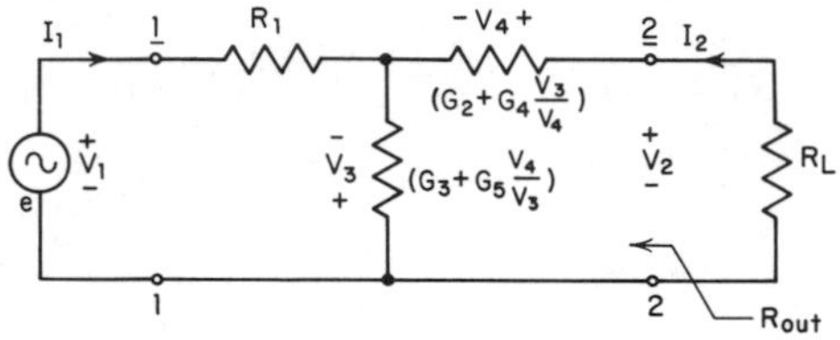

Fig. 3.2

Upon elimination of I_1 we obtain the answer given by Eq. 3.12. R_{out} is obtained as before.

Conclusions to this solution

We have here an example illustrating the standard procedure of finding the matrix of a given network. We apply the definitions of the twoport parameters. This example also demonstrates the fact that an active network may be shown without explicit sources provided one or more immittances employ ratios between the variables. Solutions employing the Compensation Theorem in this way are not necessarily faster than other solutions, but they demonstrate the importance of the marvelous tool for the handling of function sources provided by the Compensation Theorem.

SOME FINAL THOUGHTS

One often hears the statement that the Superposition Theorem does not hold for dependent sources; yet we used it here and obtained correct answers. The following thoughts may clarify the issue. If the network is undisturbed, there is no noticeable difference between dependent and independent sources. Thus we may temporarily replace all dependent sources by independent sources without risk of changing any currents and voltages in the system. Now eliminating all sources except one, we may encounter the seemingly contradictory case of a variable being zero everywhere except in the source we kept from the undisturbed network. A little consideration will show that the reasoning is logical and correct, although the procedure is somewhat unusual.

We learned that the conventional linear network has four rather than two equivalent generators—two fictitious generators in addition to the Thévenin and Norton generators. There are many ways in which we can produce the additional two generators, one being the application of the Compensation Theorem. In a general linear network (one that contains both dependent and independent sources), the conventional Thévenin Theorem fails to produce a Thévenin generator, and similarly the conventional Norton Theorem fails to produce a Norton generator (although a cross-breed of the two theorems may be formulated, which produces everything). The Equivalent Generator Theorem, however, directly produces both the Thévenin generator and the Norton generator and therefore replaces the Thévenin Theorem and the Norton Theorem.

3
CB, CE, and CC Transformations

Transformation from one transistor connection to another occurs very frequently in transistor network calculations. Not only must we master the fastest method known to carry out such transformations, but we must also know other ways of carrying out such transformations so that one method can be used as a check on another method. No doubt the most satisfactory method, generally, is to use the author's Matrix Table with built-in transformation formulas, but occasionally other methods are quicker. Thus we may use the Equation System Comparison Method or the Arm Interchange Method. To provide the greatest possible clarity, different notations have been used for the three connections: no primes for Common-Base- or CB-connection; single primes for Common-Emitter- or CE-connection; double primes for Common-Collector- or CC-connection. Often the primes can be left out without any risk of misunderstandings. Since any one of the transistor terminals may be grounded, terms such as "Grounded-Base-connection" have been avoided.

An effort has been made to show the mathematical distinction between such quantities as a, α, β', α'', and b''. Students notoriously make mistakes by not keeping such quantities clearly apart. It goes without saying that the reader who does not maintain a strict sign convention will soon be lost in calculation difficulties. All voltage and current directions must be clearly indicated before the formula writing begins.

PROBLEM 1

A transistor is known through its immittance matrices

$$|\mathbf{z}| = \begin{vmatrix} \mathbf{z}_{11} & \mathbf{z}_{12} \\ \mathbf{z}_{21} & \mathbf{z}_{22} \end{vmatrix} \qquad |\mathbf{y}| = \begin{vmatrix} \mathbf{y}_{11} & \mathbf{y}_{12} \\ \mathbf{y}_{21} & \mathbf{y}_{22} \end{vmatrix}$$

(A) Write the matrix equations and the long-hand equations and draw the double-source equivalent networks.

(B) Using long-hand equations only, transform from z to y parameters, writing the y equation system in terms of z parameters.

(C) In the z equivalent network, replace the series-form generators by shunt-form generators, and show that the y equivalent network can be obtained in this manner.

(D) Using the network equivalents obtained in (A), and leaving the 2, $\underline{2}$ end open, determine the input immittance in various ways.

(E) If each matrix element has the general form $\mathbf{z} = r + jx$, $\mathbf{y} = g + jb$, where r, x, g, and b may be positive or negative, what possible forms can the input immittance calculated in (D) assume?

(F) If a network equivalent in the form of an active TEE is used, labeled in z parameters, what is the effect upon the input immittance calculated in (D) of the function source, which appears due to the relationship $\mathbf{z}_{12} \neq \mathbf{z}_{21}$?

Solution

(A) The z and y matrix equations and long-hand equations are shown below. The requested network equivalents are shown in Fig. 1.1.

$$\begin{vmatrix} \mathbf{V}_1 \\ \mathbf{V}_2 \end{vmatrix} = \begin{vmatrix} \mathbf{z}_{11} & \mathbf{z}_{12} \\ \mathbf{z}_{21} & \mathbf{z}_{22} \end{vmatrix} \begin{vmatrix} \mathbf{I}_1 \\ \mathbf{I}_2 \end{vmatrix} \tag{1.1}$$

$$\begin{vmatrix} \mathbf{I}_1 \\ \mathbf{I}_2 \end{vmatrix} = \begin{vmatrix} \mathbf{y}_{11} & \mathbf{y}_{12} \\ \mathbf{y}_{21} & \mathbf{y}_{22} \end{vmatrix} \begin{vmatrix} \mathbf{V}_1 \\ \mathbf{V}_2 \end{vmatrix} \tag{1.2}$$

$$\mathbf{V}_1 = \mathbf{z}_{11}\mathbf{I}_1 + \mathbf{z}_{12}\mathbf{I}_2 \tag{1.3}$$

$$\mathbf{V}_2 = \mathbf{z}_{21}\mathbf{I}_1 + \mathbf{z}_{22}\mathbf{I}_2 \tag{1.4}$$

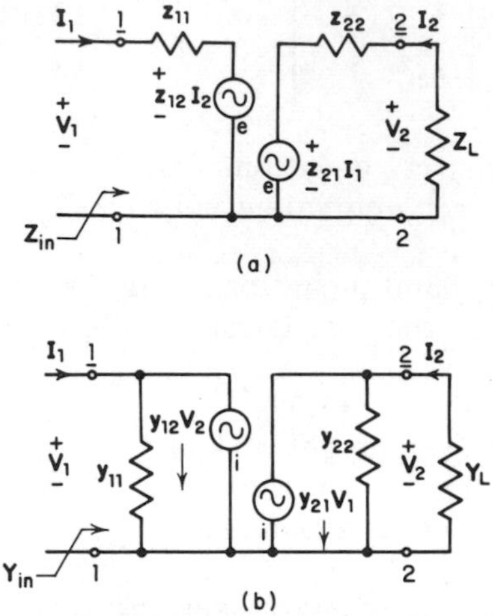

Fig. 1.1

$$\left.\begin{aligned} \mathbf{I}_1 &= \mathbf{y}_{11}\mathbf{V}_1 + \mathbf{y}_{12}\mathbf{V}_2 \quad (1.5) \\ \mathbf{I}_2 &= \mathbf{y}_{21}\mathbf{V}_1 + \mathbf{y}_{22}\mathbf{V}_2 \quad (1.6) \end{aligned}\right\}$$

(B) We solve Eqs. 1.3 and 1.4 for $\mathbf{I}_1$ and also for $\mathbf{I}_2$, setting $\mathbf{z}_{11}\mathbf{z}_{22} - \mathbf{z}_{12}\mathbf{z}_{21} = \mathbf{\Delta}_z$, thus obtaining

$$\left.\begin{aligned} \mathbf{I}_1 &= (\mathbf{z}_{22}/\mathbf{\Delta}_z)\mathbf{V}_1 + (-\mathbf{z}_{12}/\mathbf{\Delta}_z)\mathbf{V}_2 \quad (1.7) \\ \mathbf{I}_2 &= (-\mathbf{z}_{21}/\mathbf{\Delta}_z)\mathbf{V}_1 + (\mathbf{z}_{11}/\mathbf{\Delta}_z)\mathbf{V}_2 \quad (1.8) \end{aligned}\right\}$$

It is, of course, much quicker to look up the y parameters in the matrix table.

(C) The requested network equivalent is shown in Fig. 1.2. Comparing it with the network equivalent in Fig. 1.1b, we may at first fail to see any agreement, since for example $\mathbf{y}_{11} \neq 1/\mathbf{z}_{11}$. Still the two equivalents must agree, since there are no discrepancies from a topological point of view. Investigating the first source, we may write with the aid of Eq. 1.6:

$$\frac{\mathbf{z}_{12}\mathbf{I}_2}{\mathbf{z}_{11}} = \frac{\mathbf{z}_{12}\mathbf{z}_{21}}{\mathbf{z}_{11}\mathbf{\Delta}_z}\mathbf{V}_1 + \frac{\mathbf{z}_{12}}{\mathbf{\Delta}_z}\mathbf{V}_2$$

The second term here represents, in accordance with Eq. 1.7, the current source $\mathbf{y}_{12}\mathbf{V}_2$, so that full agreement now exists with respect to the source. To the first term we can apply the Compensation Theorem, turning it into an impedance, which in parallel with $\mathbf{z}_{11}$ provides $\mathbf{y}_{11}$. Thus full agreement also exists with respect to

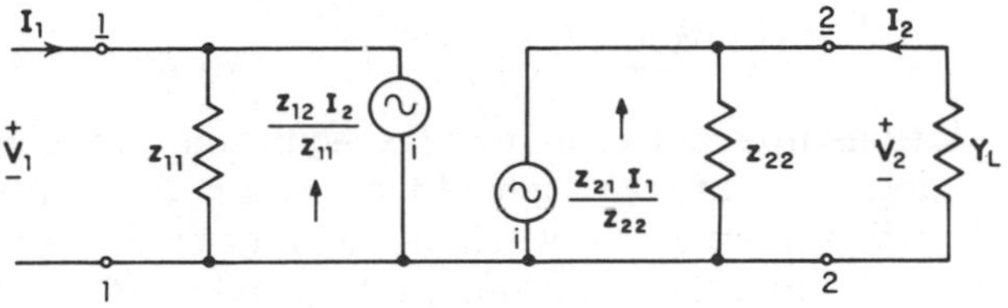

Fig. 1.2

the first generator immittance. Similarly, we can show that full agreement exists for the right-hand side of the network equivalent. We may note that both function sources may be genuine function sources, namely, if the transistor is driven by a current source. Nothing has been said about how it is driven. Thus, in employing the Superposition Theorem, one must be careful not to overlook the fact that a certain source may be a genuine function source, demanding that its variable be taken from the undisturbed network.

(D) Since $\mathbf{z}_{11}$ is the input impedance with the 2, $\underline{2}$ end open, the quickest answer is obtained if we write $\mathbf{Z}_{in} = \mathbf{z}_{11}$. Using y parameters we simply look up the answer in the matrix table, writing $\mathbf{Z}_{in} = 1/\mathbf{Y}_{in} = \mathbf{y}_{22}/\Delta_y$.

(E) The formula $\mathbf{Z}_{in} = \mathbf{z}_{11}$ is complete and will answer all our questions without any need for further investigation. Since r_{11} may be negative, the most striking result is that the system may not be stable, depending upon the nature of the driving generator, about which nothing has been said in the problem formulation. Thus under all circumstances, power from the driving generator may enter the port 1,$\underline{1}$, going right, and at the same time, power due to transistor instability may be transmitted in the other direction. Even if the transistor oscillates, we can, in the laboratory, obtain a reading of $\mathbf{Z}_{in}$, but it may not have any practical meaning. It is bound to be quite different from the value obtained when the transistor is merely amplifying. Due to the reactance, $\pm x$, the input impedance could have practically any complex value.

(F) Since $\mathbf{Z}_{in} = \mathbf{z}_{11}$, the function-source, $\mathbf{z}_m\mathbf{I}_1$, has no effect whatsoever on $\mathbf{Z}_{in}$. Only the first element in the z matrix has any influence on the input impedance in this case. Two transistors may vary greatly in amplification, due to $\mathbf{z}_m\mathbf{I}_1$, and still have the same value of $\mathbf{z}_{11}$. In practical engineering, however, $\mathbf{\Delta}_z$ is one of the design criteria; for one thing its value must fall inside a certain range of values to guarantee stability.

Conclusions to this solution

The relationships between matrix equations, long-hand equations, and z and y parameters should be clear from this solution. While the y double-source network equivalent can be shown on inspection of the y equation system, we learned in (C) that this network equivalent can also be obtained by means of the Generator Transformation Theorem. In (D) and (E) we discussed input immittance and complex matrix elements, the most important consideration here being that the transistor may become unstable, and thus lap into a surge, or oscillate at some specific frequency. The possibility of r_{11} being negative in $\mathbf{z}_{11} = r_{11} + jx_{11}$ is not at all far-fetched. It does not mean necessarily that we are using some peculiar transistor with unusual characteristics. Any transistor that for one reason or another has become unstable (or deliberately is made unstable) must show negative resistance or at least zero resistance at the port under consideration, whether the $1,\underline{1}$ or $2.\underline{2}$.

PROBLEM 2

An audio transistor is known by its matrix

$$|k| = \begin{vmatrix} k_{11} & k_{12} \\ k_{21} & k_{22} \end{vmatrix}$$

(A) Determine the parameters a_{12}, b_{11}, b_{21}, and b_{22}.

(B) Write an expression for the current-transfer function, $\mathbf{A}_I(\omega) = \mathbf{I}_2/\mathbf{I}_1$, when the transistor is loaded by the admittance $\mathbf{Y}_L$.

(C) Describe the variations of $|\mathbf{A}_I(\omega)|$ as a function of frequency when the load admittance has the value $\mathbf{Y}_L = (2 + j)10^{-5}$.

Solution

(A) The answers are most readily obtained by the use of Matrix Table I in Appendix C. From this table we obtain

$$a_{12} = \frac{k_{22}}{k_{21}} \qquad b_{11} = -\frac{\Delta k}{k_{12}} \qquad b_{21} = -\frac{k_{11}}{k_{12}} \qquad b_{22} = -\frac{1}{k_{12}} \tag{2.1}$$

where

$$\Delta_k = k_{11}k_{22} - k_{12}k_{21} \tag{2.2}$$

(B) The k parameter matrix and long-hand equations are, from Appendix C,

$$\begin{vmatrix} \mathbf{I}_1 \\ \mathbf{V}_2 \end{vmatrix} = \begin{vmatrix} k_{11} & k_{12} \\ k_{21} & k_{22} \end{vmatrix} \begin{vmatrix} \mathbf{V}_1 \\ \mathbf{I}_2 \end{vmatrix} \tag{2.3}$$

$$\mathbf{I}_1 = k_{11}\mathbf{V}_1 + k_{12}\mathbf{I}_2 \tag{2.4}$$

$$\mathbf{V}_2 = k_{21}\mathbf{V}_1 + k_{22}\mathbf{I}_2 \tag{2.5}$$

Solving for $\mathbf{I}_2/\mathbf{I}_1$ in Eqs. 2.4 and 2.5 we obtain, with $\mathbf{V}_2 = -\mathbf{I}_2/\mathbf{Y}_L = -\mathbf{Z}_L\mathbf{I}_2$,

$$\mathbf{A}_I(\omega) = \mathbf{I}_2/\mathbf{I}_1 = -k_{21}/(\mathbf{\Delta}_k + k_{11}\mathbf{Z}_L) \tag{2.6}$$

(C) $\mathbf{Y}_L = 2 \times 10^{-5} + j10^{-5} = G_L + jB_L = G_L + j\omega C_L/\omega$ is a capacitive load, whose capacitance apparently decreases as the frequency is increased, so that the load admittance stays constant. Thus, provided the transistor parameters remain constant throughout the a-f range, the current transfer function is also constant.

Conclusions to this solution

In this problem we had some further exercise on transistor parameters and transfer functions. In solving the last part of this problem, students often fail to observe that the load capacitance is frequency dependent in such a way as to make the current-transfer function independent of frequency.

PROBLEM 3

A CB-connected video transistor amplifier operates at a sufficiently low frequency to allow all capacitances to be disregarded. An internally appearing base resistance, r_{bb}, positioned as shown in Fig. 3.1, cannot be neglected, however. The twoport (1,$\underline{1}$) (2,$\underline{2}$) is described by a known h matrix.

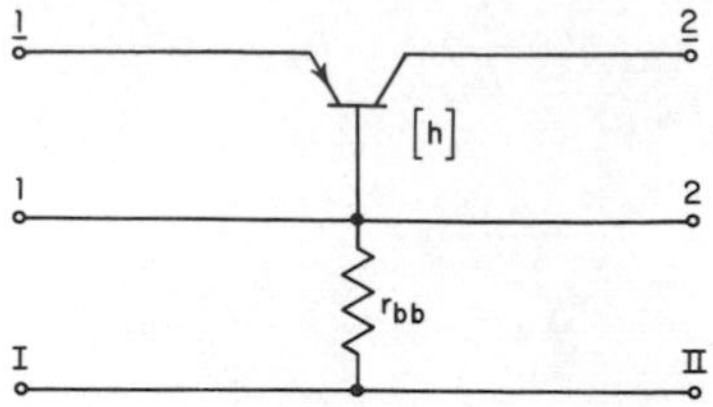

Fig. 3.1

(A) Change the given transistor (1,1) (2,2) into an r TEE. (Assume r_m of the given transistor to have a fixed value.)

(B) Allowing the approximations, $r_{bb}h_{22} \ll 1$ and $h_{12} \ll 1$, find the H matrix for the total network.

Solution

(A) We first change the given h parameters into r parameters, and then add r_{bb} to $r_b = r_{12}$ in the equivalent TEE, obtaining

$$\begin{vmatrix} r_{11} & r_{12} \\ r_{21} & r_{22} \end{vmatrix} = \begin{vmatrix} \dfrac{\Delta h}{h_{22}} & \dfrac{h_{12}}{h_{22}} \\ \dfrac{-h_{21}}{h_{22}} & \dfrac{1}{h_{22}} \end{vmatrix} \rightarrow \begin{vmatrix} \left(\dfrac{\Delta h}{h_{22}} + r_{bb}\right) & \left(\dfrac{h_{12}}{h_{22}} + r_{bb}\right) \\ \left(\dfrac{-h_{21}}{h_{22}} + r_{bb}\right) & \left(\dfrac{1}{h_{22}} + r_{bb}\right) \end{vmatrix} = \begin{vmatrix} \bar{r}_{11} & \bar{r}_{12} \\ \bar{r}_{21} & \bar{r}_{22} \end{vmatrix} \tag{3.1}$$

Note that r_{bb} appears in all four elements. The value of $\bar{r}_{21}$ follows, since $\bar{r}_{21} - \bar{r}_{12}$ must equal r_m.

(B) The equivalent TEE for the total network is read off from Eq. 3.1 and is shown in Fig. 3.2. All we have to do now is to express the $\bar{r}$ parameters in H parameters. The determinant is

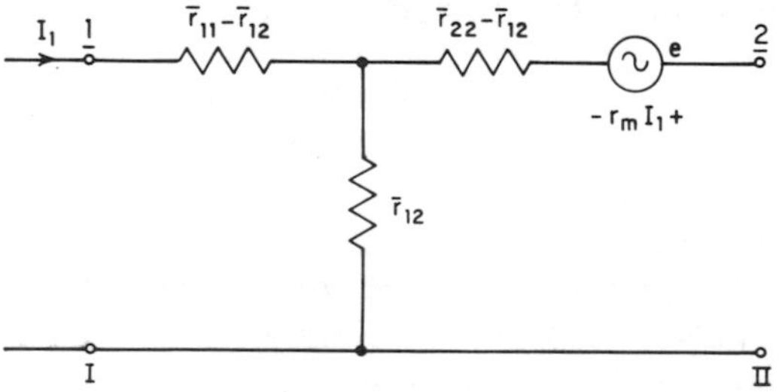

Fig. 3.2

$$\bar{\Delta}_r = \bar{r}_{11}\bar{r}_{22} - \bar{r}_{12}\bar{r}_{21} \doteq \frac{1}{h_{22}}\ [h_{11} + r_{bb}(1 + h_{21})] \tag{3.2}$$

Accordingly,

$$H_{11} = \bar{\Delta}_r/\bar{r}_{22} \doteq h_{11} + r_{bb}(1 + h_{21}) \tag{3.3}$$

$$H_{12} = \bar{r}_{12}/\bar{r}_{22} \doteq (h_{12} + r_{bb}h_{22}) \tag{3.4}$$

$$H_{21} = (-\bar{r}_{21})/\bar{r}_{22} \doteq h_{21} \tag{3.5}$$

$$H_{22} = 1/\bar{r}_{22} \doteq h_{22} \tag{3.6}$$

Conclusions to this solution

The simplicity achieved by changing from h to r matrix is apparent, allowing us to add r_{bb} directly. Note that the appearance of r_{bb} in the matrix depends on the assumption made.

PROBLEM 4

Looking back in his notebook, an electronics engineer found that he had calculated $A_V(\omega)$ for an (h CB) audio-frequency transistor as follows:

$$A_V(\omega) = V_2/V_1 = 0.960/[(1{,}025 \times 10^{-6}) + (65/20{,}000)] = 225 \tag{A}$$

and $A_I(\omega)$ as follows:

$$A_I(\omega) = I_2/I_1 = -0.960/[1 + (10^{-6} \times 20{,}000)] = 0.942 \tag{B}$$

From this information, the engineer was able to determine the matrices and determinants for all six parameters. Repeat this feat.

Solution

The h parameter matrix and long-hand equations are

$$\begin{vmatrix} V_1 \\ I_2 \end{vmatrix} = \begin{vmatrix} h_{11} & h_{12} \\ h_{21} & h_{22} \end{vmatrix} \begin{vmatrix} I_1 \\ V_2 \end{vmatrix} \tag{4.1}$$

$$\left.\begin{aligned} V_1 &= h_{11}I_1 + h_{12}V_2 \qquad (4.2) \\ I_2 &= h_{21}I_1 + h_{22}V_2 \qquad (4.3) \end{aligned}\right\}$$

from which we derive the amplification formulas:

$$A_V(\omega) = \frac{V_2}{V_1} = \frac{-h_{21}}{\Delta_h + h_{11}G_L} \tag{4.4}$$

$$A_I(\omega) = I_2/I_1 = \frac{h_{21}}{1 + h_{22}R_L} \tag{4.5}$$

Comparing (A) and (B) with Eqs. 4.4 and 4.5, we are justified in drawing the conclusion that $R_L = 20{,}000$ ohms, $h_{21} = -0.96$, $h_{22} = 10^{-6}$ mho, $h_{11} = 65$, and $\Delta_h = 1{,}025 \times 10^{-6}$. Accordingly,

$$h_{12} = (h_{11}h_{22} - \Delta_h)/h_{21} = [(65 \times 10^{-6}) - (1{,}025 \times 10^{-6})]/-0.96 = 10^{-3} \tag{4.6}$$

The h parameter matrix and determinant are therefore the ones indicated below. All the additional matrices and determinants are obtained by means of the matrix tables in Appendix C.

$$\begin{vmatrix} 1{,}025 & 1{,}000 \\ 0.96 \times 10^6 & 10^6 \end{vmatrix}_r \qquad \begin{vmatrix} 15.4 \times 10^{-3} & -15.4 \times 10^{-6} \\ -14.8 \times 10^{-3} & 15.8 \times 10^{-6} \end{vmatrix}_g$$

$$\Delta_r = 65 \times 10^6 \qquad \Delta_g = 154 \times 10^{-10}$$

$$\begin{vmatrix} 65 & 10^{-3} \\ -0.960 & 10^{-6} \end{vmatrix}_h$$

$$\Delta_h = 1{,}025 \times 10^{-6}$$

$$\begin{vmatrix} 976 \times 10^{-6} & -976 \times 10^{-3} \\ 937 & 63.4 \times 10^3 \end{vmatrix}_k \qquad \begin{vmatrix} 1{,}070 \times 10^{-6} & 67.75 \\ 1.042 \times 10^{-6} & 1.042 \end{vmatrix}_a$$

$$\Delta_k = 976 \qquad \Delta_a = 1{,}042 \times 10^{-6}$$

$$\begin{vmatrix} 1{,}000 & 65 \times 10^3 \\ 10^{-3} & 1.025 \end{vmatrix}_b$$

$$\Delta_b = 960 \tag{4.7}$$

Conclusions to this solution

This solution merely provides a review of routine ties. The values in 4.7 furnish us with a complete set of parameters for

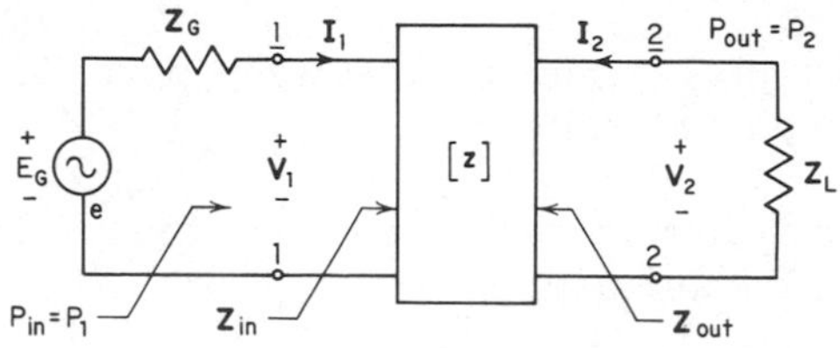

Fig. 5.1

a practical transistor and may be used in trying out some parameter relationships in the following.

PROBLEM 5

Given is the transistor amplifier shown in Fig. 5.1, in which the transistor is known through its complex z matrix. Determine:

(A) The matrix and long-hand equations for the entire network

(B) The voltage transfer function, $\mathbf{A}_V(\omega) = \mathbf{V}_2/\mathbf{V}_1$

(C) The current transfer function, $\mathbf{A}_I(\omega) = \mathbf{I}_2/\mathbf{I}_1$

(D) The imput impedance, $\mathbf{Z}_{\text{in}}$, using more than one method

(E) The output impedance, $\mathbf{Z}_{\text{out 1}}$, for the entire system, using more than one method

(F) The available gain, $G_{\text{ava}} = P_2/P_{1\ \text{ava}}$

(G) Starting from the equation system in (A), derive a TEE-equivalent for the entire system.

Solution

(A) The matrix and long-hand equations for the entire system are, with $\mathbf{Z}_{11G} = (\mathbf{z}_{11} + \mathbf{Z}_G)$,

$$\begin{vmatrix} E_G \\ \mathbf{V}_2 \end{vmatrix} = \begin{vmatrix} \mathbf{Z}_{11G} & \mathbf{z}_{12} \\ \mathbf{z}_{21} & \mathbf{z}_{22} \end{vmatrix} \begin{vmatrix} \mathbf{I}_1 \\ \mathbf{I}_2 \end{vmatrix} \tag{5.1}$$

$$E_G = \mathbf{Z}_{11G}\mathbf{I}_1 + \mathbf{z}_{12}\mathbf{I}_2 \tag{5.2}$$

$$\mathbf{V}_2 = \mathbf{z}_{21}\mathbf{I}_1 + \mathbf{z}_{22}\mathbf{I}_2 \tag{5.3}$$

For $\mathbf{Z}_G = 0$ and $\mathbf{Z}_{11G} = \mathbf{z}_{11}$ the above equations describe, with $E_G = \mathbf{V}_1$, the twoport proper, located between ports 1,$\underline{1}$ and 2,$\underline{2}$. Note that E_G has zero phase angle.

(B) The voltage transfer function for the entire network, obtained from Eqs. 5.2 and 5.3, is, with $\mathbf{I}_2 = -\mathbf{V}_2/\mathbf{Z}_L$,

$$\mathbf{A}_E(\omega) = \frac{\mathbf{V}_2}{E_G} = \frac{\mathbf{z}_{21}}{\mathbf{Z}_{11G} + \mathbf{\Delta}_{z1}\mathbf{Y}_L} \qquad (5.4)$$

Here $\mathbf{\Delta}_{z1} = \mathbf{Z}_{11G}\mathbf{z}_{22} - \mathbf{z}_{12}\mathbf{z}_{21}$. By setting $\mathbf{Z}_{11G} = \mathbf{z}_{11}$ and $E_G = \mathbf{V}_1$, we obtain the voltage-transfer function for the twoport proper:

$$\mathbf{A}_V(\omega) = \frac{\mathbf{V}_2}{\mathbf{V}_1} = \frac{\mathbf{z}_{21}}{\mathbf{z}_{11} + \mathbf{\Delta}_z\mathbf{Y}_L} \qquad (5.5)$$

where $\mathbf{\Delta}_z = \mathbf{z}_{11}\mathbf{z}_{22} - \mathbf{z}_{12}\mathbf{z}_{21}$.

(C) The current-transfer function is from Eqs. 5.2 and 5.3, with $\mathbf{Z}_{22L} = (\mathbf{z}_{22} + \mathbf{Z}_L)$:

$$\mathbf{A}_I(\omega) = \frac{\mathbf{I}_2}{\mathbf{I}_1} = \frac{-\mathbf{z}_{21}}{\mathbf{Z}_{22L}} = \frac{-\mathbf{z}_{21}}{\mathbf{z}_{22} + \mathbf{Z}_L} \qquad (5.6)$$

(D) With $\mathbf{Z}_G = 0$, $E_G = \mathbf{V}_1$, and $\mathbf{V}_2 = -\mathbf{Z}_L\mathbf{I}_2$, we obtain from Eqs. 5.2 and 5.3:

$$\mathbf{Z}_{\text{in}} = \mathbf{V}_1/\mathbf{I}_1 = (\mathbf{\Delta}_z + \mathbf{z}_{11}\mathbf{Z}_L)/\mathbf{Z}_{22L} = (\mathbf{z}_{11} + \mathbf{\Delta}_z\mathbf{Y}_L)/(1 + \mathbf{z}_{22}\mathbf{Y}_L) \qquad (5.7)$$

As an alternative, we may use determinants and Cramer's Rule, writing from Eqs. 5.2 and 5.3, with the vertical bars designating determinants:

$$\mathbf{I}_1 = \frac{\mathbf{\Delta}_{I1}}{\mathbf{\Delta}_{z2}} = \begin{vmatrix} \mathbf{V}_1 & \mathbf{z}_{12} \\ 0 & \mathbf{Z}_{22L} \end{vmatrix} \Bigg/ \begin{vmatrix} \mathbf{z}_{11} & \mathbf{z}_{12} \\ \mathbf{z}_{21} & \mathbf{Z}_{22L} \end{vmatrix} = \frac{\mathbf{Z}_{22L}\mathbf{V}_1}{\mathbf{\Delta}_{z2}} \qquad (5.8)$$

where $\mathbf{\Delta}_{z2} = \mathbf{z}_{11}\mathbf{Z}_{22L} - \mathbf{z}_{12}\mathbf{z}_{21} = \mathbf{z}_{11}(\mathbf{z}_{22} + \mathbf{Z}_L) - \mathbf{z}_{12}\mathbf{z}_{21}$. Solving for $\mathbf{V}_1/\mathbf{I}_1$ in Eq. 5.8, we obtain the result in Eq. 5.7.

(E) The output immittance for the entire system can be obtained directly from Eq. 5.4 by the Output Immittance Theorem:

$$\mathbf{Z}_{\text{out}\,1} = \mathbf{\Delta}_{z1}/\mathbf{Z}_{11G} \qquad (5.9)$$

As another approach, we may use the Applied Source Method and obtain $\mathbf{Z}_{out\,1}$ from Eqs. 5.2 and 5.3.

(F) With $\mathbf{Z}_G = R_G + jX_G$, the available power from the driving generator is $P_{1\,ava} = E_G^2/8R_G$ if we consider the instantaneous value of the driving voltage to be $e_G(t) = E_G \cos \omega t$. This power is not generally secured in the network shown in Fig. 5.1, since the requirement, $\mathbf{Z}_{in} = R_G - jX_G$ is not always fulfilled. Nevertheless, we are entirely free to derive a power ratio with reference to $P_{1\,ava}$. The output power is $R_L I_2^2/2$, and the available gain becomes

$$G_{ava} = \frac{P_2}{P_{1\,ava}} = 4R_G R_L \left(\frac{I_2}{E_G}\right)^2 = 4R_G R_L \left|\frac{\mathbf{I}_2}{E_G}\right|^2 \qquad (5.10)$$

Then from Eqs. 5.2 and 5.3,

$$G_{ava} = 4R_G R_L \left|\frac{-\mathbf{z}_{21}}{\mathbf{Z}_{11G}\mathbf{Z}_L + \mathbf{\Delta}_{z1}}\right|^2 \qquad (5.11)$$

which expression can be further elaborated upon.

(G) The matrix in Eq. 5.1 already describes the entire network, except for the load impedance. To obtain an equivalent TEE, we only have to rewrite Eq. 5.3 as follows:

$$\mathbf{V}_2 = \mathbf{z}_{12}\mathbf{I}_1 + \mathbf{z}_{22}\mathbf{I}_2 + \mathbf{z}_m\mathbf{I}_1 \qquad (5.12)$$

where $\mathbf{z}_m = (\mathbf{z}_{21} - \mathbf{z}_{12})$. Due to the inequality, $\mathbf{z}_{21} \neq \mathbf{z}_{12}$, a voltage source appears in the output arm of the so far passive TEE, turning it into the active TEE shown in Fig. 5.2, which represents the entire network and thus includes the load impedance $\mathbf{Z}_L$.

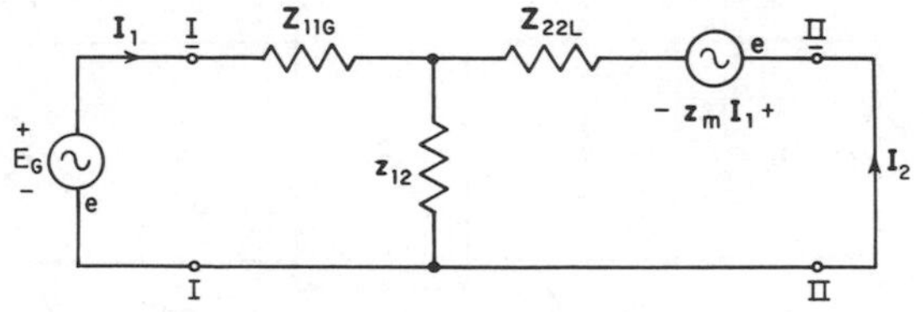

Fig. 5.2

Conclusions to this solution

It has been shown how the generator immittance and the load immittance can be included in the matrix, and how the use of proper symbols makes this possible without much complication. Accordingly, we can distinguish between four different determinants: the one for the twoport between ports 1,1 and 2,2; the same extended to include the generator immittance; the same extended to include the load immittance; and finally, the determinant that includes everything. Since different determinants exist, one must be careful not to mistake one for another; mistakes are often made on this basis.

PROBLEM 6

Given the transistor amplifier shown in Fig. 6.1, in which the transistor is known through its complex y matrix, determine:

(A) The matrix and long-hand equations for the entire network

(B) The voltage transfer function, $\mathbf{A}_V(\omega) = \mathbf{V}_2/\mathbf{V}_1$

(C) The current transfer function, $\mathbf{A}_I(\omega) = \mathbf{I}_2/\mathbf{I}_1$

(D) The input admittance, $\mathbf{Y}_{in}$, using more than one method

(E) The output admittance, $\mathbf{Y}_{out\,1}$ for the entire system, using more than one method

(F) The available gain, $G_{ava} = P_2/P_{1\,ava}$.

(G) Starting from the equation system in (A), derive a PI equivalent for the entire network.

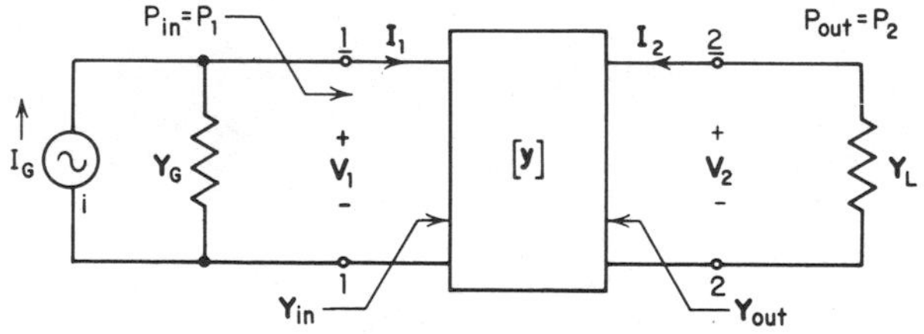

Fig. 6.1

Solution

(A) The matrix and long-hand equations for the entire system are, with $\mathbf{Y}_{11G} = (\mathbf{y}_{11} + \mathbf{Y}_G)$,

$$\begin{vmatrix} \mathbf{I}_G \\ \mathbf{I}_2 \end{vmatrix} = \begin{vmatrix} \mathbf{Y}_{11G} & \mathbf{y}_{12} \\ \mathbf{y}_{21} & \mathbf{y}_{22} \end{vmatrix} \begin{vmatrix} \mathbf{V}_1 \\ \mathbf{V}_2 \end{vmatrix} \tag{6.1}$$

$$\mathbf{I}_G = \mathbf{Y}_{11G}\mathbf{V}_1 + \mathbf{y}_{12}\mathbf{V}_2 \tag{6.2}$$

$$\mathbf{I}_2 = \mathbf{y}_{21}\mathbf{V}_1 + \mathbf{y}_{22}\mathbf{V}_2 \tag{6.3}$$

For $\mathbf{Y}_G = 0$, $\mathbf{Y}_{11G} = \mathbf{y}_{11}$, and $I_G = \mathbf{I}_1$, the above equations describe the twoport proper, located between the ports $1,\underline{1}$ and $2,\underline{2}$. Note that I_G has zero phase angle. Two matrices have already been introduced. A third one results if we lump the load admittance into $\mathbf{y}_{22}$, writing $\mathbf{Y}_{22L} = (\mathbf{y}_{22} + \mathbf{Y}_L)$. Finally a fourth matrix is obtained if we make use of $\mathbf{Y}_{11G}$ and $\mathbf{Y}_{22L}$ simultaneously. Accordingly, we must distinguish between the following four determinants:

$$\mathbf{\Delta}_y = \mathbf{y}_{11}\mathbf{y}_{22} - \mathbf{y}_{12}\mathbf{y}_{21} \tag{6.4}$$

$$\mathbf{\Delta}_{y1} = \mathbf{\Delta}_y + \mathbf{y}_{22}\mathbf{Y}_G \tag{6.5}$$

$$\mathbf{\Delta}_{y2} = \mathbf{\Delta}_y + \mathbf{y}_{11}\mathbf{Y}_L \tag{6.6}$$

$$\mathbf{\Delta}_{y12} = \mathbf{\Delta}_y + \mathbf{y}_{11}\mathbf{Y}_L + \mathbf{y}_{22}\mathbf{Y}_G + \mathbf{Y}_G\mathbf{Y}_L \tag{6.7}$$

These determinants are all used in the following.

(B) The voltage-transfer function for the entire network is the same as for the twoport proper and is obtained from Eqs. 6.2 and 6.3, with $\mathbf{I}_2 = -\mathbf{Y}_L\mathbf{V}_2$:

$$\mathbf{A}_V(\omega) = \frac{\mathbf{V}_2}{\mathbf{V}_1} = \frac{-\mathbf{y}_{21}}{\mathbf{Y}_{22L}} = \frac{-\mathbf{y}_{21}}{\mathbf{y}_{22} + \mathbf{Y}_L} \tag{6.8}$$

(C) The current-transfer function for the entire network is obtained from Eqs. 6.2 and 6.3. With $\mathbf{V}_2 = -\mathbf{I}_2/\mathbf{Y}_L = -\mathbf{Z}_L\mathbf{I}_2$, it is

$$\mathbf{A}_{I1}(\omega) = \frac{\mathbf{I}_2}{I_G} = \frac{\mathbf{y}_{21}}{\mathbf{Y}_{11G} + \mathbf{\Delta}_{y1}\mathbf{Z}_L} = \frac{\mathbf{y}_{21}}{\mathbf{y}_{11} + \mathbf{Y}_G + (\mathbf{\Delta}_y + \mathbf{y}_{22}\mathbf{Y}_G)\mathbf{Z}_L} \tag{6.9}$$

If we here set $\mathbf{Y}_G = 0$, $\mathbf{Y}_{11G} = \mathbf{y}_{11}$, and $I_G = \mathbf{I}_1$, Eq. 6.9 describes the desired current-transfer function and takes the form

$$\mathbf{A}_I(\omega) = \frac{\mathbf{I}_2}{\mathbf{I}_1} = \frac{\mathbf{y}_{21}}{\mathbf{y}_{11} + \mathbf{\Delta}_y\mathbf{Z}_L} \tag{6.10}$$

(D) With $\mathbf{Y}_G = 0$, $I_G = \mathbf{I}_1$, we obtain from Eqs. 6.2 and 6.3:

$$\mathbf{Y}_{in} = (\mathbf{\Delta}_y + \mathbf{y}_{11}\mathbf{Y}_L)/(\mathbf{y}_{22} + \mathbf{Y}_L) = \mathbf{\Delta}_{y2}/\mathbf{Y}_{22L} \tag{6.11}$$

As an alternative, we may use determinants and Cramer's Rule in the same manner as in problem 5D.

(E) Using the Output Immittance Theorem, we obtain for the entire network from Eq. 6.9:

$$\mathbf{Y}_{out\ 1} = (\mathbf{\Delta}_y + \mathbf{y}_{22}\mathbf{Y}_G)/(\mathbf{y}_{11} + \mathbf{Y}_G) = \mathbf{\Delta}_{y1}/\mathbf{Y}_{11G} \tag{6.12}$$

Since $\mathbf{Y}_{in}$ is already available, we could have obtained $\mathbf{Y}_{out}$ as a second alternative merely by interchanging subscripts in the formula for $\mathbf{Y}_{in}$, that is, Eq. 6.11. As a third alternative, we may use the Applied Source Method.

(F) By the same reasoning that was applied in problem 5F, we obtain the available gain as

$$G_{ava} = \frac{P_2}{P_{1\ ava}} = 4G_G G_L \left(\frac{V_2}{I_G}\right)^2 = 4G_G G_L \left|\frac{\mathbf{V}_2}{I_G}\right|^2 \tag{6.13}$$

Then from Eqs. 6.2 and 6.3

$$G_{ava} = 4G_G G_L \left|\frac{-\mathbf{y}_{21}}{\mathbf{Y}_{11G}\mathbf{Y}_L + \mathbf{\Delta}_{y1}}\right|^2 = \frac{4G_G G_L y_{21}^2}{|(\mathbf{y}_{11} + \mathbf{Y}_G)\mathbf{Y}_L + \mathbf{\Delta}_y + \mathbf{y}_{22}\mathbf{Y}_G|^2}$$

which may be further elaborated upon.

(G) By the same reasoning that was applied in problem 5G, we obtain an active PI with the series arm, $-\mathbf{y}_{12}$, and the downwards directed current source, $\mathbf{y}_m\mathbf{V}_1 = (\mathbf{y}_{21} - \mathbf{y}_{12})\mathbf{V}_1$. The first leg in the PI is $(\mathbf{Y}_{11G} + \mathbf{y}_{12})$, and the second leg in the PI is $(\mathbf{Y}_{22L} + \mathbf{y}_{12})$, with the output port left open.

Conclusions to this solution

The conclusions are largely the same as those drawn with reference to problem solution 5. The similarity between solutions pertaining to a series input and z parameters on the one hand, and parallel input and y parameters on the other hand, should be noticed.

PROBLEM 7

Using the method of the "floating" matrix, start out from the (gCE) transistor

$$|g|_{CE} = \begin{vmatrix} 2/28 & -1/28 \\ 18/28 & 5/28 \end{vmatrix}$$

and

(A) Transform it into an (hCC) transistor and then proceed to transform it into an (rCB) transistor.

(B) Transform this (rCB) transistor back to a (gCE) transistor and show that the initially given matrix is obtained.

Solution

(A) We begin by inserting the given information in the complete "floating" third-order matrix given in Appendix C. Since the basic parameter is the g parameter in this matrix, and since the transistor employs CE-connection, the four matrix elements given above fall directly into the four corners of the third-order matrix, which therefore takes the form shown in 7.1:

$$\begin{vmatrix} 2/28 & -1/28 & -1/28 \\ -20/28 & 24/28 & -4/28 \\ 18/28 & -23/28 & 5/28 \end{vmatrix} \tag{7.1}$$

$$|h|_{CC} = \begin{vmatrix} 14 & 1/2 \\ -10 & 1/2 \end{vmatrix} \tag{7.2}$$

The remaining five elements can now be filled in on the basis that all column sums must be zero and all row sums zero. The immediate request is for an (hCC) transistor, and we are therefore interested in the upper left four elements, 2/28,–1/28,–20/28, and 24/28. These are y parameter values, however, and we must now use the "built-in" formulas in the complete third-order matrix to secure h parameters in the CC-connection matrix. Accordingly, we read off

$$\frac{2}{28} = \frac{1}{h_{11}''} \qquad \frac{-1}{28} = \frac{-h_{12}''}{14} \qquad \frac{-20}{28} = \frac{h_{21}''}{14} \qquad \frac{24}{28} = h_{22}'' - \frac{(1/2)(-10)}{14}$$

$$\therefore h_{11}'' = 14 \qquad \therefore h_{12}'' = 1/2 \qquad \therefore h_{21}'' = -10 \qquad \therefore h_{22}'' = 1/2 \tag{7.3}$$

The resulting matrix is shown in 7.2. We are next requested to find the corresponding (rCB) transistor. If 7.2 is the starting point and 7.1 unknown, we insert the information from 7.2 into the complete third-order matrix with 7.1 as result. Since the elements of interest are the ones in the right lower corner of 7.1, the only work we have to perform is to transform from g to r parameters. Again using the "built-in" transformation formulas, we write

$$\frac{24}{28} = \frac{r_{22}}{\Delta_r} = r_{22}\Delta_g = r_{22}\frac{1}{28} \qquad \frac{-4}{28} = \frac{-r_{12}}{\Delta_r} = -r_{12}\Delta_g = -r_{12}\frac{1}{28}$$

$$\therefore r_{22} = 24 \qquad \therefore r_{12} = 4$$

$$\frac{-23}{28} = \frac{-r_{21}}{\Delta_r} = -r_{21}\Delta_g = -r_{21}\frac{1}{28} \qquad \frac{5}{28} = \frac{r_{11}}{\Delta_r} = r_{11}\Delta_g = r_{11}\frac{1}{28}$$

$$\therefore r_{21} = 23 \qquad \therefore r_{11} = 5 \tag{7.4}$$

Here we obtained direct transformations for each r element by utilizing the well-known relationship, $\Delta_r = 1/\Delta_g$. Without the aid of this information, we would have to calculate Δ_r, which we can do by writing

$$\Delta_r = r_{11}r_{22} - r_{12}r_{21} = \left(\frac{5\Delta_r}{28}\right)\left(\frac{24\Delta_r}{28}\right) - \left(\frac{4\Delta_r}{28}\right)\left(\frac{23\Delta_r}{28}\right) = 28 \tag{7.5}$$

The desired (rCB) matrix is as follows:

$$|r|_{CB} = \begin{vmatrix} 5 & 4 \\ 23 & 24 \end{vmatrix} \tag{7.6}$$

(B) If 7.6 is the only available information, we construct the third order matrix from it and thus obtain 7.1. In doing this, we merely retrace the steps we took in (A). Inspecting the corners of the third order matrix, we directly find the required (gCE) transistor.

Conclusions to this solution

This is our first example of the use of the floating-matrix technique, facilitated by the author's complete third-order matrix, which has "built-in" transformation formulas.[1] Generally, this is the fastest method known to transform from one connection to another, whatever the parameters. Note, however, that other methods exist, such as the Equation System Comparison Method. As an exercise, the student may carry out each one of the indicated transformations, using this method as an alternative.

PROBLEM 8

(A) Using the "floating" matrix method, start out from a (gCC) transistor and transform it to an (rCE) transistor.

(B) Employing the Equation System Comparison Method, transform the (r CE) transistor back to a (gCC) transistor and show that it is identical to the one we started out with in (A).

(C) Same as (B), except that we now use the Arm Interchange Method for the transformation.

Solution

(A) The (gCC) transistor matrix, positioned properly in the "floating" matrix, is shown in 8.1.

$$\begin{vmatrix} g_{11}'' & g_{12}'' & - \\ g_{21}'' & g_{22}'' & - \\ - & - & - \end{vmatrix} \tag{8.1}$$

$$\begin{vmatrix} g_{11}'' & g_{12}'' & -(g_{11}''+g_{12}'') \\ g_{21}'' & g_{22}'' & -(g_{21}''+g_{22}'') \\ -(g_{11}''+g_{21}'') & -(g_{12}''+g_{22}'') & (g_{11}''+g_{22}''+g_{12}''+g_{21}'')=g'' \end{vmatrix} \tag{8.2}$$

The matrix completed according to the zero-column and zero-row rule is shown in 8.2. The corner elements now represent the CE-connected transistor, but in terms of g parameters. We wish to obtain them in terms of r parameters. Accordingly, we write:

[1]Stockman, H. E.. "Transistor Transformation Matrix," *Electro-Technology*, vol. 72, No. 3, Sept. 1963. An early paper on this kind of transformation was presented by Jacob Shekel in *Proceedings of the IRE*, vol. 40, No. 11, Nov. 1952, pp. 1493-1497.

$$g_{11}'' = \frac{r_{22}'}{\Delta r'} \qquad -(g_{11}'' + g_{12}'') = \frac{-r_{12}'}{\Delta r'}$$

$$-(g_{11}'' + g_{21}'') = \frac{-r_{21}'}{\Delta r'} \qquad g'' = \frac{r_{11}'}{\Delta r'} \tag{8.3}$$

Making use of the relationship $\Delta_r{}' = 1/\Delta_g'$ and calculating Δ_g' as follows,

$$\Delta_g' = g_{11}''g'' - [(-g_{11}'' - g_{12}'')(-g_{11}'' - g_{21}'')] = g_{11}''g_{22}'' - g_{12}''g_{21}'' = \Delta_g'' \tag{8.4}$$

we may rewrite 8.3 in the following fashion:

$$r_{22}' = g_{11}''/\Delta_g' \qquad r_{12}' = (g_{11}'' + g_{12}'')/\Delta_g' \tag{8.5}$$

$$r_{21}' = (g_{11}'' + g_{21}'')/\Delta_g' \qquad r_{11}' = g''/\Delta_g'$$

The (rCE) matrix requested in (A) is therefore

$$\begin{vmatrix} r_{11}' & r_{12}' \\ r_{21}' & r_{22}' \end{vmatrix} = \begin{vmatrix} g''/\Delta_g' & (g_{11}'' + g_{12}'')/\Delta_g' \\ (g_{11}'' + g_{21}'')/\Delta_g' & g_{11}''/\Delta_g' \end{vmatrix} = |r|_{CE} \tag{8.6}$$

(B) We begin by drawing the key network diagrams (see Fig. 8.1). Expressing the variables in Fig. 8.1a in terms of the variables in Fig. 8.1b, we write the equation systems:

$$V_1' = r_{11}'I_1' + r_{12}'I_2' \tag{8.7}$$

$$V_2' = r_{21}'I_1' + r_{22}'I_2' \tag{8.8}$$

$$V_1'' - V_2'' = r_{11}'I_1'' + r_{12}'(-I_1'' - I_2'') \tag{8.9}$$

$$-V_2'' = r_{21}'I_1'' + r_{22}'(-I_1'' - I_2'') \tag{8.10}$$

from which

$$V_1'' = (r_{11}' + r_{22}' - r_{12}' - r_{21}')I_1'' + (r_{22}' - r_{12}')I_2'' = r_{11}''I_1'' + r_{12}''I_2''$$

$$V_2'' = (r_{22}' - r_{21}')I_1'' + r_{22}'I_2'' = r_{21}''I_1'' + r_{22}''I_2''$$

(8.11) and (8.12)

Accordingly

$$r_{11}'' = (r_{11}' + r_{22}' - r_{12}' - r_{21}') \qquad r_{12}'' = (r_{22}' - r_{12}')$$

$$r_{21}'' = (r_{22}' - r_{21}') \qquad r_{22}'' = r_{22}' \tag{8.13}$$

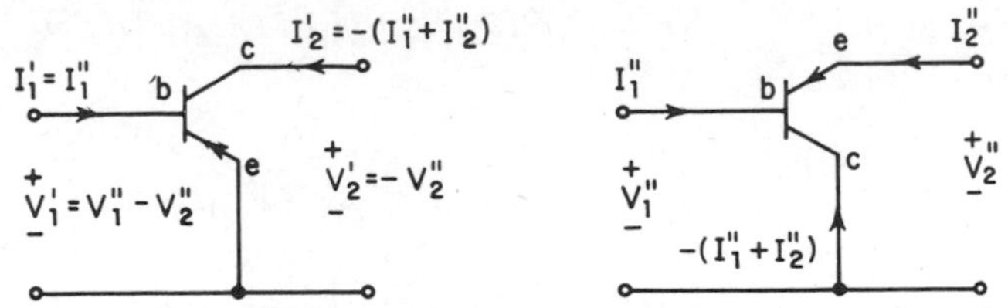

(a) Given CE connection (b) Unknown CC connection

Fig. 8.1

Inserting values from (8.6), we obtain:

$$r_{11}'' = g_{22}''/\Delta_g' \qquad r_{12}'' = -g_{12}''/\Delta_g'$$
$$r_{21}'' = -g_{21}''/\Delta_g' \qquad r_{22}'' = g_{11}''/\Delta_g' \tag{8.14}$$

These matrix elements represent the (rCC) transistor. What we want, however, is the (gCC) transistor. Since the calculations already have become lengthy, we consult Matrix Table 2 in Appendix C, making use of the equality $\Delta_r'' = 1/\Delta_g''$. We have already shown in 8.4 that $\Delta_g' = \Delta_g''$. We can therefore write $\Delta_r'' = 1/\Delta_g'$, and with capital letters symbolizing the desired matrix elements, we obtain:

$$G_{11}'' = r_{22}''/\Delta_r'' = g_{11}'' \qquad G_{12}'' = -r_{12}''/\Delta_r'' = g_{12}''$$
$$G_{21}'' = -r_{21}''/\Delta_r'' = g_{21}'' \qquad G_{22}'' = r_{11}''/\Delta_r'' = g_{22}'' \tag{8.15}$$

Thus we have recovered the original (gCC) matrix that we initially inserted into 8.1 in solution (A). This was quite a tedious solution, however.

(C) We begin by drawing the network equivalents (see Fig. 8.2). Here Fig. 8.2b is obtained merely by interchanging the positions of the mid-arm and the output arm in Fig. 8.2a. It is seen that I_1' and I_1'' have the same direction and that the function source in Fig. 8.2b is controlled by I_1'' ($r_m'I_1' = r_m'I_1''$). Applying the parameter definitions to the network in Fig. 8.2b, we obtain rather directly:

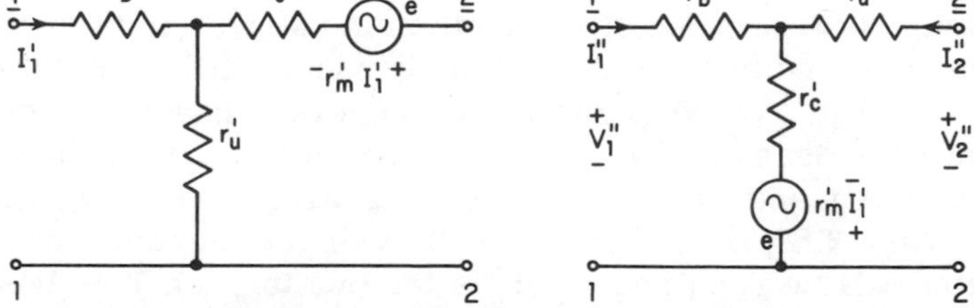

(a) Given CE connection (b) Unknown CC connection

Fig. 8.2

$$r_{11}'' = \left.\frac{V_1''}{I_1''}\right|_{I_2''=0} = r_b' + r_c' - r_m' \qquad r_{12}'' = \left.\frac{V_1''}{I_2''}\right|_{I_1''=0} = r_c'$$

$$r_{21}'' = \left.\frac{V_2''}{I_1''}\right|_{I_2''=0} = r_c' - r_m' \qquad r_{22}'' = \left.\frac{V_2''}{I_2''}\right|_{I_1''=0} = r_c' + r_u' \qquad (8.16)$$

This method yields the desired parameters in terms of base, emitter, collector, and mutual resistance, while the previous methods produced matrix elements. That the results obtained agree with those in 8.13 is evident if we use the key:

$$\begin{aligned} r_b' &= r_{11}' - r_{12}' & r_c' &= r_{22}' - r_{12}' \\ r_u' &= r_{12}' & r_m' &= r_{21}' - r_{12}' \end{aligned} \qquad (8.17)$$

by the use of which 8.16 yields 8.13.

Conclusions to this solution

The "floating" matrix solution in (A), employing the complete third-order matrix (see footnote) is a fast and elegant method, even when algebraical expressions are used. It is generally the number-one method to use, although it is employed very sparingly in today's transistor literature. The Equation System Comparison Method is long and tedious, particularly when algebraical expressions are used. With complex matrix elements the calculations sometimes go entirely out of hand, while the matrix method handles complex numbers just about as easily as real numbers. On the other hand, when small real numbers are used, the Equation System Comparison Method is workable, and can then be used as a check on the results obtained with the matrix method.

We note that both methods produce matrix elements. In contrast to this, the Arm Interchange Method produces electrode resistances together with the mutual resistance, but otherwise appears as a variation of the Equation System Comparison Method. Neither method is as fast as the "floating" matrix method, and this is particularly true when storage elements appear in the networks. Nevertheless, one of the three methods usually fits a certain problem better than the other two, but you never know which one until you have considered the specific problem at hand. It all depends on what the given and desired parameters are, whether we are concerned with a TEE or a PI, and whether or not an additional transformation will be required, such as the one in 8.17. It is best to be equally familiar with all three methods.

PROBLEM 9

A transistor amplifier employing a (gCB) transistor is described by the network matrix

$$|g|_{CB} = \begin{vmatrix} 15.39 \times 10^{-3}\,\mho & -15.39 \times 10^{-6}\,\mho \\ -14.77 \times 10^{-3}\,\mho & g_{22} \end{vmatrix}$$

The amplifier is provided with a load admittance consisting of the conductance $G_L = 10^{-4}$ mho, shunted by the elastance $S_L = 10^9$ daraf. This gives the amplifier an upper cutoff angular velocity, $\omega_c = 115{,}800$ rad/sec.

(A) Determine the unknown matrix element, g_{22}.

(B) Construct the gTEE, the rPI, and the hPI and label them with the proper numerical quantities.

(C) Calculate the output power P_2 as function of V_1^2 and discuss the commonly used relation determining the 3-db upper cutoff frequency.

Solution

(A) A block diagram of the amplifier is shown in Fig. 9.1. One way of determining the missing matrix element, g_{22}, is to write an equation for $\mathbf{A}_V(\omega) = \mathbf{V}_2/\mathbf{V}_1$ at the cutoff frequency, so that the element, g_{22}, becomes the only unknown. The equation system takes the form

$$\left.\begin{aligned} \mathbf{I}_1 &= g_{11}\mathbf{V}_1 + g_{12}\mathbf{V}_2 \\ \mathbf{I}_2 &= g_{21}\mathbf{V}_1 + g_{22}\mathbf{V}_2 = -\mathbf{Y}_L\mathbf{V}_2 \end{aligned}\right\} \qquad \begin{aligned} (9.1) \\ (9.2) \end{aligned}$$

from which

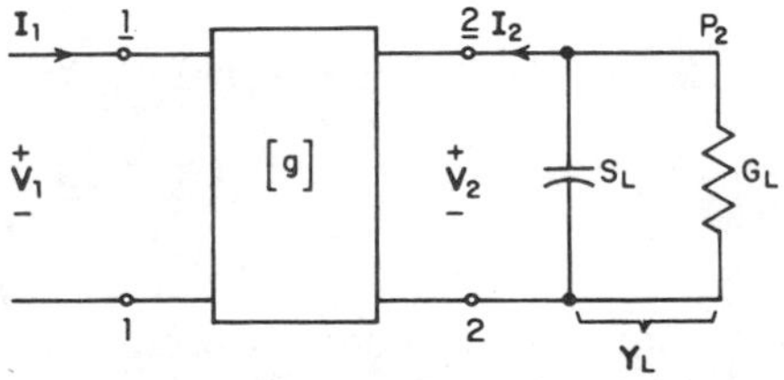

Fig. 9.1

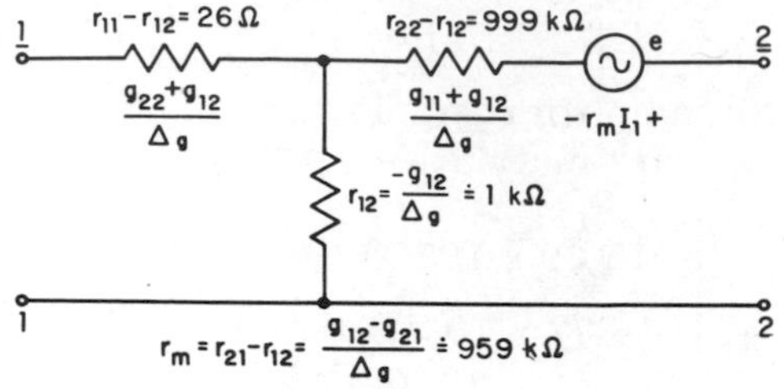

Fig. 9.2

$$\mathbf{A}_V(\omega) = \frac{\mathbf{V}_2}{\mathbf{V}_1} = -\frac{g_{21}}{g_{22} + \mathbf{Y}_L} = -\frac{g_{21}}{g_{22} + G_L + jB_L} \tag{9.3}$$

where $jB_L = j\omega C_L = j\omega/S_L$. Defining the cutoff frequency as the frequency at which the amplification has fallen to $1/\sqrt{2}$ of its medium-frequency value, we write

$$\frac{g_{21}}{\sqrt{(g_{22} + G_L)^2 + B_{Lc}^{\;2}}} = \left(\frac{1}{\sqrt{2}}\right)\left(\frac{g_{21}}{g_{22} + G_L}\right) \tag{9.4}$$

from which

$$g_{22} = \omega_c C_L - G_L = 115,\ 800 \times 10^{-9} - 10^{-4} \doteq 15.80\,\mu\text{mho} \tag{9.5}$$

This is the desired answer.

(B) The gTEE is merely the rTEE labeled in terms of the g parameter. This TEE is shown in Fig. 9.2. The g parameters are determined as follows:

$$\Delta_g = g_{11}g_{22} - g_{12}g_{21} = (15.39 \times 10^{-3})(15.80 \times 10^{-6}) - (-15.39 \times 10^{-6}) \times (-14.77 \times 10^{-3}) \doteq 154 \times 10^{-10}$$

$$(g_{22} + g_{12})/\Delta_g = [(15.80 \times 10^{-6}) + (-15.39 \times 10^{-6})]/(154 \times 10^{-10}) \doteq 26\,\Omega$$

$$(g_{11} + g_{12})/\Delta_g = [(15.39 \times 10^{-3}) + (-15.39 \times 10^{-6})]/(154 \times 10^{-10}) \doteq 999\text{k}\Omega$$

$$(g_{12} - g_{21})/\Delta_g = [(-15.39 \times 10^{-6}) - (-14.77 \times 10^{-3})]/(154 \times 10^{-10}) \doteq 959\text{k}\Omega$$

$$-g_{12}/\Delta_g = -(15.39 \times 10^{-6})/(154 \times 10^{-10}) \doteq 1\,\text{k}\Omega \tag{9.6}$$

The rPI is merely the gPI labeled in terms of the r parameters. This PI is shown in Fig. 9.3. The network element values have al-

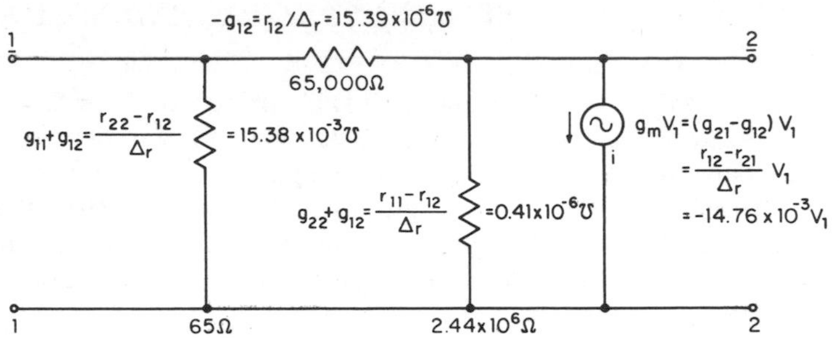

Fig. 9.3

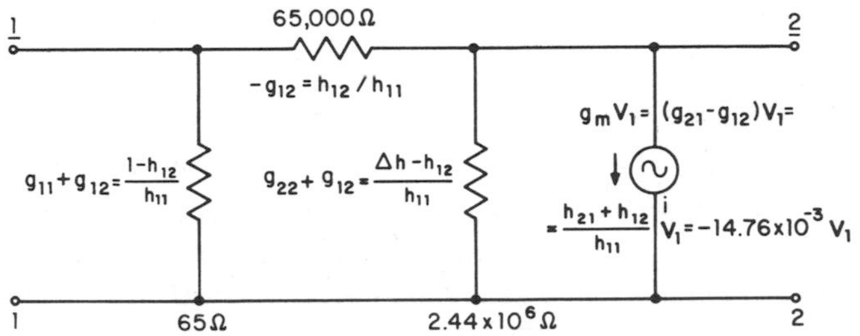

Fig. 9.4

ready been calculated as part of 9.6 and are properly introduced in Fig. 9.3. The *h* PI is the same PI as far as numerical values are concerned, and Fig. 9.4 shows this PI with the proper *h* formulas inserted.

We may be interested in using one of the equivalent networks to determine how much voltage amplification this amplifier gives in its pass band at medium frequency. From Eq. 9.3 we obtain:

$$\mathbf{A}_V(\omega) = \frac{\mathbf{V}_2}{\mathbf{V}_1} = -\frac{g_{21}}{g_{22} + G_L} = -\frac{-14.77 \times 10^{-3}}{(15.80 \times 10^{-6}) + 10^{-4}} \doteq 128 \qquad (9.7)$$

(C) The output power is $P_2 = G_L V_2^2 = G_L|\mathbf{A}_V(\omega)\mathbf{V}_1|^2$. Thus from Eq. 9.7 with $\mathbf{V}_1 = V_1$,

$$P_2 = G_L \left| \frac{-g_{21}}{g_{22} + G_L} V_1 \right|^2 \doteq 10^{-4} \times 128^2 V_1^2 = 1.63\, V_1^2 \text{ watt} \qquad (9.8)$$

At the cutoff point this power is down to half its value, that is, 0.81 V_1^2 watt. The fact that the power in the load immittance is reduced to one half at the cutoff frequency, $\omega_c/2\pi$ gives us one method of determining this frequency. Another method already used in Eq. 9.4 is the same thing pertaining to voltage rather than power; we note the frequency at which the output voltage has fallen to $1/\sqrt{2}$ of its mid-frequency value. Both these criteria imply that as the cutoff frequency is approached, the resistive part in the denominator equals the reactive part, meaning that the phase angle becomes 45°. Thus the cutoff frequency can be determined in two additional ways. Setting the resistive part equal to the reactive part, or in this particular problem, the conductance part equal to the susceptance part, we write:

$$g_{22} + G_L = B_L = \omega_c C_L \qquad (9.5a)$$

Using the phase angle criterion, we write:

$$tan^{-1}\, \omega_c C_L/(g_{22} + G_L) = 45° \qquad \therefore\ \omega_c C_L/(g_{22} + G_L) = 1 \qquad (9.9)$$

Since no instantaneous values appear in this problem, the voltages could be either maximum values or rms values, and usually we mean maximum values. In the power formula 9.8, however, we must be specific, since rms values must be used. Thus if maximum values are employed, we must divide them by $\sqrt{2}$.

Conclusions to this solution

Usually the matrix is given, but here we had an example of an incomplete matrix. However, this does not change the basic procedure of network calculations. We learned that a given transistor has just one numerical TEE and one numerical PI, and that it is merely a technicality as to which parameters we should like to use for labeling, although the r and g parameters are naturals. In (C) we reviewed four methods for determining the cutoff frequency of an amplifier.

PROBLEM 10

Given the r CB transistor amplifier shown in Fig. 10.1.

(A) Draw the equivalent r TEE and give all parameters, including Δ_r, using a shunt-form generator in the output arm. Define clearly the origin of the quantities, a and α, and indicate in the following both rigorous and approximate relationships. Determine the values, r_u, r_b, r_c, r_m, α, β, assuming that the latter may be calculated from the approximate formula, $\beta \doteq \alpha/(1 - \alpha)$. Also derive formulas for $A_I(\omega)$, $A_V(\omega)$, $A_E(\omega)$, R_{in}, R_{out}, and $R_{out\,1}$.

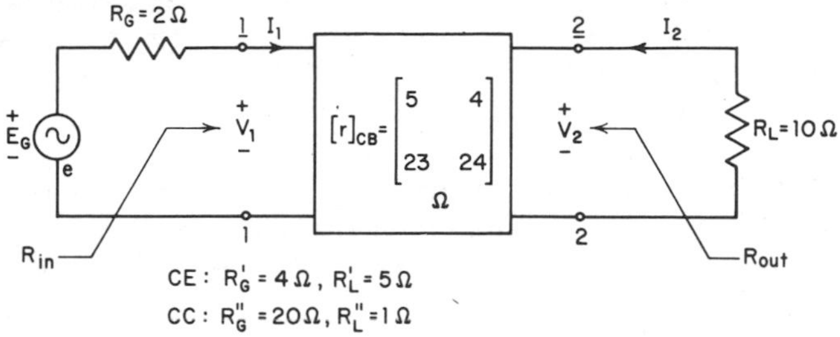

Fig. 10.1

(B) Obtain by means of matrix tables the corresponding g parameters with Δ_g, and draw and label the corresponding g PI.

(C) Obtain from matrix tables the h, k, a, and b parameters, and also determine Δ_h, Δ_k, Δ_a, and Δ_b.

(D) Obtain, either by means of the Equation System Comparison Method or the "Floating" Matrix Method, the (gCE) matrix, determining Δ_g' and labeling the corresponding g PI and the corresponding r TEE. Calculate $A_I'(\omega)$, $A_V'(\omega)$, $A_E'(\omega)$, R_{in}', R_{out}', and $R_{out\,1}'$.

(E) Discuss the quantities, b and β, and derive the formula for β used in (A).

(F) Extend the above calculations to the CE-connection h, k, a, and b parameters, always stating the Δ-quantities.

(G) By means of a similar procedure to that used in (D), obtain the CC-connection parameters and Δ_g'', and draw and label the corresponding g PI. Calculate $A_I''(\omega)$, $A_V''(\omega)$, $A_E''(\omega)$, R_{in}'', R_{out}'', and $R_{out\,1}''$.

(H) Define clearly the quantities, c and γ, and state their relationships to previously derived quantities of the same nature.

(I) Extend above calculations to the CC-connection h, k, a, and b parameters, always stating the Δ-quantities.

(J) Make up a table, expressing a in terms of b and c, b in terms of a and c, and a few additional typical relationships, including α, β, and γ.

(K) Determine $A_V(\omega)$ for all CB-connection parameters (that is, the r, g, h, k, a, and b parameters), $A_V'(\omega)$ for all CE-connection parameters, and $A_V''(\omega)$ for all CC-connection parameters, using the port-termination values shown in Fig. 10.1.

(L) Tabulate all values for $A_1(\omega)$, $A_V(\omega)$, R_{in}, and similarly all values for the corresponding single-prime and double-prime quantities, drawing conclusions about similarities and differences between the three connections.

(M) Make up a table from which one can see at a glance how the determinants and the inverse determinant relationships, such as $\Delta_g = 1/\Delta_r$, vary from one connection to another.

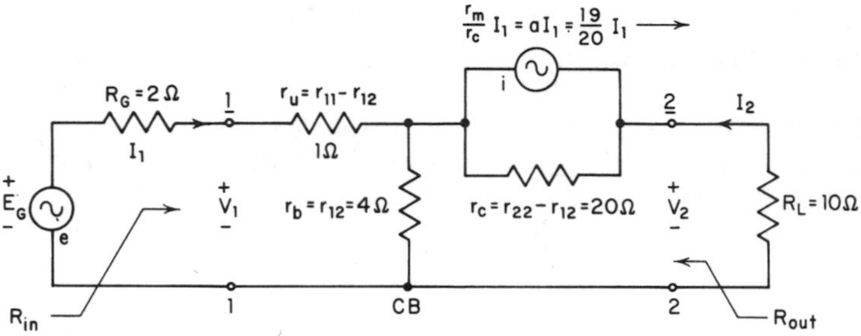

Fig. 10.2

Solution

(A) The required rTEE is shown in Fig. 10.2. From the given matrix:

$$r_{11} = 5\,\Omega \qquad r_u = r_{11} - r_{12} = 1\Omega \tag{10.1}$$

$$r_{12} = 4\Omega \qquad r_b = r_{12} = 4\Omega \tag{10.2}$$

$$r_{21} = 23\Omega \qquad r_c = r_{22} - r_{12} = 20\Omega \tag{10.3}$$

$$r_{22} = 24\,\Omega \qquad r_m = r_{21} - r_{12} = 19\,\Omega \tag{10.4}$$

$$\Delta_r = r_{11}r_{22} - r_{12}r_{21} = (5 \times 24) - (4 \times 23) = 28\,\Omega^2 \tag{10.5}$$

With a used as a notation for r_m/r_c, we obtain by definition

$$a = r_m/r_c = 19/20 = 0.950 \tag{10.6}$$

The quantity α is by definition the negative of the output-to-input current ratio when the output port is closed; thus

$$\alpha = -I_2/I_1 \Big|_{V_2=0} \tag{10.7}$$

The r parameter equation system, based upon the given matrix is

$$\left.\begin{aligned} V_1 &= r_{11}I_1 + r_{12}I_2 \quad (10.8)\\ V_2 &= r_{21}I_1 + r_{22}I_2 \quad (10.9)\end{aligned}\right\}$$

from which we obtain the current ratio

$$A_I(\omega)\Big|_{R_L=0} = \frac{I_2}{I_1}\Big|_{R_L=0} = -\frac{r_{21}}{r_{22}+R_L}\Big|_{R_L=0} = -\alpha \tag{10.10}$$

Accordingly

$$\alpha = r_{21}/r_{22} = (r_m + r_b)/(r_c + r_b) = 23/24 = 0.958 \tag{10.11}$$

so that

$$\alpha \doteq a \;\; if \;\; r_b \ll r_m,\; r_b \ll r_c \tag{10.12}$$

Accordingly, we obtain the following exact formulas:

$$\alpha = \frac{a + r_b/r_c}{1 + r_b/r_c} \tag{10.13}$$

$$a = \alpha - \frac{r_b}{r_c}(1-\alpha) \tag{10.14}$$

It is seen that α is larger than a. The quantity, β, is obtained from the suggested formula and is:

$$\beta \doteq \frac{\alpha}{1-\alpha} = \frac{23/24}{1-23/24} = 23 \tag{10.15}$$

Note that this is an approximation. The current transfer ratio is from Eq. 10.10:

$$A_I(\omega) = \frac{I_2}{I_1} = -\frac{r_{21}}{r_{22}+R_L} = -\frac{23}{34} = -0.677 \tag{10.16}$$

The voltage transfer ratio is from Eqs. 10.8 and 10.9:

$$A_V(\omega) = \frac{V_2}{V_1} = \frac{r_{21}}{r_{11} + \Delta_r G_L} = \frac{115}{39} = 2.95 \qquad (10.17)$$

If we extend r_{11} by R_G, we obtain:

$$\Delta_{r1} = (r_{11} + R_G)r_{22} - r_{12}r_{21} = \Delta_r + R_G r_{22} = 76 \qquad (10.18)$$

and thus

$$A_E(\omega) = \frac{V_2}{E_G} = \frac{r_{21}}{r_{11} + R_G + \Delta_{r1} G_L} = \frac{115}{73} = 1.58 \qquad (10.19)$$

The input resistance is from Eqs. 10.8 and 10.9:

$$R_{in} = \frac{V_1}{I_1} = \frac{\Delta_r + r_{11}R_L}{r_{22} + R_L} = \frac{39}{17} = 2.29\Omega \qquad (10.20)$$

Similarly the output resistances are:

$$R_{out} = \left.\frac{V_2}{I_2}\right|_V = \frac{\Delta_r}{r_{11}} = \frac{28}{5} = 5.60\,\Omega \qquad (10.21)$$

$$R_{out1} = \left.\frac{V_2}{I_2}\right|_E = \frac{\Delta_{r1}}{r_{11} + R_g} = \frac{76}{7} = 10.9\Omega \qquad (10.22)$$

These two results could have been obtained directly from Eqs. 10.17 and 10.19 by means of the Output Immittance Theorem.

(B) With the aid of Matrix Tables C1 and C2 in Appendix C, we obtain:

$$g_{11} = r_{22}/\Delta_r = 24/28 = 0.858\ \mho \qquad (10.23)$$

$$g_{12} = -r_{12}/\Delta_r = -4/28 = -0.143\ \mho \qquad (10.24)$$

$$g_{21} = -r_{21}/\Delta_r = -23/28 = -0.822\ \mho \qquad (10.25)$$

$$g_{22} = r_{11}/\Delta_r = 5/28 = 0.179\ \mho \qquad (10.26)$$

$$\Delta_g = 1/\Delta_r = 1/28 = 0.0357\mho^2 \qquad (10.27)$$

The required gPI is shown in Fig. 10.3. The quantities in the network equivalent are:

$$g_{11} + g_{12} = 5/7 = 0.715 \ \mho \quad (10.28)$$

$$g_{22} + g_{12} = 1/28 = 0.0357 \ \mho \quad (10.29)$$

$$g_m = g_{21} - g_{12} = (-19)/28 = -0.679 \ \mho \quad (10.30)$$

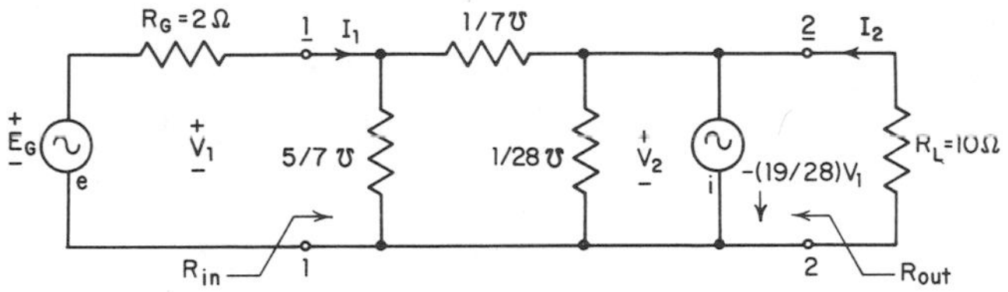

Fig. 10.3

(C) The required quantities are from Matrix Tables C1 and C2:

$$|h|_{CB} = \begin{vmatrix} 7/6 = 1.167 & 1/6 = 0.167 \\ -23/24 = -0.958 & 1/24 = 0.0416 \end{vmatrix} \quad \Delta_h = \frac{5}{24} = 0.208 \quad (10.31)$$

$$|k|_{CB} = \begin{vmatrix} 1/5 = 0.200 & -4/5 = -0.800 \\ 23/5 = 4.60 & 28/5 = 5.60 \end{vmatrix} \quad \Delta_k = \frac{24}{5} = 4.80 = \frac{1}{\Delta_h} \quad (10.32)$$

$$|a|_{CB} = \begin{vmatrix} 5/23 = 0.217 & 28/23 = 1.22 \\ 1/23 = 0.0435 & 24/23 = 1.043 \end{vmatrix} \quad \Delta_a = \frac{4}{23} = 0.147 \quad (10.33)$$

$$|b|_{CB} = \begin{vmatrix} 6/1 = 6.00 & 7/1 = 7.00 \\ 1/4 = 0.250 & 5/4 = 1.25 \end{vmatrix} \quad \Delta_b = \frac{23}{4} = 5.75 = \frac{1}{\Delta_a} \quad (10.34)$$

(D) We shall first make use of the Equation System Comparison Method (see Fig. 10.4). Expressing the variables in Fig. 10.4a in terms of the variables in Fig. 10.4b, we obtain:

$$V_1 = r_{11} I_1 + r_{12} I_2 \quad (10.35)$$

$$V_2 = r_{21} I_1 + r_{22} I_2 \quad (10.36)$$

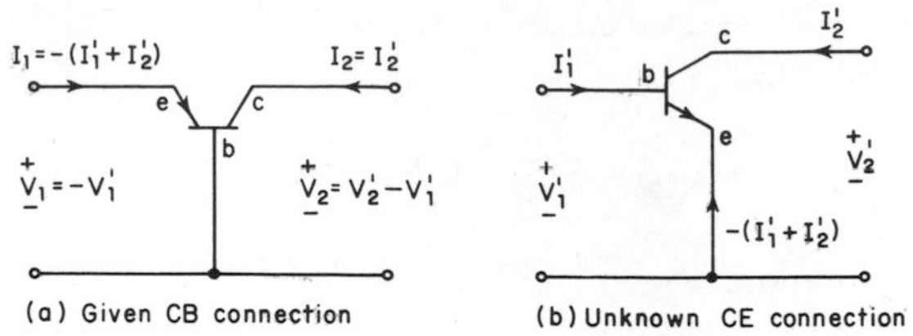

Fig. 10.4

$$-V_1' = r_{11}(-I_1' - I_2') + r_{12}I_2' \tag{10.37}$$

$$V_2' - V_1' = r_{21}(-I_1' - I_2') + r_{22}I_2' \tag{10.38}$$

from which

$$V_1' = r_{11}I_1' + (r_{11} - r_{12})I_2' = r_{11}'I_1' + r_{12}'I_2' \tag{10.39}$$

$$V_2' = (r_{11} - r_{21})I_1' + (r_{11} + r_{22} - r_{12} - r_{21})I_2' = r_{21}'I_1' + r_{22}'I_2' \tag{10.40}$$

Accordingly,

$$r_{11}' = r_{11} = 5\,\Omega \tag{10.41}$$

$$r_{12}' = (r_{11} - r_{12}) = 1\,\Omega \tag{10.42}$$

$$r_{21}' = (r_{11} - r_{21}) = -18\,\Omega \tag{10.43}$$

$$r_{22}' = (r_{11} + r_{22} - r_{12} - r_{21}) = 2\,\Omega \tag{10.44}$$

$$r_u' = r_{12}' = r_u = 1\,\Omega \tag{10.45}$$

$$r_b' = (r_{11}' - r_{12}') = 4\,\Omega = r_b \tag{10.46}$$

$$r_c' = (r_{22}' - r_{12}') = 1\,\Omega \neq r_c \tag{10.47}$$

$$r_m' = (r_{21}' - r_{12}') = -19\Omega \neq r_m \tag{10.48}$$

$$\Delta_r' = r_{11}'r_{22}' - r_{12}'r_{21}' = (5)(2) - (1)(-18) = 28\,\Omega^2 = \Delta_r \tag{10.49}$$

The CB and CE matrices are:

$$|r|_{CB} = \begin{vmatrix} 5 & 4 \\ 23 & 24 \end{vmatrix} \tag{10.50}$$

$$|r|_{CE} = \begin{vmatrix} 5 & 1 \\ -18 & 2 \end{vmatrix} \tag{10.51}$$

Note that the input and mid-arms are only interchanged, while the resistance of the output arm in the CE connection is drastically reduced. To transform to g parameters, we make use of matrix tables C1 and C2, obtaining:

$$g_{11}' = r_{22}'/\Delta_r' = 2/28 = 0.0715\,\mho \tag{10.52}$$

$$g_{12}' = -r_{12}'/\Delta_r' = -1/28 = -0.0357\,\mho \tag{10.53}$$

$$g_{21}' = -r_{21}'/\Delta_r' = 18/28 = 0.643\,\mho \tag{10.54}$$

$$g_{22}' = r_{11}'/\Delta_r' = 5/28 = 0.178\,\mho \tag{10.55}$$

$$\Delta_g' = 1/\Delta_r' = 1/28 = 0.0357\,\mho^2 \tag{10.56}$$

The required gPI and rTEE are shown in Figs. 10.5 and 10.6.

The g parameters may be obtained more directly if we replace Eqs. 10.35 to 10.38 with g parameter equations, eliminating the use of matrix tables. We obtain:

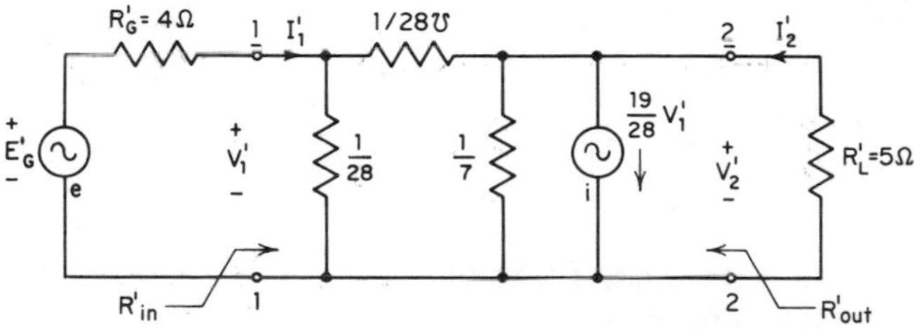

Fig. 10.5

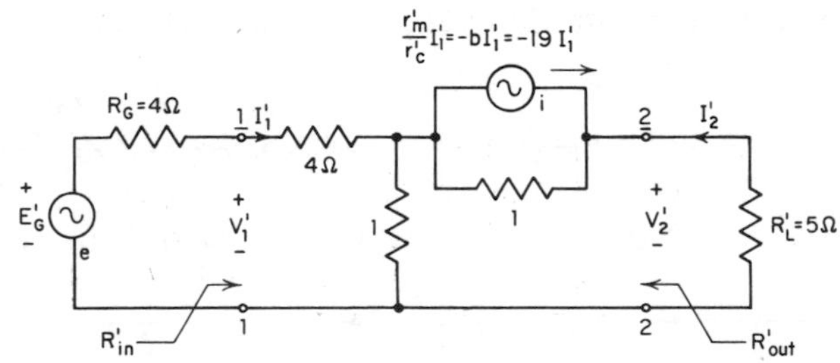

Fig. 10.6

$$\left.\begin{aligned} I_1 &= g_{11}V_1 + g_{12}V_2 \\ I_2 &= g_{21}V_1 + g_{22}V_2 \end{aligned}\right\} \quad \begin{aligned}(10.57)\\(10.58)\end{aligned}$$

$$\left.\begin{aligned} -I_1' - I_2' &= g_{11}(-V_1') + g_{12}(V_2' - V_1') \\ I_2' &= g_{21}(-V_1') + g_{22}(V_2' - V_1') \end{aligned}\right\} \quad \begin{aligned}(10.59)\\(10.60)\end{aligned}$$

from which

$$I_1' = (g_{11} + g_{12} + g_{21} + g_{22})V_1' - (g_{12} + g_{22})V_2' = g_{11}'V_1' + g_{12}'V_2' \tag{10.61}$$

$$I_2' = \quad -(g_{21} + g_{22})V_1' \quad + g_{22}V_2' = g_{21}'V_1' + g_{22}'V_2' \tag{10.62}$$

where the parameters have the values previously given by Eqs. 10.52 to 10.55.

Employing the Arm Interchange Method, we start out from Fig. 10.7a and interchange the positions of the input arm and the mid-arm, thus obtaining the network equivalent shown in Fig. 10.7b. Applying the parameter definitions, and noticing that the current in r_u retains its initial direction, we write:

$$r_{11}' = \left.\frac{V_1'}{I_1'}\right|_{I_2'=0} = r_b + r_u \qquad r_{12}' = \left.\frac{V_1'}{I_2'}\right|_{I_1'=0} = r_u$$

$$r_{21}' = \left.\frac{V_2'}{I_1'}\right|_{I_2'=0} = r_u - r_m \qquad r_{22}' = \left.\frac{V_2'}{I_2'}\right|_{I_1'=0} = r_c + r_u - r_m$$

A comparison with Eqs. 10.41 to 10.48 and 10.1 to 10.4 shows that complete agreement exists.

Finally, we shall again make use of the "Floating" Matrix Method. The procedure is here exceedingly simple, since we may use the g parameters in Eqs. 10.23 to 10.26 as given information,

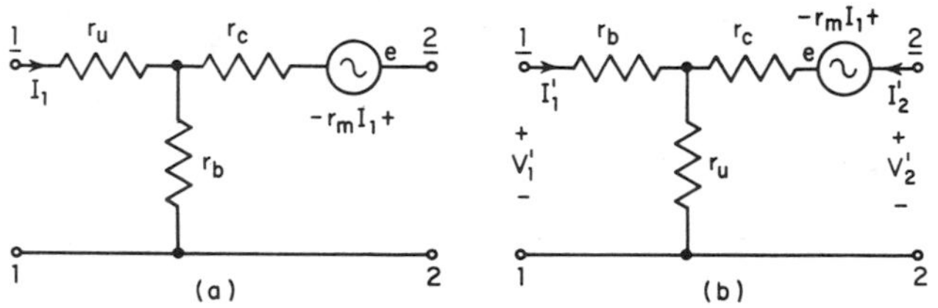

Fig. 10.7

resulting in the matrix to the left in 10.63. We now fill in the empty positions, obtaining:

$$\begin{vmatrix} \bar{g}_{11} & \bar{g}_{12} & \bar{g}_{13} \\ \bar{g}_{21} & 24/28 & -4/28 \\ \bar{g}_{31} & -23/28 & 5/28 \end{vmatrix} \longrightarrow \begin{vmatrix} 1/14 & -1/28 & -1/28 \\ -5/7 & 6/7 & 1/7 \\ 9/14 & -23/28 & 5/28 \end{vmatrix} \tag{10.63}$$

Thus:

$$|g|_{\text{CE}} = \begin{vmatrix} g_{11}' & g_{12}' \\ g_{21}' & g_{22}' \end{vmatrix} = \begin{vmatrix} 1/14 & -1/28 \\ 9/14 & 5/28 \end{vmatrix} \tag{10.64}$$

The matrix to the right in 10.63 results from the "zero row," "zero column" consideration. When we go into the third-order matrix, we employ the four positions in the right bottom corner; when we go out, we utilize the four extreme corner positions. This is the fastest method.

The required quantities are:

$$A_I'(\omega) = -r_{21}'/(r_{22}' + R_L') = 18/7 = 2.57 \tag{10.65}$$

$$A_V'(\omega) = r_{21}'/(r_{11}' + \Delta_r' G_L') = -90/53 = -1.70 \tag{10.66}$$

$$\Delta_{r1}' = (r_{11}' + R_G')r_{22}' - r_{12}'r_{21}' = \Delta_r' + R_G' r_{22}' = 36\Omega^2 \tag{10.67}$$

$$A_E'(\omega) = r_{21}'/(r_{11}' + R_G' + \Delta_{r1}' G_L') = -10/9 = -1.11 \tag{10.68}$$

$$R_{\text{in}}' = (\Delta_r' + r_{11}' R_L')/(r_{22}' + R_L') = 53/7 = 7.57\Omega \tag{10.69}$$

$$R_{\text{out}}' = \Delta_r'/r_{11}' = 28/5 = 5.60\Omega \tag{10.70}$$

$$R_{\text{out}\,1}' = \Delta_{r1}'/(r_{11}' + R_D') = 36/9 = 4.00\,\Omega \tag{10.71}$$

(E) In the r TEE in Fig. 10.6 we have introduced r_m'/r_c' as $-b$, obtaining $b = 19$. Following the established pattern, we shall introduce β to mean the output-to-input current ratio when the load resistance has zero value. Thus by definition:

$$b = -r_m'/r_c' = 19 \tag{10.72}$$

$$\beta = I_2'/I_1' \,|_{V_2' = 0} \tag{10.73}$$

Accordingly, both α and β are represented by positive numbers. From Eq. 10.10:

$$A_I{}'(\omega)\,\Big|_{R_L{}'=0} = I_2{}'/I_1{}'\,\Big|_{R_L{}'=0} = -r_{21}{}'/(r_{22}{}' + R_L{}')\,\Big|_{R_L{}'=0} = \beta \qquad (10.74)$$

$$\beta = -r_{21}{}'/r_{22}{}' = -(r_m{}' + r_u{}')/(r_c{}' + r_u{}') = 9 \qquad (10.75)$$

so that

$$\beta \doteq b \quad \text{if} \quad r_u{}' \ll r_m{}',\ r_u{}' \ll r_c{}' \qquad (10.76)$$

We can easily derive the following exact formulas:

$$\beta = (b - r_u{}'/r_c{}')/(1 + r_u{}'/r_c{}') \qquad (10.77)$$

$$b = \beta + r_u{}'(1 + \beta)/r_c{}' \qquad (10.78)$$

Note that β and b may differ considerably. Starting out to derive some useful cross-relationships, we write:

$$b = \frac{-r_m{}'}{r_c{}'} = \frac{r_{21} - r_{12}}{r_{22} - r_{12} - (r_{21} - r_{12})} = \frac{r_m}{r_c - r_m} = \frac{r_m/r_c}{1 - r_m/r_c} \qquad (10.79)$$

so that

$$b = a/(1 - a) \qquad (10.80)$$

$$a = b/(1 + b) \qquad (10.81)$$

Note that these formulas are exact. Similarly, for β:

$$\beta = \frac{-r_{21}{}'}{r_{22}{}'} = \frac{-(r_{11} - r_{21})}{r_{11} + r_{22} - r_{12} - r_{21}} = \frac{r_{21}/r_{22} - r_{11}/r_{22}}{1 - r_{21}/r_{22} + (r_{11} - r_{12})/r_{22}} \qquad (10.82)$$

Thus:

$$\beta = \frac{\alpha - r_{11}/r_{22}}{1 - \alpha + (r_{11} - r_{12})/r_{22}} \qquad (10.83)$$

$$\alpha = \frac{\beta + \dfrac{r_{11}}{r_{11} + r_{22} - r_{12}}}{1 + \beta} \times \frac{r_{11} + r_{22} - r_{12}}{r_{22}} \qquad (10.84)$$

Not always permissible approximations are

$$\beta \doteq \frac{\alpha}{1-\alpha} \tag{10.85}$$

$$\alpha \doteq \frac{\beta}{1+\beta} \tag{10.86}$$

Summarizing our numerical results, we have

$$\begin{aligned} a &= 19/20 = 0.950 \qquad & \alpha &= 23/24 = 0.958 \\ b &= 19 & \beta &= 9 \end{aligned} \tag{10.87}$$

We are at an advantage to work with a and b, since the formulas are simpler and exact. Additional formulas can be produced by combinations of the above ones, for example:

$$b = \frac{\alpha - r_b/(r_b + r_c)}{1 - [\alpha(r_b + r_c)/r_c] + r_b/r_c} \times \frac{r_b + r_c}{r_c} \tag{10.88}$$

For handy reference between the various formulas, see Table 10.1 in solution J.

(F) The desired results are:

$$|h|_{CE} = \begin{vmatrix} 14 & 1/2 \\ 9 & 1/2 \end{vmatrix} \qquad \Delta_h{}' = \frac{5}{2} = 2.50 \tag{10.89}$$

$$|k|_{CE} = \begin{vmatrix} 1/5 & -1/5 \\ -18/5 & 28/5 \end{vmatrix} \qquad \Delta_k{}' = \frac{2}{5} = 0.400 \tag{10.90}$$

$$|a|_{CE} = \begin{vmatrix} -5/18 & -14/9 \\ -1/18 & -1/9 \end{vmatrix} \qquad \Delta_a{}' = \frac{-1}{18} = -0.0556 \tag{10.91}$$

$$|b|_{CE} = \begin{vmatrix} 2 & 28 \\ 1 & 5 \end{vmatrix} \qquad \Delta_b{}' = -18 = \frac{1}{\Delta_a{}'} \tag{10.92}$$

(G) Making use of the already available third-order matrix in (10.63), we select the four elements in the upper left corner, obtaining

$$|g|_{cc} = \begin{vmatrix} 1/14 & -1/28 \\ -5/7 & 6/7 \end{vmatrix} \qquad \Delta_g'' = \left(\frac{1}{14}\times\frac{6}{7}\right) - \left(\frac{1}{28}\times\frac{5}{7}\right) = \frac{1}{28}\,℧^2 \tag{10.93}$$

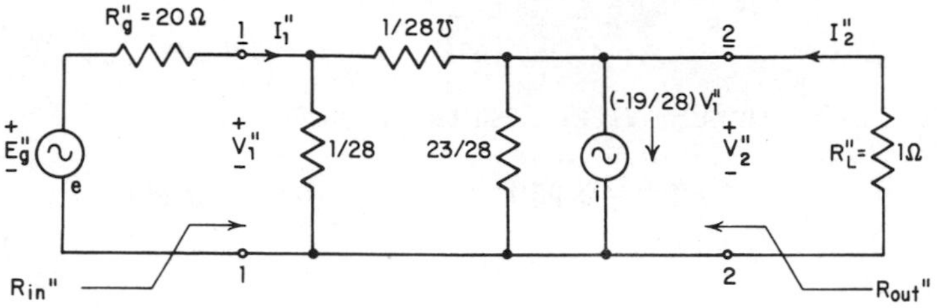

Fig. 10.8

The requested gPI is shown in Fig. 10.8. The r parameters, obtained with the aid of the matrix tables, are:

$$r_{11}'' = 24\,\Omega \tag{10.94}$$

$$r_{12}'' = 1\,\Omega \tag{10.95}$$

$$r_{21}'' = 20\,\Omega \tag{10.96}$$

$$r_{22}'' = 2\,\Omega \tag{10.97}$$

$$r_u'' = r_{22}'' - r_{12}'' = 1\,\Omega \tag{10.98}$$

$$r_b'' = r_{11}'' - r_{12}'' = 23\,\Omega \tag{10.99}$$

$$r_c'' = r_{12}'' = 1\,\Omega \tag{10.100}$$

$$r_m'' = r_{21}'' - r_{12}'' = 19\Omega \tag{10.101}$$

$$\Delta_r'' = r_{11}''r_{22}'' - r_{12}''r_{21}'' = (24 \times 2) - (1 \times 20) = 28\,\Omega^2 = \Delta_r' = \Delta_r \tag{10.102}$$

Instead of using the "Floating" Matrix Method to obtain Eq. 10.93, we may again make use of the Equation System Comparison Method, previously used with reference to Fig. 10.4. This transformation has already been carried out in problem 8 of this chapter. The required transfer functions and immittances are:

$$A_I''(\omega) = -r_{21}''/(r_{22}'' + R_L) = -20/3 = -6.67 \tag{10.103}$$

$$A_V''(\omega) = r_{21}''/(r_{11}'' + \Delta_r''G_L'') = 5/13 = 0.385 \tag{10.104}$$

$$\Delta_{r1}'' = (r_{11}'' + R_G'')r_{22}'' - r_{12}''r_{21}'' = \Delta_r'' + R_G''r_{22} = 68\Omega^2 \tag{10.105}$$

$$A_E''(\omega) = r_{21}''/(r_{11}'' + R_G'' + \Delta_{r1}''G_L'') = 5/28 = 0.179 \tag{10.106}$$

$$R_{\text{in}}'' = (\Delta_r'' + r_{11}''R_L'')/(r_{22}'' + R_L'') = 52/3 = 17.3\,\Omega \tag{10.107}$$

$$R_{\text{out}}'' = \Delta_r''/r_{11}'' = 7/6 = 1.17\,\Omega \tag{10.108}$$

$$R_{\text{out }1} = \Delta_{r1}''/(r_{11}'' + R_G'') = 17/11 = 1.55\,\Omega \tag{10.109}$$

(H) Following the established pattern, we introduce the definitions

$$c = r_m''/r_u'' = 19 \tag{10.110}$$

$$\gamma = -I_2''/I_1'' \,\Big|\, V_2''=0 \tag{10.111}$$

from which

$$A_I''(\omega) \,\Big|\, R_L''=0 = I_2''/I_1'' \,\Big|\, R_L''=0 = -r_{21}''/(r_{22}'' + R_L'') \,\Big|\, R_L''=0 = -\gamma \tag{10.112}$$

and

$$\gamma = r_{21}''/r_{22}'' = (r_m'' + r_c'')/(r_u'' + r_c'') = 10 \tag{10.113}$$

so that, from an academic point of view,

$$\gamma \doteq c \qquad \text{if} \qquad r_c'' \ll r_m'',\ r_c'' \ll r_u'' \tag{10.114}$$

We can easily derive the following exact formulas:

$$\gamma = (c + r_c''/r_u'')/(1 + r_c''/r_u'') \tag{10.115}$$

$$c = \gamma - r_c''(1 - \gamma)/r_u'' \tag{10.116}$$

Proceeding, we may develop the following typical formulas, suited for Table 1:

$$\gamma = \beta + 1, \qquad \beta = \gamma - 1 \tag{10.117}$$

$$c = \beta(1 + r_u'/r_c') + 1 \tag{10.118}$$

$$\beta = (c - 1)/(1 + r_u'/r_c') \tag{10.119}$$

(I) The required matrices and parameters are as follows:

$$|h|_{CC} = \begin{vmatrix} 14 & 1/2 \\ -10 & 1/2 \end{vmatrix} \qquad \Delta_h'' = 12 \tag{10.120}$$

$$|k|_{CC} = \begin{vmatrix} 1/24 & -1/24 \\ 5/6 & 7/6 \end{vmatrix} \qquad \Delta_k'' = \frac{1}{12} = \frac{1}{\Delta_h''} \tag{10.121}$$

$$|a|_{CC} = \begin{vmatrix} 6/5 & 7/5 \\ 1/20 & 1/10 \end{vmatrix} \qquad \Delta_a'' = \frac{1}{20} \tag{10.122}$$

$$|b|_{CC} = \begin{vmatrix} 2 & 28 \\ 1 & 24 \end{vmatrix} \qquad \Delta_b'' = 20 = \frac{1}{\Delta_a''} \tag{10.123}$$

(J) The desired table is Table 10.1 shown below. The numbers refer to equation numbers in the text. Many of the formulas have not yet been worked out and are left as additional exercises for the interested reader.

TABLE 10.1

	a	b	c	α	β	γ
a	(—)	(81)	( )	(14)	( )	( )
b	(80)	(—)	( )	(88)	(78)	( )
c	( )	( )	(—)	( )	(118)	(116)
α	(13)(12)	( )	( )	(—)	(84)(86)	( )
β	( )	(76)(77)	(119)	(15)(83)(85)	(—)	(117)
γ	( )	( )	(114)(115)	( )	(117)	(—)

(K) For a given parameter, there is only one formula for each quantity, independent of the connection. Thus, for CB-connection,

$$A_v(\omega) = \frac{r_{21}}{r_{11} + \Delta_r G_L} = \frac{-g_{21}}{g_{22} + G_L} = \frac{-h_{21}}{\Delta_h + h_{11} G_L} = \frac{k_{21}}{1 + k_{22} G_L}$$

$$= \frac{1}{a_{11} + a_{12} G_L} = \frac{\Delta b}{b_{22} + b_{12} G_L} = 2.95 \qquad (10.124)$$

Similarly, for CE-connection and for CC-connection, using all six formulas,

$$A_v'(\omega) = -1.70 \qquad (10.125)$$

$$A_v''(\omega) = 0.385 \qquad (10.126)$$

Note that R_G and R_L are different for different connections in accordance with Fig. 10.1.

(L) The required results are shown in Table 10.2 below.

TABLE 10.2

	CB	CE	CC
$A_I(\omega)$	−0.676 less than 1	2.57 medium	−6 high
$A_V(\omega)$	2.95 medium	−1.70 medium	0.385 less than 1
R_{in} Ω	2.30 low	7.57 medium	17.3 high
$R_{out\,1}$ Ω	10.90 high	4.00 medium	1.55 low

Note that each connection has its individual generator and load resistance. If the same generator resistance and the same load resistance were used independently of connection, the results in Table 10.2 would be quite different and would deviate from practical operational conditions.

(M) The presentation in Table 10.3 clarifies the relationships.

TABLE 10.3

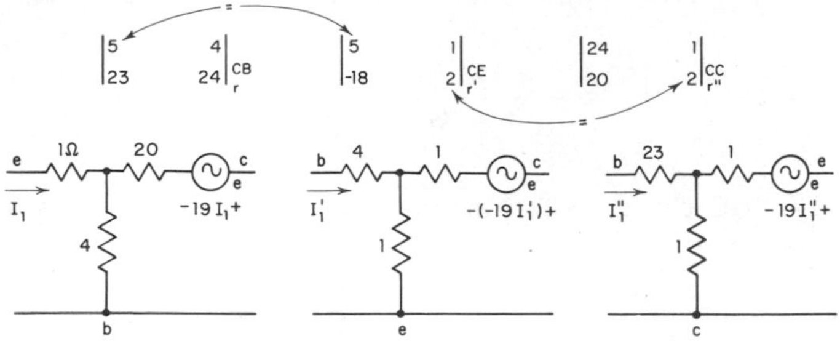

$\Delta_r = 28 = \frac{1}{\Delta_g}$ =	$\Delta'_r = 28 = \frac{1}{\Delta_g'}$ =	$\Delta''_r = 28 = \frac{1}{\Delta_g''}$
$\Delta_h = \frac{5}{24} = \frac{1}{\Delta_k}$	$\Delta'_h = \frac{5}{2} = \frac{1}{\Delta_k'}$	$\Delta''_h = 12 = \frac{1}{\Delta_k''}$
$\Delta_a = \frac{4}{23} = \frac{1}{\Delta_b}$	$\Delta'_a = -\frac{1}{18} = \frac{1}{\Delta_b'}$	$\Delta''_a = \frac{1}{20} = \frac{1}{\Delta_b''}$

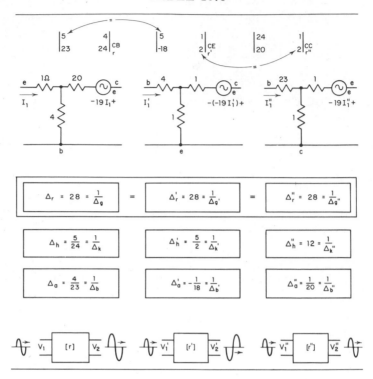

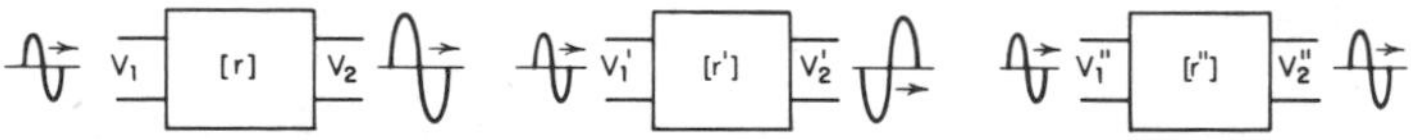

Conclusions to this solution

This solution allows us a comparison by numbers between the three transistor connections. Both the Equation System Comparison Method, the Arm Interchange Method, and the "Floating" Matrix Method have been used in the transformations, and again we have found the latter method to be the quickest one. Use of the basic pattern of the six quantities a, b, c, α, β, and γ, as suggested by the author, streamlines the presentation and makes possible logical formula writing. Table 10.1 gives a few of the many relationships between the six quantities. Table 10.2 gives a nutshell presentation of the characteristics of properly terminated CB, CE, and CC amplifiers. From this table we learn that the CE amplifier usually represents the medium case and is most likely to fit most applications. The CB amplifier is often selected when we want a low input impedance, the CC amplifier when we want a high input impedance. Similarly, the CB amplifier is often employed to give a high output impedance, and the CC amplifier to give a low output impedance (being an emitter follower, it corresponds to the cathode follower in the tube family). These are rules with many exceptions, however. As an example, if high input impedance is what we want, we can also produce it by using a CE amplifier with a large series resistor in the input arm. Finally, in Table 10.3, a comparison has been made between the three connections, bringing out certain significant relationships, such as the common determinant Δ_γ. The block diagrams at the bottom of the table indicate the phase relationship between the output voltage and the input voltage.

SOME FINAL THOUGHTS

We have learned several different ways of transistor-connection transformation, and how to obtain a certain quantity, such as c, in terms of other quantities, such as γ, r_c'' and r_u''. In calculation work, we must be able to carry out such transformations at a moment's notice. Some readers may prefer to make up a list of important formulas as they go along, since such a formula list will save considerable time. Some textbooks give formula collections that are very useful, but it takes time for the reader to glance through several such books and determine under what conditions a certain formula holds. You cannot find anything comparable to a formula collection of your own, with guidance notes which you will recognize instantly.

The reader may have noticed the use in preceeding problems of the author's "classroom model transistors," in which small "round" numbers replace the actual figures that represent matrix elements and parameters. These "model" transistors simulate real transistors surprisingly well, possessing acceptable α and β values, and readily yielding amplification. In intricate problems, these "model" transistors save a considerable amount of time; the reader might well imagine the length of the last problem if transistors with four-figure parameters had been used. In spite of the sometimes enormous time-saving contributed by the "model" transistors, they provide about the same educational value as real transistors.

4
Transistor Amplifiers

We are now ready to apply the knowledge we have gained to transistor amplifiers. Initially, we shall concern ourselves only with single-stage amplifiers, but this involves the calculation of many important quantities, such as various amplifications, gain and port immittances, and also the plotting of some response curves. We shall also extend the "Floating" Matrix Method to encompass complex numbers. Then the subject matter changes to multistage amplifiers, and here we shall learn to use the time-saving Matrix Multiplication Method. This method is almost without competition if the individual transistors are already represented by matrices, but even when this is not the case, the method is often the fastest one. Other methods are used for comparison. Generally, the reader who familiarizes himself with the various matrix methods used in transistor problem solutions is a step ahead in the game. They are becoming so important in this field that other methods tend to be reduced to the rank of checking methods. The checking thereby provided is quite reliable since the methods are, in principle, different. Essentially, the only way an error made in the application of one method can be repeated in the use of another method is by a misinterpretation of the problem formulation or of the final calculation results.

PROBLEM 1

A transistor amplifier is represented by the equivalent network shown in Fig. 1.1.

(A) Using h parameters, write the basic equations and derive the voltage- and current-transfer functions.

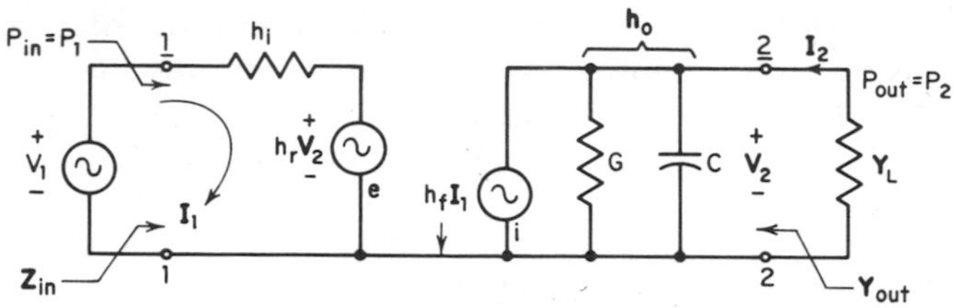

Fig. 1.1

(B) Determine the output admittance $\mathbf{Y}_{out}$ by employing: (B1) the Applied Source Method, (B2) the Output Immittance Theorem, (B3) the Network Element Combination Method, (B4) the Function-Source Output Immittance Theorem (with $1-\mathbf{k}$ in the denominator), (B5) the "Open-Short" Output Immittance Theorem, and (B6) the "Half-Output" Output Immittance Theorem.

(C) Determine the input impedance $\mathbf{Z}_{in}$.

(D) Calculate (D1) output power and power gain, and (D2) discuss the occurrence of maxima in the output-power and the gain curves, for $\mathbf{Y}_L = G_L$ and $C = 0$.

Note: Methods B4, B5, and B6 employ theorems used by the author.[1] The Function-Source Output Immittance Theorem depicts a series-form or shunt-form generator in which the function source is either $\mathbf{kV}_{20}$ or $\mathbf{kI}_{20}$.[2] The theorem claims that the output impedance is $\mathbf{Z}_k/(1-\mathbf{k})$, with the sign in the parenthesis pertaining to the case of a voltage source opposing $\mathbf{V}_{20}$ and with $\mathbf{Z}_k$ signifying the impedance in series with the voltage source. The "Open-Short" Output Immittance Theorem states that the ratio of the open-circuit voltage and the short-circuit current, with proper sign, constitutes the output impedance. This same statement results from a combination of the Thévenin theorem and the Norton theorem. The "Half-Output" Output Immittance Theorem states that

$$\mathbf{A}_V(\omega)\Big|_{Z_L=\infty} = 2\mathbf{A}_V(\omega)\Big|_{\mathbf{Z}_L=\mathbf{Z}_{out}}$$

[1]Stockman, H. E., "Three Output Immittance Theorems," *Electronics Industries*, January 1958. Also by the same author: "Time-Saving Network Calculations," Sine-Ser Co., 1956. SINE-SER Co.,

[2]Stockman, H. E., "Output Impedance Theorem," *Wireless Engineer* (correspondence). No. 3, March 1954. See also "A New Tool for Easier Network Synthesis," *Electronic Design*, vol. 13, pp. 20-21, Feb. 1, 1965 and also continued discussion in *Electronic Design*, vol. 13, pp. 26-30, April 12, 1965.

and thus represents another method of obtaining the output immittance. For further information on this and other theorems, see the references listed in footnote 1.

Solution

(A) The equation system takes the form

$$\left.\begin{aligned} V_1 &= h_i \mathbf{I}_1 + h_r \mathbf{V}_2 \quad (1.1)\\ \mathbf{I}_2 &= h_f \mathbf{I}_1 + \mathbf{h}_0 \mathbf{V}_2 \quad (1.2) \end{aligned}\right\}$$

We note that V_1 is real and that it is utilized as reference quantity. With $\mathbf{V}_2 = -\mathbf{Z}_L \mathbf{I}_2$ and $\mathbf{\Delta}_h = h_i \mathbf{h}_0 - h_f h_r$, we obtain the transfer functions

$$\mathbf{A}_V(\omega) = \mathbf{V}_2/V_1 = -h_f/(\mathbf{\Delta}_h + h_i \mathbf{Y}_L) \quad (1.3)$$

$$\mathbf{A}_I(\omega) = \mathbf{I}_2/I_1 = h_f/(1 + \mathbf{h}_0 \mathbf{Z}_L) \quad (1.4)$$

(B1) Applied Source Method—We rewrite the equation system (1.1) (1.2) for shorted input and apply the current $\mathbf{I}_{20}$ to the output, obtaining

$$\left.\begin{aligned} 0 &= h_i \mathbf{I}_{10} + h_r \mathbf{V}_{20} \quad (1.5)\\ \mathbf{I}_{20} &= h_f \mathbf{I}_{10} + \mathbf{h}_0 \mathbf{V}_{20} \quad (1.6) \end{aligned}\right\}$$

from which

$$\mathbf{Y}_{\text{out}} = \frac{\mathbf{I}_{20}}{\mathbf{V}_{20}} = \frac{\mathbf{\Delta}_h}{h_i} \quad (1.7)$$

(B2) Output Immittance Theorem—We obtain the answer in Eq. 1.7 from a direct inspection of the denominator of Eq. 1.3.

(B3) Network Element Combination Method—With the input port 1, $\underline{1}$ closed, the current becomes $\mathbf{I}_1 = -h_r \mathbf{V}_2/h_i$. Inserting this value in the current function source, we obtain $h_f \mathbf{I}_1 = -h_f h_r \mathbf{V}_2/h_i$. Now applying the Compensation Theorem, we obtain the network element $-h_f h_r/h_i$. Port 2, $\underline{2}$ is now associated with a network free from function sources. We can therefore apply the Network Element Combination Method. Accordingly,

$$\mathbf{Y}_{\text{out}} = \mathbf{h}_0 + (-h_f h_r / h_i) = \Delta_h / h_i \tag{1.7A}$$

(B4) Function-Source Output Immittance Theorem —In this problem we can easily produce $k\mathbf{V}_{20}$, since $\mathbf{I}_1 = -h_r \mathbf{V}_{20}/h_i$. Turning the network associated with port 2,$\underline{2}$ into a series-form generator, and noting that its voltage source is aiding instead of opposing this voltage, we conclude that the output impedance becomes, with $\mathbf{Z}_k = 1/\mathbf{h}_0$,

$$\mathbf{Z}_{\text{out}} = \frac{\mathbf{Z}_k}{1+\mathbf{k}} = \frac{1/\mathbf{h}_0}{1 - h_f h_r / h_i \mathbf{h}_0} = \frac{h_i}{\Delta_h} \tag{1.7B}$$

(B5) "Open-Short" Output Immittance Theorem—In accordance with this theorem we formulate the ratio,

$$\mathbf{Y}_{\text{out}} = -\mathbf{I}_{2\,\text{sh}} / \mathbf{V}_{2\,\text{op}} = (-h_f/h_i)/(-h_f/\Delta_h) = \frac{\Delta_h}{h_i} \tag{1.7C}$$

(B6) "Half-Output" Output Immittance Theorem—In accordance with this theorem we write

$$\frac{-h_f}{\Delta_h} = 2\frac{-h_f}{\Delta_h + h_i \mathbf{Y}_{\text{out}}} \quad \text{or} \quad \mathbf{Y}_{\text{out}} = \frac{\Delta_h}{h_i} \tag{1.7D}$$

(C) The input impedance is obtained directly from the equation system (1.1) (1.2):

$$\mathbf{Z}_{\text{in}} = \frac{V_1}{\mathbf{I}_1} = \frac{h_i + \Delta_h \mathbf{Z}_L}{1 + \mathbf{h}_0 \mathbf{Z}_L} \tag{1.8}$$

(D1) The output power is $V_{2\,\text{rms}}^2 / R_L$. Thus, from Eq. 1.3,

$$P_2 = \frac{V_{2\,\text{rms}}^{\;2}}{R_L} = \frac{h_f^{\,2} V_{1\,\text{rms}}^{\;2}}{R_L(\Delta_h + h_i G_L)^2} \text{ watt} \tag{1.9}$$

To calculate the gain, we must first determine the input power, which is from the equation system (1.1) (1.2):

$$P_1 = \frac{V_{1\,\text{rms}}^{\;2}}{R_{\text{in}}} = \frac{(1 + h_0 R_L) V_{1\,\text{rms}}^{\;2}}{h_i + \Delta_h R_L} \tag{1.10}$$

Accordingly,

$$G = \frac{P_2}{P_1} = \frac{h^2 f}{R_L(\Delta_h + h_i G_L)^2} \times \frac{h_i + \Delta_h R_L}{(1 + h_o R_L)}$$

or

$$G = \frac{h^2{}_f R_L}{h_i + (h_i h_o + \Delta_h) R_L + h_o \Delta_h R_L{}^2} \qquad (1.11)$$

(D2) The output power has a maximum for $R_L = R_{out}$. The gain has a maximum for a different value of R_L; see the solution in Chapter 1 to problem 9.

Conclusions to this solution

This solution makes use of the popular "irfo" h parameters. In part B a number of methods are used for the determination of output immittance—some very fast, some rather slow. It should be noted, however, that a method that gives a long solution in one problem occasionally gives a short solution in another problem. The Applied Source Method employed in B1 gives a rather quick solution. The Output Immittance Theorem in B2 is, as usual, the fastest method. The Network Element Combination Method used in B3 is here lengthy, because of the fact that we must get rid of a function source. The Function-Source Output Immittance Theorem in B4 is equally lengthy. The "Open-Short" and "Half-Output" Output Immittance Theorems give rather short solutions and can be employed by the busy engineer. Output immittance is often calculated in transistor problems, and it is important for the engineer to know what method to use in each application.

PROBLEM 2

In the design of a transistor video amplifier, the CB-connection double-source equivalent in Fig. 2.1a was found inadequate. Measurements indicated that the physical transistor possessed reactive properties, and it was found that the introduction of the collector capacitance, C_c, and a certain amount of dissipation in the mid-branch return provided the more adequate network equivalent shown in Fig. 2.1b. Here the dissipation is secured by means of a series resistance r_b' (the "base-spreading" resistance). All parameters and variables in Fig. 2.1a are real numbers.

(A) The physical transistor represented by Fig. 2.1a has an

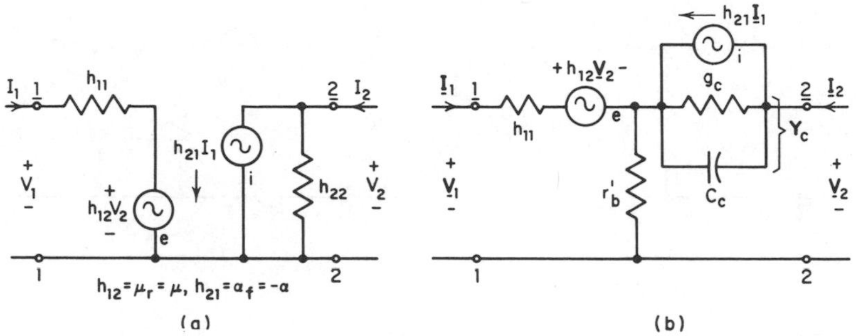

Fig. 2.1

emitter resistance, r_u, and a collector resistance, r_c, which may be considered numerically known. Use valid approximations to determine simple formulas for h_{11} and h_{22}.

(B) Allowing strong approximations, determine the $\underline{h}$ matrix for the new network in Fig. 2.1b.

(C) Write an expression for the instantaneous output voltage in a load resistor, R_L, when the input voltage is $v_1(t) = V_1 \cos(\omega_1 t + \beta)$. For simplicity, set $r_b{}' = 0$.

(D) Determine the transient voltage across the load resistor, R_L, when the input voltage consists of a step voltage $\underline{|E_1}$, $t = 0$. For simplicity, consider the system nonenergized, and $r_b{}' = 0$.

Solution

(A) From Matrix Table I, and with $r_m/r_c = \alpha \doteq 1$,

$$h_{11} = \frac{\Delta r}{r_{22}} = \frac{r_{11}r_{22} - r_{12}r_{21}}{r_{22}} = r_{11} - \frac{r_{12}r_{21}}{r_{22}}$$

$$= r_u + r_b - \frac{r_b(r_m + r_b)}{r_b + r_c} \doteq r_u + r_b - \frac{r_b r_m}{r_c} \doteq r_u \tag{2.1}$$

and

$$h_{22} = \frac{1}{r_{22}} = \frac{1}{r_b + r_c} \doteq \frac{1}{r_c} \tag{2.2}$$

(B) The equation system pertaining to Fig. 2.1b. is

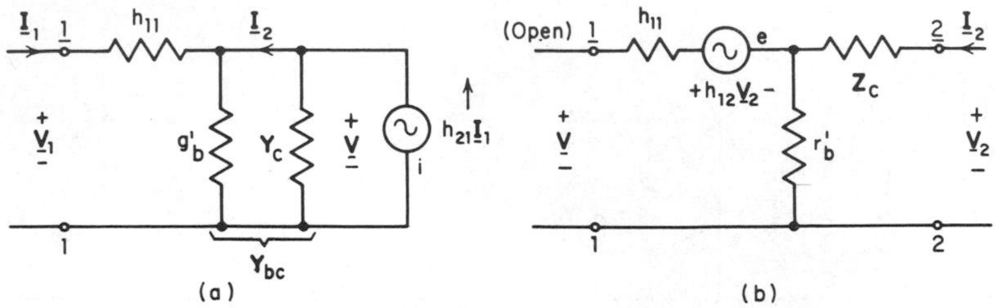

Fig. 2.2

$$\left.\begin{aligned}\underline{\mathbf{V}}_1 &= \underline{\mathbf{h}}_{11}\underline{\mathbf{I}}_1 + \underline{\mathbf{h}}_{12}\underline{\mathbf{V}}_2 \\ \underline{\mathbf{I}}_2 &= \underline{\mathbf{h}}_{21}\underline{\mathbf{I}}_1 + \underline{\mathbf{h}}_{22}\underline{\mathbf{V}}_2\end{aligned}\right\} \qquad \begin{aligned}(2.3)\\(2.4)\end{aligned}$$

With $\mathbf{Y}_{bc} = (g_b' + \mathbf{Y}_c)$, we formally obtain the four $\underline{h}$ parameters by port manipulation and begin by determining $\underline{h}_{11}$ by short-circuiting the port 2,$\underline{2}$. Interpreting the shunt generator thus produced as a series generator, we directly read off the equation (see Fig. 2.2a):

$$\underline{\mathbf{V}}_1 - h_{21}\mathbf{Z}_{bc}\underline{\mathbf{I}}_1 - (h_{11} + \mathbf{Z}_{bc})\underline{\mathbf{I}}_1 = 0$$

from which

$$\underline{\mathbf{h}}_{11} = \underline{\mathbf{V}}_1/\underline{\mathbf{I}}_1 \Big|_{\underline{\mathbf{V}}_2 = 0} = h_{11} + \mathbf{Z}_{bc}(1 + h_{21}) \qquad (2.5)$$

Since $r_c \gg r_b'$ and the capacitance, C_c, is relatively small, we may set $Z_{bc} \doteq r_b'$ so that Eq. 2.5 becomes

$$\underline{\mathbf{h}}_{11} = \underline{h}_{11} \doteq r_u + r_b'(1 - \alpha) \qquad (2.6)$$

To determine $\underline{h}_{12}$ from the network equivalent in Fig. 2.2b, we employ the Voltage Proportioning Method, obtaining the equation:

$$\underline{\mathbf{V}}_1 = h_{12}\underline{\mathbf{V}}_2 + r_b'\underline{\mathbf{V}}_2(r_b' + \mathbf{Z}_c) \qquad (2.7)$$

from which

$$\underline{\mathbf{h}}_{12} = \underline{\mathbf{V}}_1/\underline{\mathbf{V}}_2 \Big|_{\underline{\mathbf{I}}_1 = 0} = h_{12} + r_b'/(r_b' + \mathbf{Z}_c)$$

If we make the approximation $r_b' + \mathbf{Z}_c \doteq \mathbf{Z}_c$, this becomes

$$\underline{\mathbf{h}}_{12} = \mu + r_b'(g_c + j\omega C_c) \qquad (2.8)$$

To determine $\underline{\mathbf{h}}_{21}$, we again make use of Fig. 2.2a, formulating

$$\left.\begin{aligned} \underline{\mathbf{I}}_1 + \underline{\mathbf{I}}_2 - g_b'\underline{\mathbf{V}} &= 0 \\ h_{21}\underline{\mathbf{I}}_1 - \underline{\mathbf{I}}_2 - \mathbf{Y}_c\underline{\mathbf{V}} &= 0 \end{aligned}\right\} \qquad \begin{aligned}(2.9)\\(2.10)\end{aligned}$$

from which

$$\underline{\mathbf{h}}_{21} = \underline{\mathbf{I}}_2/\underline{\mathbf{I}}_1 \Big|_{\underline{\mathbf{V}}_2 = 0} = (g_b'h_{21} - \mathbf{Y}_c)/(g_b' + \mathbf{Y}_c) \tag{2.11}$$

where we may disregard $\mathbf{Y}_c$. Thus,

$$\underline{\mathbf{h}}_{21} = \underline{h}_{21} \doteq -\alpha \tag{2.12}$$

To determine $\underline{\mathbf{h}}_{22}$, we again make use of Fig. 2.2b, writing the equation

$$\underline{\mathbf{h}}_{22} = \underline{\mathbf{I}}_2/\underline{\mathbf{V}}_2 \Big|_{\underline{\mathbf{I}}_1 = 0} = 1/(r_b' + \mathbf{Z}_c') \doteq \mathbf{Y}_c = g_c + j\omega C_c \tag{2.13}$$

While the above approximations may not always be completely valid, they result in $\underline{h}$ parameters that describe the desired matrix, which has the following determinant:

$$\underline{\Delta}_h \doteq (r_u)(g_c + j\omega C_c) + \mu\,\alpha \tag{2.14}$$

This result may be modified by the use of lesser approximations, or possibly stronger approximations. Usually, we carry through this kind of calculation with numerical values, and we can then secure approximations which are truly justified. To keep the quantities apart, some readers may like to use the designations I_{20}, V_{20}, I_{10}, and V_{10} when the twoport is driven from its 2-end.

(C) The network in Fig. 2.3 may be used for the calculation of the periodic steady-state output voltage when the voltage $v_1(t)$ is applied to the input. Except for the presence of the capacitor, C_c,

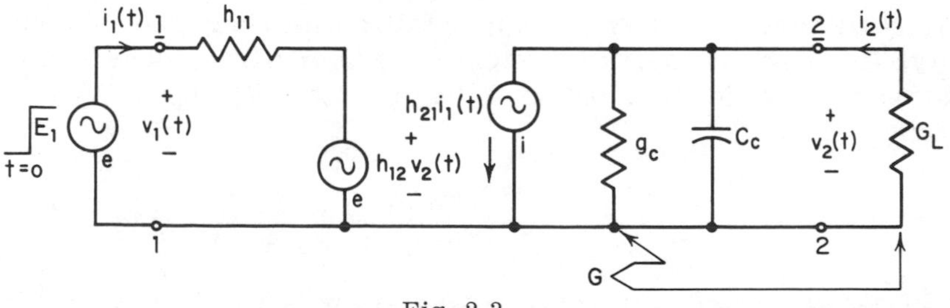

Fig. 2.3

and except for the fact that we use instantaneous values, the network in Fig. 2.3 is the same as that initially shown in Fig. 2.1a. Using complex quantities, and applying Ohm's law to the right-hand side of the network in Fig. 2.3, with $(g_c + G_L) = G$, we write

$$\mathbf{V}_2 = \frac{-h_{21}}{G + j\omega_1 C_c} \mathbf{I}_1 = \frac{-h_{21}}{G + j\omega_1 C_c} \times \frac{\mathbf{V}_1 - h_{12}\mathbf{V}_2}{h_{11}}$$

or, with $\mathbf{V}_1 = V_1 e^{j\beta}$,

$$\mathbf{V}_2 = \alpha V_1 \frac{\angle \beta + \tan^{-1}[-\omega_1 C_c r_u/(\mu\alpha + Gr_u)]}{\sqrt{(\mu\alpha + Gr_u)^2 + \omega_1^2 C_c^2 r_u^2}}$$

and finally we obtain,

$$v_2(t) = \alpha V_1 \times \frac{1}{\sqrt{(\mu\alpha + Gr_u)^2 + \omega_1^2 C_c^2 r_u^2}} \times \cos\left(\omega_1 t + \beta - \tan^{-1} \frac{\omega_1 C_c r_u}{\mu\alpha + Gr_u}\right) \qquad (2.15)$$

This is the required instantaneous output voltage.

(D) While our calculations refer to the network shown in Fig. 2.3, we shall here start out from the matrix already derived. Setting $r_b' = 0$, we find that Eqs. 2.6, 2.8, 2.12, 2.13, and 2.14 yield the following total matrix and determinant, with $(g_c + G_L) = G$:

$$\begin{vmatrix} r_u & \mu \\ -\alpha & (sC_c + G) \end{vmatrix} \qquad (2.16)$$

$$\overline{\Delta}_h \doteq r_u C_c (s + s_1) \qquad (2.17)$$

$$s_1 = (\mu\alpha + r_u G)/r_u C_c \qquad (2.18)$$

We shall here employ transform notation with a bar above the quantity. The original equation system (2.3) (2.4) in transform interpretation now yields the output voltage, with $v_1(t)$ appearing as the transform, E_1/s:

$$\overline{V}_2 \doteq \frac{E_1}{s} \times \frac{-\overline{h}_{21}}{\overline{\Delta}_h} = \frac{\alpha E_1}{r_u C_c} \times \frac{1}{s(s + s_1)} \qquad (2.19)$$

Here we make use of the transform-pair formula,

$$\frac{A}{s(s+s_1)} \rightarrow \frac{A}{s_1}(1-e^{-s_1 t}) \tag{2.20}$$

The transient output voltage determined by means of the Laplace Transform Method is accordingly

$$v_2(t) \doteq \frac{\alpha E_1}{\mu\alpha + r_u G}\left(1 - e^{-\frac{\mu\alpha + r_u G}{r_u C_c} t}\right) \tag{2.21}$$

It is seen that as we apply the step voltage to the transistor input, an exponentially rising output voltage is obtained.

As an alternative solution, we could have started out as in part C and derived a transform equation from the network in Fig. 2.3 without formulating any matrix. Turning this procedure around, we could have provided a periodic steady-state solution from the matrix, rather than adapted the procedure used in part C. Had we not been bound by a specific problem formulation, our most rational approach to a general solution would have been to use the s variable right away and to derive the system matrix in this variable. The solution given in part C would then start from a transform formula such as Eq. 2.19, with E_1/s replaced by $\mathbf{V}_1$, and proceed as follows:

$$\mathbf{V}_2 \doteq \frac{\alpha \mathbf{V}_1}{r_u C_c (j\omega_1 + s_1)} = \alpha \mathbf{V}_1 \frac{\underline{/\beta + tan^{-1}(-\omega_1/s_1)}}{r_u C_c \sqrt{\omega_1^2 + s_1^2}} \tag{2.22}$$

or, for $\mathbf{V}_1 = V_1$,

$$v_2(t) \doteq \alpha V_1 \frac{1}{r_u C_c \sqrt{\omega_1^2 + s_1^2}} \cos\left(\omega_1 t + \beta - tan^{-1}\frac{\omega_1}{s_1}\right) \tag{2.23}$$

This agrees with the result in Eq. 2.15, provided we insert the expression for s_1 from 2.18.

Conclusions to this solution

This problem gave us some exercise in the art of making approximations. It is often easier to make the right kind of approximations in numerical expressions than in algebraic ones. On the other hand, if the answer indicates that too strong approximations have been made, algebraic solutions give us a better chance for tracing the approximations to one particular origin.

In problems involving transients, we should notice the advantage of introducing transform variables right away and to carry out the solution in the s-language. The transient solution then follows in a natural fashion and to obtain the periodic steady-state solution, we merely set $s = j\omega$ and follow through with the Symbolic Method. We can, of course, obtain the entire solution by means of the Laplace Transform, but this procedure is generally longer and more tedious than that of obtaining the periodic steady-state solution by means of the Symbolic Method (at least for simple problems).

PROBLEM 3

A CE-connected transistor audio amplifier is known by its (rCB) matrix (see Fig. 3.1).

(A) Calculate $A_I'(\omega) = I_2'/I_1'$, R_{in}', R_{out}', α, and β.

(B) With the load resistance R_L' varied from 10,000 ohm to 300, 000 ohm, plot log-log curves for $A_I'(\omega)$ and R_{in}'.

(C) With the generator resistance R_G' varied from 10 ohm to 20,000 ohm, plot a log-log curve for R_{out}'.

(D) For $R_G' = 100$ ohm, determine the optimum load resistance $R_{L\,opt}'$ to yield maximum power and the maximum power $P_{2\,max}'$.

Solution

(A) The twoport is described by the matrix equation

$$\begin{vmatrix} V_1' \\ V_2' \end{vmatrix} = \begin{vmatrix} r_{11}' & r_{12}' \\ r_{21}' & r_{22}' \end{vmatrix} \begin{vmatrix} I_1' \\ I_2' \end{vmatrix} \tag{3.1}$$

and the long-hand equation system

$$V_1' = r_{11}'I_1' + r_{12}'I_2' \tag{3.2}$$

$$V_2' = r_{21}'I_1' + r_{22}'I_2' \tag{3.3}$$

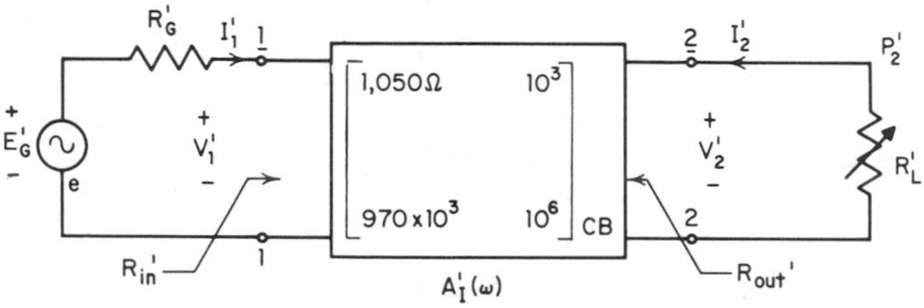

Fig. 3.1

With $V_2' = -R_L'I_2'$ we obtain, using triple-subscript symbols,

$$A_I'(\omega) = \frac{I_2'}{I_1'} = -\frac{r_{21}'}{r_{22}' + R_L'} = -\frac{r_{21}'}{r_{222}'} \tag{3.4}$$

The input resistance is

$$R_{in}' = \frac{V_1'}{I_1'} = \frac{\Delta_r' + r_{11}'R_L'}{r_{22}' + R_L'} = \frac{\Delta_{r2}'}{r_{222}'} \tag{3.5}$$

where

$$\Delta_r' = r_{11}'r_{22}' - r_{12}'r_{21}' \qquad \Delta_{r2}' = r_{11}'(r_{22}' + R_L') - r_{12}'r_{21}' \tag{3.6}$$

The output resistance may be obtained from Eq. 3.5 by the interchanging of subscripts and is

$$R_{out}' = \frac{V_{20}'}{I_{20}'} = \frac{\Delta_r' + r_{22}'R_G'}{r_{11}' + R_G'} = \frac{\Delta_{r1}'}{r_{111}'} \tag{3.7}$$

where

$$\Delta_{r1}' = (r_{11}' + R_G')r_{22}' - r_{12}'r_{21}' \tag{3.8}$$

Since Eq. 3.4 describes an open port, 1, $\underline{1}$ it cannot be used for an immediate application of the Output Immittance Theorem. If instead we had available the voltage transfer function

$$A_E'(\omega) = \frac{V_2'}{E_G'} = \frac{r_{21}'}{r_{11}' + R_G' + G_L'(\Delta_r' + r_{22}'R_G')} \tag{3.9}$$

the Output Immittance Theorem would immediately give the correct result in Eq. 3.7.

We calculate α and β as follows:

$$A_I'(\omega)\Big|_{R_L'=0} = \frac{I_2'}{I_1'}\Big|_{R_L'=0} = \frac{-r_{21}'}{r_{22}'} = \beta \tag{3.10}$$

$$\beta = \frac{-r_{21}'}{r_{22}'} \tag{3.11}$$

$$A_I(\omega)\Big|_{R_L=0} = \frac{I_2}{I_1}\Big|_{R_L=0} = \frac{-r_{21}}{r_{22}} = -\alpha \tag{3.12}$$

$$\alpha = \frac{r_{21}}{r_{22}} \tag{3.13}$$

As an alternative we may use the formula developed in the solution to problem 9 in Chapter 3:

$$\alpha \doteq \frac{\beta}{1+\beta} \tag{3.14}$$

To find the numerical values of all the above quantities, we must first obtain the CE matrix from the given CB matrix. This calculation has already been carried out in the problem solution just referred to, from which we obtain:

$$r_{11}' = r_{11} = 1{,}050\,\Omega \qquad r_{12}' = r_{11} - r_{12} = 50\,\Omega$$

$$r_{21}' = r_{11} - r_{21} = -968{,}950\,\Omega \qquad r_{22}' = r_{11} + r_{22} - r_{12} - r_{21} = 30{,}050\,\Omega \tag{3.15}$$

$$\Delta_r' = \Delta_r = 80 \times 10^6\,\Omega^2$$

$$A_I'(\omega) = \frac{968{,}950}{30{,}050 + R_L'} \doteq \frac{970}{30 + \overline{R}_L'} \tag{3.16}$$

$$R_{in}' \doteq \frac{80 + \overline{R}_L'}{30 + \overline{R}_L'} \times 10^3 \tag{3.17}$$

$$R_{out}' \doteq \frac{80 + 30\overline{R}_G'}{1 + \overline{R}_G'} \times 10^3 \tag{3.18}$$

$$R_{out}' \Big|_{R_G' = 100\,\Omega} \doteq 75{,}400\,\Omega \tag{3.19}$$

$$\alpha \doteq \frac{970}{1{,}000} = 0.970 \tag{3.20}$$

$$\beta \doteq \frac{970}{30} = 32.3 \tag{3.21}$$

Here the bar-values are in kilohm. Equation 3.13 gives the same result as 3.14, properly approximated. Equation 3.19 introduces the value of R_G' used in part D.

(B) Approximated values are given in Table 3.1, from which

the curves for $A_I'(\omega)$ and R_{in}' are plotted in Fig. 3.2. As may be expected, the current amplification falls off as the load resistance is increased. We note that the input resistance decreases as the load resistance increases. This is a feedback effect; an increasing load resistance decreases the output mesh current in the equivalent active TEE, reducing the bucking voltage across the shunt-leg of the TEE. Thus the transistor takes more current from the signal source, E_G', which implies a reduction in input resistance.

TABLE 3.1*

R_L'	$30 + R_L'$	$A_I'(\omega)$	$80 + R_L'$	R_{in}'
0	30	32.3	80	2.67
10	40	24.2	90	2.25
30	60	16.2	110	1.83
50	80	12.1	130	1.63
70	100	9.70	150	1.50
100	130	7.46	180	1.39
150	180	5.39	230	1.28
300	330	2.94	380	1.15
∞	∞	0	∞	1.00

*Resistance unit: kilohm

TABLE 3.2

R_G'	$1.05 + R_G'$	Δ_{r1}'	R_{out}'
.01	1.06	80.3	75.7
.10	1.15	83.0	72.2
.20	1.25	86.0	68.7
.50	1.55	95.0	61.2
1.00	2.05	110	53.7
2.00	3.05	140	45.9
5.00	6.05	230	38.0
10.00	11.1	380	34.4
20.00	21.1	680	32.2
∞	∞	∞	30.0

(C) Approximated values are given in Table 3.2, from which the curve for the output resistance is plotted (see Fig. 3.3). It is seen that the output resistance decreases when the generator resistance is increased (again the result of feedback). As the port current to the equivalent active TEE is reduced, the function-source voltage $r_m'I_1'$ is also reduced. But this source voltage, due

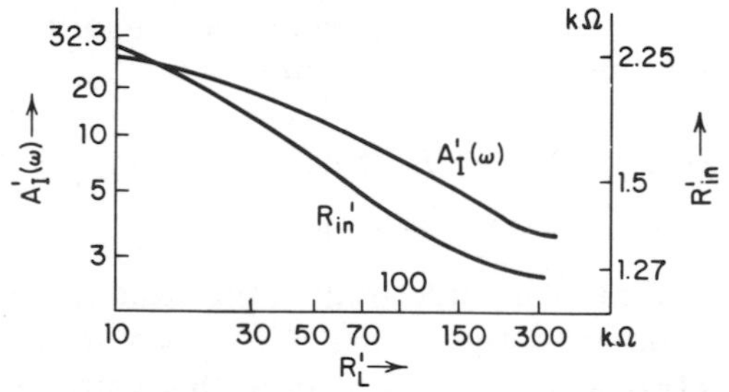

Fig. 3.2

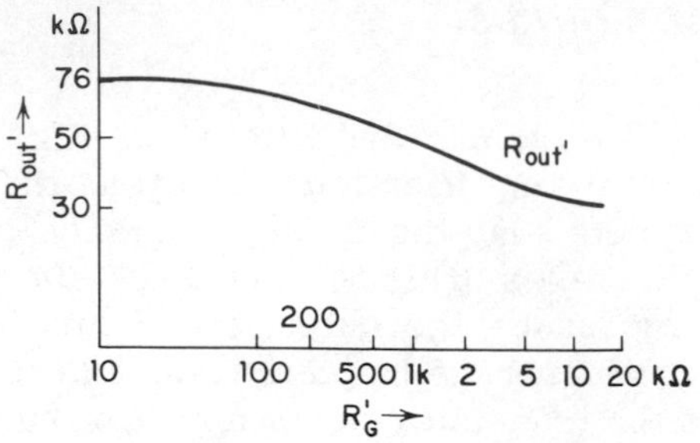

Fig. 3.3

to the sign situation, opposes the voltage applied to the port 2, $\underline{2}$ from, say, an impedance bridge. Accordingly, the counter voltage gets weaker, and the bridge current stronger, which means that the output resistance falls off.

(D) To calculate the output power we make use of Eq. 3.9, setting $P_2' = (V_2')^2/2R_L$, thus obtaining

$$P_2' = (r_{21}')^2(E_G')^2/2[\sqrt{R_L'}(r_{11}' + R_G') + (\Delta_r' + r_{22}'R_G')/\sqrt{R_L'}]^2 \tag{3.22}$$

This expression has a maximum when the square root of the denominator, u, has a minimum, thus

$$du/dR_L' = [(R_{L\,opt}')^{-1/2}(r_{11}' + R_G') - (R_{L\,opt}')^{-3/2} \times (\Delta_r' + r_{22}'R_G')]/\sqrt{2} = 0 \tag{3.23}$$

from which

$$R_{L\,opt}' = (\Delta_r' + r_{22}'R_G')/(r_{11}' + R_G') \tag{3.24}$$

For $R_G' = 100$ ohm we find from Eq. 3.19 that $R_{L\,opt}' \doteq 75{,}400$ ohm. A quicker way of obtaining the result in Eq. 3.24 is to apply the Maximum Power Transfer Theorem, which in this case states that $R_{L\,opt}' = R_{out}'$, verified by the identity of Equations 3.7 and 3.24. To determine the maximum output power, we merely insert $R_{L\,opt}'$ in Eq. 3.22, obtaining, with $R_G' = 100$ ohm,

$$P_2'{}_{max} = (r_{21}')^2(E_G')^2/8(r_{11}' + R_G')(\Delta_r' + r_{22}R_G') \doteq 1.23(E_G')^2 \tag{3.25}$$

V_2' and E_G' are treated as maximum amplitude, not rms, values.

As a variation in determining $P_{2\,max}'$, we may transform to a single-mesh network at port 2, $\underline{2}$, call the voltage source E^* and the series resistance R^* noting that $R^* = R_{out}'$. We can then use a ready-made formula, writing

$$P_{2\,\max}{}' = \frac{(E*)^2}{8R*} = (E_G{}')^2 \left. \frac{r_{21}{}^2/(r_{11}{}' + R_G{}')}{8(\Delta_r{}' + r_{22}{}'R_G{}')/(r_{11}{}' + R_G{}')} \right|_{R_G{}' = 100\,\Omega}$$

$$\doteq 1.23(E_G{}')^2 \qquad (3.26)$$

which result agrees with that in Eq. 3.25.

Conclusions to this solution

This problem solution reminds us of the necessity of keeping CB and CE parameters apart, and here the use of primes offers one way of securing correct results. Mix-up of parameters is a common source of errors in problems of this type. Most of the solution is of routine character. Plots such as the ones in Fig. 3.2 and Fig. 3.3 portray the behavior of the amplifier, and these curves may be directly compared with those obtained from laboratory measurements. The use of logarithmic axes is practical, and a horizontal logarithmic axis for frequency plots is recommended. In plotting curves such as those shown, it is always a good idea for the reader to carry on a reasoning on the side, making sure that the plotted change in immittance is substantiated by the internal feedback action. Brief indications of how such reasoning is done are included in the solution. In calculating output power, we must always make clear whether the current and voltage symbols we enter are maximum amplitude values or rms values. The former ones are more generally useful, since they allow the direct writing of instantaneous values without the need of any numerical factors. The produced single-mesh network represents the equivalent Thévenin generator for the given network; thus the generator resistance is the output resistance.

PROBLEM 4

Discuss typical internal feedback phenomena occurring in transistor networks at low frequency. (Do not use classical feedback theory).

(A) Begin with a voltage-source-driven CB-connected transistor, using its r TEE equivalent, and discuss the feedback taking place due to the existence of its mid-arm. Also consider the question of voltage and current phase reversal.

(B) Discuss a voltage-source-driven CE-connected transistor in the same manner.

(C) Discuss a voltage-source-driven CC-connected transistor in the same manner.

(D) Make up a table showing the voltage and current phase reversals that appear, indicating also the nature of the feedback.

(E) The voltage source V_1 is now replaced by a series-form generator (V_1, R_G), in which R_G is 100 ohm. Using the matrix,

$$|r|_{CB} = \begin{vmatrix} 1{,}050 \; ohm & 1{,}000 \\ 970{,}000 & 1{,}000{,}000 \end{vmatrix}$$

carry out a mathematical analysis for the CB-connection, calculating $A_I(\omega)$, $A_V(\omega)$, R_{in}, and $R_{out\,1}$ (which includes R_G). Use the load-resistance value, R_L = 100,000 ohm.

(F) Same assignment as in part E, but pertaining to the CE-connection, with R_G' = 1,000 ohm and R_L' = 20,000 ohm.

(G) Same assignment as in part E but pertaining to the CC-connection, with R_G'' = 10,000 and R_L'' = 500 ohm.

(H) Tabulate the results obtained in parts E, F, and G.

(I) Derive formulas for the collector resistance in CE-connection and for the base resistance in CC-connection.

(J) Analyze the CC-connected transistor with the function source located in the shunt leg of the TEE, and discuss the operation of the practical "emitter follower."

Solution

(A) The rTEE for the CB-connected voltage-source-driven transistor is shown in Fig. 4.1. The r matrices for all three connections are given in Equations 4.1, 4.2, and 4.3.

$$|r|_{CB} = \begin{vmatrix} r_{11} & r_{12} \\ r_{21} & r_{22} \end{vmatrix} \tag{4.1}$$

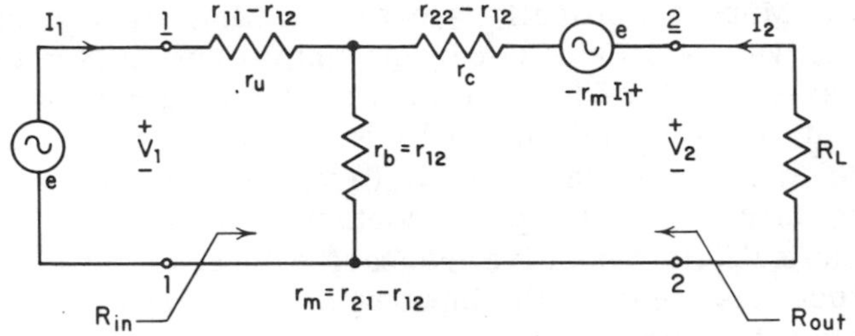

Fig. 4.1

$$|r|_{CE} = \begin{vmatrix} r_{11}' & r_{12}' \\ r_{21}' & r_{22}' \end{vmatrix} \tag{4.2}$$

$$|r|_{CC} = \begin{vmatrix} r_{11}'' & r_{12}'' \\ r_{21}'' & r_{22}'' \end{vmatrix} \tag{4.3}$$

The matrix in Eq. 4.1, in which $r_{12} = r_b$ is the feedback parameter, is the given matrix, all matrix elements and parameters being positive quantities, and $r_{21} > r_{12}$ (the requirement for r_m positive). Accordingly, the function source $r_m I_1$ provides a current which has opposite direction to the indicated current, I_2. This may be verified by the study of the deflection on a conventional dc milliammeter connected in the circuit. (The current direction in this text is opposite to the electron-flow direction.) The CB-connected transistor therefore has a 180° phase shift in output current, but no phase shift in output voltage. These results have been entered in Table 4.1. When a voltage V_1 is applied to port 1,1, the source $r_m I_1$ provides a current in the second mesh, which current sets up an aiding voltage, with reference to V_1, across the mid-arm resistance r_b.

We may study the same occurrences with reference to the double-source equivalent in Fig. B6a in Appendix B. Here $\mathbf{z}_{12}\mathbf{I}_2 = r_{12}I_2 = r_b I_2$ represents the feedback voltage, which due to the 180° phase shift in $\mathbf{I}_2$ aids the applied voltage $\mathbf{V}_1$. Accordingly, the current $\mathbf{I}_1$ becomes enhanced due to the feedback action. Both equivalent networks convey to us the information that the function-source voltage in the output mesh is increased, and thus the voltage amplification is increased, due to the feedback action. If we now adopt the definition that an increase in voltage amplification due to feedback action signifies positive feedback, we conclude that the CB-connected amplifier has positive feedback. If we use as a criterion the definition that positive feedback results when the feedback voltage aids the applied signal voltage, we again conclude that the feedback is positive. More specifically, we are dealing with current-controlled positive feedback. The current amplification is not of direct interest here, since we apply a signal voltage rather than a signal current, but if we glance ahead to Eq. 4.5, we note that $|I_2/I_1|$ is smaller than 1 and thus $\alpha < 1$. (We are here using a junction transistor. In contrast, the point-contact transistor has $\alpha > 1$ and may display sufficient positive feedback to become unstable.)

The feedback controls the input resistance. The enhanced current I_1 makes the transistor appear to the source V_1 as a load of reduced resistance. Thus, the input resistance may become much smaller than $r_{11} = (r_b + r_u)$, and this is more often a disadvantage than an advantage. If we connect an impedance meter to the port 2, $\underline{2}$ to determine the output resistance, and close the port 1, $\underline{1}$ we may consider that we apply a voltage V_{20} which yields a current I_{20}. Since the current in the emitter arm of the TEE now has the opposite direction to that indicated in Fig. 4.1, it follows that the direction of the function source $r_m I_{10}$ is reversed. Applying the Compensation Theorem, we find that r_m is now a negative resistance. Thus we find that $r_m I_{10}$ aids V_{20} and thus tends to reduce the output resistance, since for a given voltage V_{20}, an enhanced current I_{20} results. The very large resistance, r_c, appears, in the output arm of the amplifier, however, swamping the negative resistance so that the resulting output resistance becomes quite large, in fact larger than the output resistance obtainable with the other two connections. It is a rather striking fact that a negative resistance appears in the collector arm, and this is shown mathematically in a note at the end of the problem solution.

(B) In the CE-connection the matrix element $r_{12}' = r_u$ in Eq. 4.2 represents the feedback parameter. We have merely interchanged the emitter and base leads, and accordingly, $r_{11}' = r_{11}$, $r_b' = r_b$, and $r_u' = r_u$ (see Fig. 4.2). It is logical to expect that the reversal of the input arms will reverse the direction of the voltage produced by the function source in the collector arm. This means that the nu-

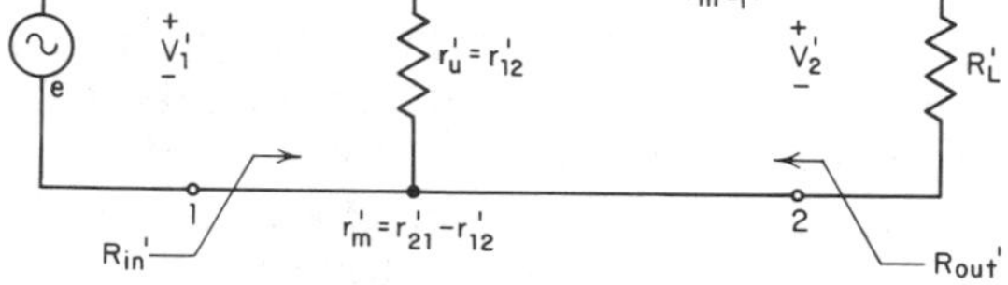

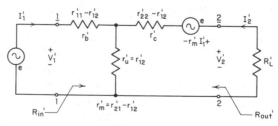

Fig. 4.2

merical values of r_m and r_{21} are negative, as is verified by later calculations. Thus the function source $r_m'I_1'$ provides a current of the same direction as the indicated current I_2'. The CE-connected transistor therefore has no phase shift in output current, but a 180° phase shift in output voltage. These results have been entered in Table 4.1. When a voltage V_1' is applied to port 1,$\underline{1}$, the source $r_m'I_1'$ provides a current in the second mesh, which current sets up an opposing voltage, with reference to V_1', across the mid-arm resistance r_u'. We may study the same occurrences with references to the double-source equivalent in Fig. B6a in Appendix B, where we now consider all quantities to be prime quantities, representative of the CE-connection. Now $\mathbf{z}_{12}'\mathbf{I}_2' = r_{12}'I_2' = r_u'I_2'$ represents the feedback voltage, which opposes the applied voltage $\mathbf{V}_1$, indicating that the CE-connected amplifier has negative feedback. Since $\mathbf{I}_1$ in Fig. B6 is reduced, the voltage produced by the source in the secondary mesh is reduced, so that less voltage amplification is obtained than during nonfeedback conditions, again implying that the feedback is negative. More specifically, we are dealing with current-controlled negative feedback. If we glance ahead to Eq. 4.8 we find that the current amplification may exceed unity to a considerable extent ($\beta > 1$). We may therefore expect the CE-connected amplifier to have considerable gain.

If we extend r_u' by an external resistance, an emitter degenerated amplifier results which has all the typical characteristics of a negative feedback amplifier. The feedback then has a strong effect on the port immittances. The reduced current I_1' makes the transistor appear to the source V_1' as a load of increased resistance. Thus the input resistance may become much larger than $r_{11}' = r_{11} = (r_b' + r_u') = (r_b + r_u)$ and very much larger than the input resistance of the CB-connected transistor—usually a very useful characteristic. If we connect an impedance meter to port 2,$\underline{2}$ to determine the output resistance, and close port 1,$\underline{1}$, we may consider that we apply a voltage V_{20}', which yields a current I_{20}'. Since the current in the emitter arm now has the opposite direction to that indicated in Fig. 4.1, the source in the collector arm experiences still another phase reversal, appearing with the plus to the right and opposing the applied voltage V_{20}'. This is precisely the opposite situation to the one we experienced for the CB-connected amplifier. In the case of the CB-connected amplifier, the effect of the feedback is to reduce both the input and the output resistance, but in the case of the CE-connected amplifier, the effect of the feedback is to increase both the input and the output resistance. At first, one would therefore expect that the CE-connected amplifier has an exceedingly high output resistance, but in reality, it is much lower than that obtained for the CB-connected amplifier—a fact well appreciated by amplifier designers. The reason for the relatively low output resistance is that the collector resistance r_c' is much smaller than r_c (the proper value of r_c' is calculated in Eq. 4.13). It may seem at first that we should introduce r_c in the collector arm of the CE-connected amplifier and absorb the punishment by a modification of the function source in the same arm. The reason why we cannot do this, and shape up network equivalents as we see fit, is that we impose the constraint that all transistor connections be described by formulas of exactly the same form, such as $r_m = r_{21} - r_{12}$, and $r_m' = r_{21}' - r_{12}'$. Within the "strait-jacket" of the common twoport theory, each network must modify itself in a large number of ways to portray the very different functions and operations of each transistor connection correctly, and not the least with respect to the peculiarities of internal feedback.

The CE-connected transistor amplifier reminds us very much of the Common Cathode, or CC-connected tube triode amplifier. Although the latter has exceedingly high input resistance at low frequency, its output resistance is of the same order of magnitude as that of the transistor amplifier, and the phase shifts are the same. Just as the CE-connected transistor amplifier has internal negative feedback, so does the triode tube amplifier. It is caused by the second term in the conventional "tube equation," $I_p = g_m V_g + g_p V_p$, since this term, with $V_p = -R_L I_p$, always subtracts from the first term, reducing the voltage amplification. We may say that the effect of the plate on the field at the cathode is to reduce this field at the same time as the signal on the grid is trying to increase it. This negative feedback effect was eliminated, or at least greatly reduced, by the insertion of the screen grid, invented by W. Schottky in Germany (around 1917).[1] Although the screen grid was inserted to reduce the back action of the plate on the cathode, it is widely and erroneously believed that the screen grid was inserted to reduce the coupling between the plate and the signal grid—a purpose very far from Schottky's thinking. The similarity between the CC-connected triode tube and the CE-connected triode transistor is closer than similarities between other connections, and many engineers familiar with tube amplifiers were able to adjust to the CE-connected transistor amplifier without much difficulty.

[1]Stockman, H. E., "Signs of Voltages and Currents in Vacuum Tube Circuits," *Communications*, Feb. 1944. Also see "Inherent Feedback in Triodes," *Wireless Engineer*, No. 4, April 1953, and "Multi-Electrode Transistor-Tube Analogy" (correspondence). *Proceedings of the IRE*, No. 6, June 1954.

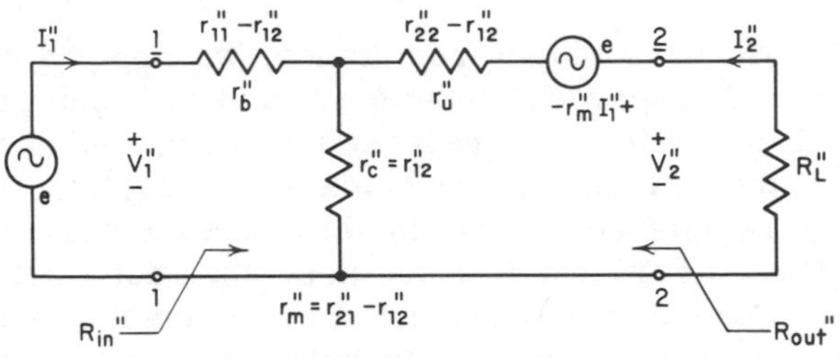

Fig. 4.3

(C) In the CC-connection the matrix element $r_{12}'' = r_c'$ in Eq. 4.3 represents the feedback parameter. We have as a further step interchanged the emitter and collector leads, thus obtaining $r_{22}'' = r_{22}'$, $r_u'' = r_u'$, and $r_c'' = r_c'$ (see Fig. 4.3). As will be shown by later calculations, the CC-connection, just like the CB-connection, has all-positive matrix elements and parameters. Accordingly, the function source $r_m''I_1''$ provides a current that has opposite direction to the indicated current I_2''. The CC-connected transistor therefore has a 180° phase shift in output current, but no phase shift in output voltage. These results have been entered in Table 4.1. When a voltage V_1'' is applied to port 1, $\underline{1}$, the source $r_m''I_1''$ provides a current in the second mesh, which current sets up an aiding voltage, with reference to V_1'', across the mid-arm resistance r_c''. As before, we may use the double-source equivalent in Fig. B6a, Appendix B, considering all quantities as double-prime quantities. Now $\mathbf{z}_{12}''\mathbf{I}_2'' = r_{12}''I_2'' = r_c''I_2''$ represents the feedback voltage, which aids the applied voltage $\mathbf{V}_1$, as was the case in the CB-connection. Thus we conclude that the CC-connected amplifier has positive feedback. More specifically, we are dealing with current-controlled positive feedback. To determine the obtainable voltage amplification, we may glance at Eq. 4.11, which indicates that the voltage amplification is less than unity. With regards to current amplification, Eq. 4.8 informs us that it is larger than that obtainable with the other two connections (see, however, the rest of the discussion).

As before, the port resistances are controlled by the feedback. Since the feedback enhances the input current, we would at first expect a low input resistance. Just the opposite obtains: an input resistance that is higher than that we can obtain with the other two connections. The reason for this is the same "strait-jacket" proposition we discussed above, which provides us with a greatly increased base resistance (the proper value of r_b'' is calculated in Eq. 4.14). In light of this information we conclude that the emitter follower is not very useful as a current amplifier, in spite of its high current amplification, since a current amplifier should have a low input resistance, not a high one.

To determine the output resistance, we apply a voltage V_{20}'' to the 2-port and observe the ensuing current I_{20}''. Since the function source $r_m''I_{20}''$ now yields a reversed voltage, aiding the applied voltage V_{20}'', the current I_{20}'' becomes enhanced, and we conclude that the output resistance is low. In this case the series resistance is $r_u'' = r_u' = r_u$, a very small resistance that does not jeopardize the low output resistance contributed by the function source. Thus we find that the rather differently behaving cathode follower and emitter follower have much in common as far as external operation goes. Both have high input resistance, low output resistance, a voltage amplification less than one, and considerable current and power amplification. In comparing tube and transistor devices with each other, and one transistor device with another transistor device, one must be careful to consider the type of drive used, whether the feedback is current controlled or voltage controlled, and other such factors. As an example, in a cathode follower, μV_k is the only dependent source and in an emitter follower, $r_m''I_1''$ is the only dependent source, provided we employ voltage drive, as we have done here. In the case of current drive, however, the cathode follower (assumed to have finite input resistance) appears with two dependent sources, whereas the emitter follower may be shown without any dependent source at all. If such matters are overlooked, the nature of the feedback may not be properly understood nor is the comparison between the devices fair.

(D) The desired table is shown as Table 4.1.

TABLE 4.1 Voltage source drive

Connection	Feedback	Current amplification	Voltage amplification
CB	Positive, as defined	180°	0°
CE	Negative, as defined	0°	180°
CC	Positive, as defined	180°	0°

(E) We calculate the following values:

$$r_b = 1{,}000\Omega \qquad r_u = 50\,\Omega$$
$$r_c = 999{,}000\,\Omega \qquad r_m = 969{,}000\,\Omega$$
$$a = r_m/rc \doteq 0.97 \qquad \alpha = r_{21}/r_{22} = 0.97$$

$$\begin{aligned}\Delta_r &= 80 \times 10^6 \Omega^2 \\ \Delta_{r1} &= \Delta_r + r_{22}R_G = 180 \times 10^6\,\Omega^2 \\ \Delta_{r2} &= \Delta_r + r_{11}R_L = 185 \times 10^6\,\Omega^2\end{aligned} \tag{4.4}$$

For completeness we have also calculated a and α. The desired quantities, calculated from the longhand equations read off from the matrix equation based on Eq. 4.1, are as follows:

$$A_I(\omega) = \frac{I_2}{I_1} = \frac{-r_{21}}{r_{22} + R_L} = -0.883 \qquad A_V(\omega) = \frac{V_2}{V_1} = \frac{r_{21}}{r_{11} + \Delta_r G_L} = 524$$

$$R_{\text{in}} = \frac{V_1}{I_1} = \frac{\Delta_{r2}}{r_{22} + R_L} \doteq 168\,\Omega \qquad R_{\text{out }1} = \frac{V_{20}}{I_{20}} = \frac{\Delta_{r1}}{r_{11} + R_G}$$

$$\doteq 156{,}000\,\Omega \tag{4.5}$$

(F) First of all we must obtain the CE-connection parameters from the CB-connection parameters used above. The transformation has already been made in problem 10 in Chapter 3, from which we obtain:

$$\begin{aligned}r_{11}' &= r_{11} = 1{,}050\,\Omega & r_{12}' &= r_{11} - r_{12} = 50\,\Omega \\ r_{21}' &= r_{11} - r_{21} = -968{,}950\,\Omega & r_{22}' &= r_{11} + r_{22} - r_{12} - r_{21} \\ & & &= 30{,}500\,\Omega\end{aligned} \tag{4.6}$$

Accordingly:

$$\begin{aligned}r_u' &= r_u = r_{12}' = 50\,\Omega & r_b' &= r_b = 1{,}000\,\Omega \\ r_c' &= 30{,}000\,\Omega & r_m' &= -r_m = -969{,}000\,\Omega \\ b &= -r_m'/r_c' \doteq 32.3 & \beta &= -r_{21}'/r_{22}' \doteq 32.3\end{aligned}$$

$$\begin{aligned}\Delta_r' &= 80 \times 10^6\,\Omega^2 = \Delta_r \\ \Delta_{r1}' &= \Delta_r' + r_{22}'R_G' = 110.1 \times 10^6\,\Omega^2 \\ \Delta_{r2}' &= \Delta_r' + r_{11}'R_L' = 101 \times 10^6\,\Omega^2\end{aligned} \tag{4.7}$$

The desired quantities are therefore

$$A_I'(\omega) = \frac{I_2'}{I_1'} = \frac{-r_{21}'}{r_{22}' + R_L'} \doteq 19.3$$

$$A_V'(\omega) = \frac{V_2'}{V_1'} = \frac{r_{21}'}{r_{11}' + \Delta_r' G_L'} \doteq -192$$

$$R_{\text{in}}' = \frac{V_1'}{I_1'} = \frac{\Delta_{r2}'}{r_{22}' + R_L'} = 2{,}020\,\Omega$$

$$R_{out\,1}' = \frac{V_{20}'}{I_{20}'} = \frac{\Delta_{r1}'}{r_{11}' + R_G'} \doteq 53{,}700\,\Omega \tag{4.8}$$

These results are entered in Table 4.2.

(G) We can obtain the CC-connection parameters either from the known CB-connection or from the known CE-connection. The latter transformation has already been carried out in problem 8 in Chapter 3, from which we obtain:

$$r_{11}'' = 1{,}000{,}000\,\Omega \qquad r_{12}'' = 30{,}000\,\Omega$$
$$r_{21}'' = 999{,}000\,\Omega \qquad r_{22}'' = r_{22}' = 30{,}050\,\Omega \tag{4.9}$$

Accordingly,

$$r_c'' = r_{12}'' = r_c' = 30{,}000\Omega \qquad r_b'' = 970{,}000\,\Omega$$
$$r_u'' = r_u' = r_u = 50\,\Omega \qquad r_m'' = -r_m' = r_m = 969{,}000\,\Omega$$
$$c = r_m''/r_u'' = 19{,}380 \qquad \gamma = r_{21}''/r_{22}'' \doteq 33.3$$

$$\Delta_r'' = \Delta_r' = \Delta_r = 80 \times 10^6\Omega^2$$
$$\Delta_{r1}'' = \Delta_r'' + r_{22}''R_G'' = 380.5 \times 10^6\Omega^2$$
$$\Delta_{r2}'' = \Delta_r'' + r_{11}''R_L'' = 580 \times 10^6\Omega^2 \tag{4.10}$$

The desired quantities are therefore

$$A_I''(\omega) = \frac{I_2''}{I_1''} = \frac{-r_{21}''}{r_{22}'' + R_L''} = -32.7 \qquad A_V''(\omega) = \frac{V_2''}{V_1''} = \frac{r_{21}''}{r_{11}'' + \Delta_r''G_L''} = 0.86$$

$$R_{in}'' = \frac{V_1''}{I_1''} = \frac{\Delta_{r2}''}{r_{22}'' + R_L''} \doteq 19{,}000\,\Omega \qquad R_{out\,1} = \frac{V_{20}''}{I_{20}''} = \frac{\Delta_{r1}''}{r_{11}'' + R_G''} \doteq 376\Omega \tag{4.11}$$

(H) The desired table is shown as Table 4.2.

TABLE 4.2

Connection			Current amplification	Voltage amplification	Input resistance	Output resistance
CB	$a = 0.97$	$\alpha = 0.97$	-0.883	524	168Ω	156,000Ω
CE	$b = 32.3$	$\beta = 32.3$	19.3	-192	2,020Ω	53,700Ω
CC	$c = 19{,}380$	$\gamma = 33.3$	-32.7	0.86	19,000Ω	376Ω

Since each transistor connection employs characteristic port terminations, the above table properly reflects the transfer functions and port immittances. The salient properties of each transistor connection can be obtained at a glance.

(I) From Eq. 4.7 we may write $b = -r_m'/r_c' = r_m/r_c'$, or

$$r_c' = r_m/b \tag{4.12}$$

As an alternative we may use $a = r_m/r_c$ in Eq. 4.4 and the formula $b = a/(1-a)$ employed in problem 10 in Chapter 3, obtaining

$$r_c' = r_c(1-a) \tag{4.13}$$

Both these formulas give the correct answer for r_c': 30,000 ohm.

The calculation of r_b'' is not quite as simple. A method that always works is to carry out the CB to CC transformation, or the CE to CC transformation, which directly yields r_b'' in terms of the specified parameters. Solution 8 in Chapter 3 gives

$$r_b'' = r_{11}'' - r_{12}'' = r_{11}' - r_{21}' \tag{4.14}$$

which is the desired formula.

(J) Starting out from the CE-connection active TEE in Fig. 4.2, we make use of the Arm Interchange Method and merely interchange the output arm and the mid-arm, obtaining in this manner the desired network shown in Fig. 4.4. The parameters of the twoport are:

$$\begin{aligned}
R_{11}'' &= \left.\frac{V_1''}{I_1''}\right|_{I_2''=0} = r_b' + r_c' - r_m' = 10^6\,\Omega \\
R_{12}'' &= \left.\frac{V_1''}{I_2''}\right|_{I_1''=0} = r_c' = 30{,}000\,\Omega \\
R_{21}'' &= \left.\frac{V_2''}{I_1''}\right|_{I_2''=0} = r_c' - r_m' = 999{,}000\,\Omega \\
R_{22}'' &= \left.\frac{V_{20}''}{I_{20}''}\right|_{I_1''=0} = r_c' + r_u' = 30{,}050\,\Omega
\end{aligned} \tag{4.15}$$

Since this is the same twoport we analyzed in Eq. 4.9, the matrices must be identical, and a comparison between Eqs. 4.15 and 4.9 shows full agreement. Accordingly, the answers obtained from the twoport in Fig. 4.4 are those given by Eq. 4.11.

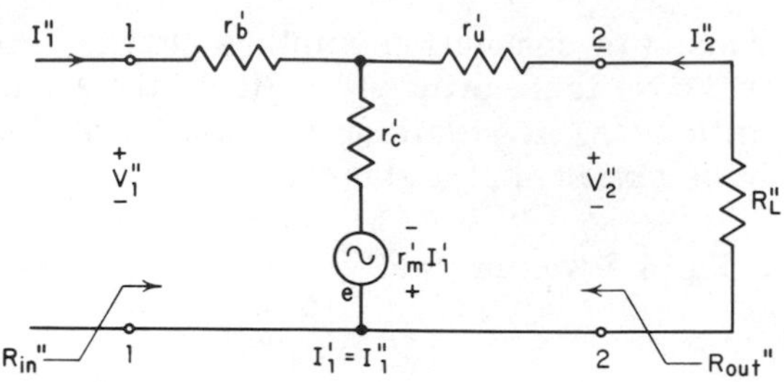

Fig. 4.4

Although the two equivalents in Fig. 4.3 and Fig. 4.4 give precisely the same results, the reasonings and explanations are different. In the emitter follower in Fig. 4.3, the input arm has the very high series resistance $r_b'' = 970{,}000$ ohm, but the input resistance is reduced to $R_{in}'' = 19{,}000$ ohm by the positive feedback action. In Fig. 4.4 the input arm has only the series resistance $r_b' = 1{,}000$ ohm. In series with r_b' appears, however, an r_c' of 30,000 ohm and the source $r_m' I_1'$ where r_m' is negative, modified by the branch $(r_u' + R_L'')$. The net effect is a resistance added to r_b' that brings the input resistance to the correct value $R_{in}'' = 19{,}000$ ohm. We can easily check this by inserting numerical values in Fig. 4.4 and writing the mesh equations.

NOTE: With reference to the CB-connected amplifier discussed in part A, the application of a voltage V_{20} leaves us with a function source $r_m I_{10}$ in the collector arm, which source we may express as a resistance by means of the Compensation Theorem. Since $I_{10} = (-r_b I_{20})/(r_b + r_u)$, with the aid of Kirchhoff'S Voltage-Sum Law,

$$V_{20} = \left(\frac{-r_m r_b}{r_b + r_u} + r_c + \frac{r_b r_u}{r_b + r_u} \right) I_{20}$$

where r_m appears as a negative resistance (the sign is opposite that of the followng two terms). Solving for the output resistance,

$$R_{out} = \frac{V_{20}}{I_{20}} = \frac{-r_b r_m + r_b r_u + r_b r_c + r_c r_u}{r_b + r_u} = \frac{r_{11} r_{22} - r_{12} r_{21}}{r_{11}} = \frac{\Delta r}{r_{11}} \tag{4.16}$$

which is the output resistance given by Eq. 4.5 for $R_G = 0$.

Conclusions to this solution

In this solution, we have made quite a thorough comparison between the CB-, CE-, and CC- connections. While we have made use of already available transformations between the three, transformations may be carried out anew by means of the "Floating" Matrix Method, the Equation Comparison Method, or the Arm Interchange Method. We have studied how feedback affects the transfer functions and port immittances, and from Table 4.2 we can obtain some guidance about the characteristics of the three connections. With reference to the internal feedback conditions in a transistor, we learned that extreme caution is necessary in the analysis and that one must be careful not to make flat statements to the effect that a certain transistor has positive or negative internal feedback. The proper statement depends first of all upon how we define positive and negative feedback and then upon what kind of drive we employ, the nature of the control, the type of network representation we choose, and the like. A high port resistance may be produced by a low resistance boosted by the appearance of a function source. Similarly, a low port resistance may be produced by a high resistance, reduced by the appearance of a function source. Thus one must be careful in drawing conclusions about the behavior of networks containing function sources in feedback systems.

The transistor amplifiers discussed here are free from storage elements, but such elements may very well be present, particularly in video and high-frequency amplifiers. The feedback will then also contribute phase shifts which are generally undesirable but which in some cases may be utilized for better amplifier performance.

PROBLEM 5

There are two mathematical conditions which, applied to a "floating" matrix, allow for the development of a general transformation matrix for CB-, CE-, and CC-transistor connections.

(A) Determine these conditions. Then specifically apply the technique to answer the following questions.

(B) If a "model" transistor, operating above its higher cutoff frequency, is described by the matrix

$$|\mathbf{z}|_{CE} = \begin{vmatrix} (5+j2) & (1+j0) \\ -(18+j5) & (2+j) \end{vmatrix}$$

what is its y CB matrix?

(C) Write an expression for the voltage amplification of a transistor amplifier using the y CB matrix obtained in part B, when the amplifier is driven by a Thévenin generator with an impedance $(1+j)$ and loaded by the admittance $(1+j)$.

(D) If, as an alternative, the load admittance can have any value, determine the value that yields maximum power output.

(E) With the matching conditions implied in (D), produce the equivalent Thévenin generator that replaces the entire network except the load, and have the laboratory build this Thévenin generator, excluding the use of energy storage components. Then let the source voltage in the Thévenin generator produce the delayed pulse indicated in Fig. 5.1. Find the transient voltage $v_2(t)$ across the load from zero time and on.

Solution

(A) The two mathematical conditions are that column sums and row sums in the third-order "floating" matrix must be individually zero, thus

$$\sum_{i=1}^{3} \mathbf{y}_{ij} \Big|_{j=1,2,3} = 0 \tag{5.1}$$

$$\sum_{j=1}^{3} \mathbf{y}_{ij} \Big|_{i=1,2,3} = 0 \tag{5.2}$$

(B) We begin by turning the z matrix elements into y matrix elements, ready to be inserted into the complete third-order matrix (see Table IV, Appendix C). From the "built-in" formulas in the complete matrix, we find the desired y matrix to be,

$$\begin{vmatrix} \mathbf{z}_{22}'/\mathbf{\Delta}_z & -\mathbf{z}_{12}'/\mathbf{\Delta}_z \\ -\mathbf{z}_{21}'/\mathbf{\Delta}_z & \mathbf{z}_{11}'/\mathbf{\Delta}_z \end{vmatrix} \tag{5.3}$$

where

$$\mathbf{\Delta}_z = \mathbf{\Delta}_z' = (5+j2)(2+j) + (18+j5) = 2(13+j7) \tag{5.4}$$

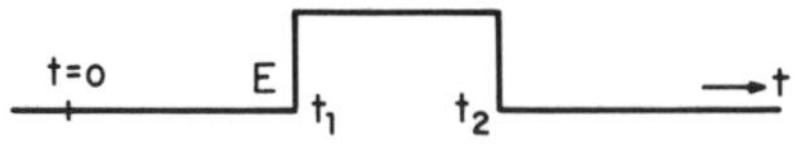

Fig. 5.1

The inserted elements are shown inside rectangular blocks in the following complete matrix, and initially all other element positions in the matrix are empty.

$$\left|\begin{array}{ccc} \boxed{(2+j)/\Delta_z} & -(1+j)/\Delta_z & \boxed{-1/\Delta_z} \\ -2(10+j3)/\Delta_z & 8(3+j)/\Delta_z & -2(2+j)/\Delta_z \\ \boxed{(18+j5)/\Delta_z} & -(23+j7)/\Delta_z & \boxed{(5+j2)/\Delta_z} \end{array}\right|_y \tag{5.5}$$

The middle column and the middle row in matrix 5.5 are now filled in in accordance with rules 5.1 and 5.2. The (yCB) matrix for the desired transistor is then the second-order matrix enclosed in the dotted frame. This matrix provides the answer to part B. The determinant to this matrix should be $1/\Delta_z$, and a check shows that

$$\Delta_y = \frac{1}{\Delta_z{}^2}\left[8(3+j)(5+j2) - 2(2+j)(23+j7)\right] = \frac{1}{\Delta_z} \tag{5.6}$$

(C) The transistor amplifier under discussion is shown in Fig. 5.2a. Changing the driving Thévenin generator into a Norton generator, and lumping its generator admittance inside the box, we end up with the simplified network shown in Fig. 5.2b. With $\mathbf{y}_{11} + \mathbf{Y}_G = \mathbf{Y}_{11}$, we obtain the equation system:

$$E_G \mathbf{Y}_G = \mathbf{Y}_{11}\mathbf{V}_1 + \mathbf{y}_{12}\mathbf{V}_2 \tag{5.7}$$

$$\mathbf{I}_2 = \mathbf{y}_{21}\mathbf{V}_1 + \mathbf{y}_{22}\mathbf{V}_2 \tag{5.8}$$

from which

$$\frac{\mathbf{V}_2}{E_g} = \frac{-\mathbf{y}_{21}\mathbf{Y}_g}{\Delta_{y1} + \mathbf{Y}_{11}\mathbf{Y}_L} \tag{5.9}$$

where

$$\Delta_{y1} = \Delta_y + \mathbf{y}_{22}\mathbf{Y}_G \tag{5.10}$$

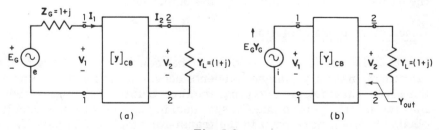

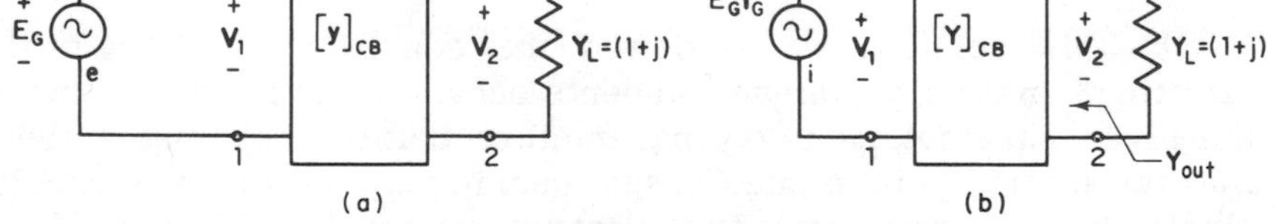

Fig. 5.2

(D) With $\mathbf{Y}_L$ not limited to the value $(1 + j)$, we apply the Output Immittance Theorem to the denominator of Eq. 5.9, obtaining

$$\mathbf{Y}_{\text{out}} = \mathbf{\Delta}_{y1}/\mathbf{Y}_{11} \tag{5.11}$$

so that

$$\mathbf{Y}_{L\ \text{opt}} = (\mathbf{\Delta}_{y1}/\mathbf{Y}_{11})^* \tag{5.12}$$

where $\mathbf{Y}_{L\,\text{opt}}$ is the optimum value of the load that gives maximum output power (the asterisk means "conjugate of"). Evaluating,

$$\mathbf{Y}_{L\ \text{opt}} = (3/388)(13 + j5) \tag{5.13}$$

(E) We conclude that the network now is the one shown in Fig. 5.2b, interpreted as a Thévenin generator. Accordingly, its voltage source and series impedance are, from Eq. 5.9,

$$\mathbf{E}^{\#} = \frac{-\mathbf{y}_{21}\mathbf{Y}_G}{\mathbf{\Delta}_{y1}} E_G \tag{5.14}$$

$$\mathbf{Z}^{\#} = R^{\#} + jX^{\#} = \frac{1}{\mathbf{Y}_{\text{out}}} = \frac{\mathbf{Y}_{11}}{\mathbf{\Delta}_{y1}} \tag{5.15}$$

The voltage source $\mathbf{E}^{\#}$ has a certain phase angle, and the series impedance $\mathbf{Z}^{\#}$ is complex. The load impedance is $\mathbf{Z}^{\#\#}$ (the conjugate of the Thévenin generator impedance). We are told that all storage elements are removed, and accordingly, the voltage source $\mathbf{E}^{\#}$ feeds two resistances in series, each one being $R^{\#}$. The output voltage is therefore half of $\mathbf{E}^{\#}$. When pulse drive is employed, we replace the sinor $\mathbf{E}^{\#}$ by the transform for the given pulse. It follows that no formal solution is required, since the above reasoning puts half of the given voltage pulse across the load resistance. During the interval $0 - t_1$, the output is zero. During the interval t_1 to t_2, the output is $E/2$, and for $t > t_2$ the output is again zero.

Conclusions to this solution

In this solution we reviewed the conditions for use of the "floating" matrix technique. Students occasionally forget to change the given parameters into y parameters before they insert them into the matrix, and in such cases meaningless results are usually obtained. When working with the transistor amplifier in part C, we notice the importance of using short-hand symbols. Although Eq. 5.9 appears here almost directly, students encountering this problem have occasionally spent pages of calculations to obtain $\mathbf{V}_2/E_G$. In the last part of the problem, we have an example of a reasoning technique that leads to a quick answer.

PROBLEM 6

Given is the transistor amplifier shown in Fig. 6.1.

(A) Transform to g parameters and then use the Equation System Comparison Method to obtain the (hCB) matrix.

(B) With the transistor amplifier described by the (hCB) matrix, obtained in (A), use the Symbolic Method to determine the voltage amplification and the output voltage $v_2(t)$ when the indicated periodic voltage is used as input.

(C) Using the Laplace Transform Method, determine the transient output voltage $v_2(t)$ when the input is the indicated step voltage. (For simplicity, consider the system nonenergized.)

Solution

(A) Staying with the CE-connection, we first use Matrix Tables 1 and 2 in Appendix C to obtain the (gCE) parameters, writing:

$$\Delta_a' = a_{11}a_{22} - a_{12}a_{21} = -1/28 \tag{6.1}$$

$$\left.\begin{matrix} g_{11}' = a_{22}/a_{12} = 44/9 & g_{12}' = -\Delta_a/a_{12} = -2/9 \\ g_{21}' = -1/a_{12} = 56/9 & g_{22}' = a_{11}/a_{12} = 13/9 \end{matrix}\right\} \tag{6.2}$$

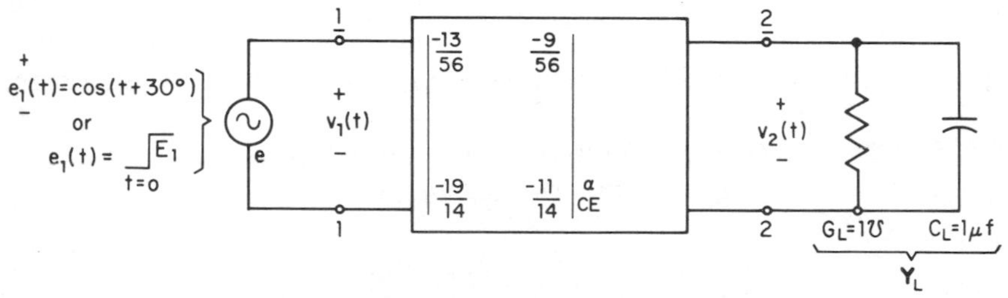

Fig. 6.1

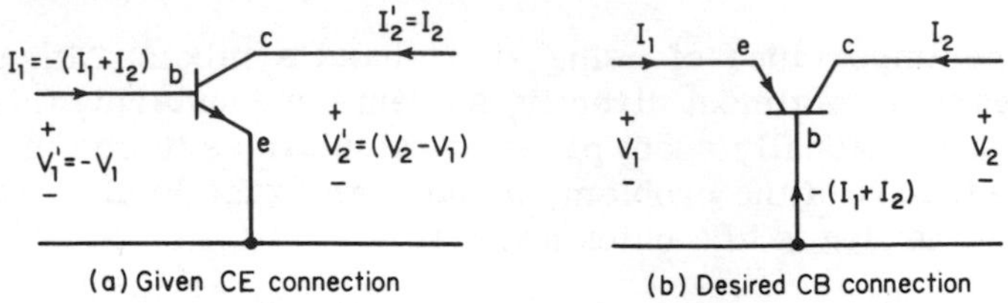

Fig. 6.2

and as a check we write

$$\Delta_a' = g_{12}'/g_{21}' = -1/28 \quad (6.3)$$

To carry out the transformation to gCB parameters, we draw the networks in Fig. 6.2, writing:

$$\left.\begin{aligned} I_1' &= g_{11}'V_1' + g_{12}'V_2' = -(I_1 + I_2) = g_{11}'(-V_1) + g_{12}'(V_2 - V_1) \quad (6.4)\\ I_2' &= g_{21}'V_1' + g_{22}'V_2' = \qquad I_2 = g_{21}'(-V_1) + g_{22}'(V_2 - V_1) \quad (6.5)\end{aligned}\right\}$$

$$\left.\begin{aligned} I_1 &= (g_{11}' + g_{12}' + g_{21}' + g_{22}')V_1 - (g_{12}' + g_{22}')V_2 \quad (6.6)\\ I_2 &= \qquad -(g_{21}' + g_{22}')V_1 + \qquad g_{22}'V_2 \quad (6.7)\end{aligned}\right\}$$

Accordingly:

$$\left.\begin{aligned} g_{11} &= (g_{11}' + g_{12}' + g_{21}' + g_{22}') = 111/9\\ g_{12} &= -(g_{12}' + g_{22}') = -11/9\\ g_{21} &= -(g_{21}' + g_{22}') = -23/3\\ g_{22} &= g_{22}' = 13/9 \end{aligned}\right\} \quad (6.8)$$

$$\Delta_g = g_{11}g_{22} - g_{12}g_{21} = 76/9 \quad (6.9)$$

Now using the matrix tables to change to h parameters, we obtain:

$$\left.\begin{aligned} h_{11} &= 1/g_{11} = 9/111 & h_{12} &= -g_{12}/g_{11} = 11/111\\ h_{21} &= g_{21}/g_{11} = -69/111 & h_{22} &= \Delta_g/g_{11} = 76/111 \end{aligned}\right\} \quad (6.10)$$

$$\Delta_h = h_{11}h_{22} - h_{12}h_{21} = 13/111 \quad (6.11)$$

The results given by Eq. 6.10 constitutes the desired hCB matrix.

(B) The matrix described by Eq. 6.10 has the long-hand equation system and transfer-function formula

$$\left.\begin{aligned} \mathbf{V}_1 &= h_{11}\mathbf{I}_1 + h_{12}\mathbf{V}_2 \quad (6.12)\\ \mathbf{I}_2 &= h_{21}\mathbf{I}_1 + h_{22}\mathbf{V}_2 \quad (6.13)\end{aligned}\right\}$$

$$\frac{\mathbf{V}_2}{\mathbf{V}_1} = \frac{-h_{21}}{\Delta_h + h_{11}\mathbf{Y}_L} \tag{6.14}$$

Here the load admittance is, with the j-term written $s_0 C_L$,

$$\mathbf{Y}_L = G_L + s_0 C_L = (1 + s_0 \times 10^{-6}) \tag{6.15}$$

so that

$$\frac{\mathbf{V}_2}{\mathbf{V}_1} = \frac{69/111}{13/111 + (9/111)(1 + s_0 \times 10^{-6})} = \frac{69}{22 + s_0 \times 9 \times 10^{-6}} \tag{6.16}$$

Since the angular velocity of the driving voltage is unity, it follows that $s_0 = j\omega_0 = j$, where the j-part is negligible compared with the real part. The voltage amplification is therefore, together with the instantaneous output voltage,

$$\mathbf{V}_2/\mathbf{V}_1 = V_2/V_1 \doteq 69/22 \doteq 3.14 \tag{6.17}$$

$$v_2(t) \doteq 3.14 \cos(t + 30°) \tag{6.18}$$

We note that the answer in Eq. 6.18 employs the particular maximum value $V_1 = 1$.

(C) In carrying out the transient solution, we start out from Eq. 6.14, with s_0 replaced by s and with V_1 replaced by E_1/s. Accordingly,

$$\overline{V}_2 = \frac{E_1}{s} \times \frac{-h_{21}}{\Delta_h + h_{11}(G_L + sC_L)} = \frac{E_1}{s} \times \frac{69}{13 + 9(1 + s \times 10^{-6})}$$

which we prefer to write

$$\overline{V}_2 = \frac{23 \times 10^6 E_1}{3} \times \frac{1}{s(s + s_1)} \tag{6.19}$$

where $s_1 = 22 \times 10^6/9$. Using the transform-pair formula

$$\frac{1}{s(s + s_1)} \rightarrow \frac{1}{s_1}\left(1 - e^{-s_1 t}\right) \tag{6.20}$$

we obtain

$$v_2(t) \doteq 3.14E_1(1 - e^{-2.44\times10^6 t}) \doteq 3.14E_1 \Big|_{t>T} \tag{6.21}$$

Here the time constant is $T = 10^{-6}/2.44$—a very small value. Thus the approximation to the right is justified in the sense that the transient rises to full value $3.14E_1$ almost instantly. The output pulse is, therefore, nearly a true copy of the input pulse, except for magnitude, and we could have introduced this result directly, skipping the calculations in part C.

Conclusions to this solution

In this solution we were given some more exercise on transistor transformations. It should be noted that we used the Equation System Comparison Method because this method was requested; actually, the "Floating" Matrix Method would have given a quicker result. In the calculation of time-domain outputs, the effect of the capacitor is so small as to be negligible, and direct answers could therefore have been written down.

PROBLEM 7

A transistor amplifier employs two transistor stages in cascade, as indicated in Fig. 7.1. G is the coupling conductance, and G_L the load conductance.

(A) Determine the individual stage amplifications and the total amplification, $A_V(\omega) = V_{II}/V_1$.

(B) Without the use of matrix algebra, replace the entire amplifier by a fictitious single-stage transistor amplifier, and calculate its output conductance, G_{out}.

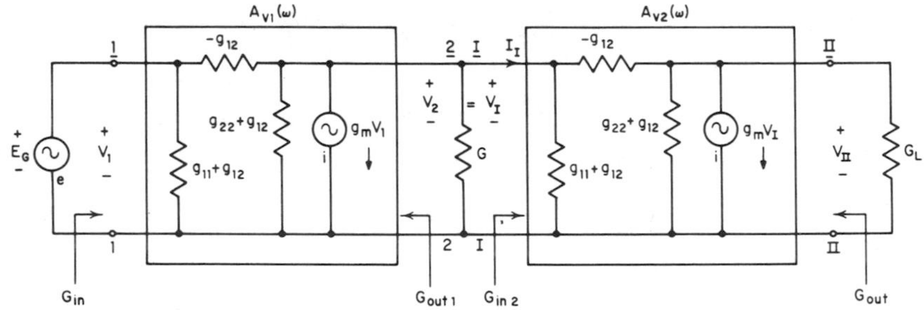

Fig. 7.1

(C) Lump the first stage into the second stage and calculate the output conductance of this modified stage. Discuss the result.

(D) How is the Output Immittance Theorem correctly applied to a cascaded transistor amplifier?

(E) What are the main considerations in the proper choice of values of G and G_L when the aim is: (1) maximum voltage output? (2) maximum power output? If possible, illustrate your viewpoints with mathematical expressions.

(F) As in part B above, replace the entire amplifier by a fictitious single stage, and determine its amplification and output conductance, using matrix algebra.

Solution

(A) As calculated from the respective long-hand equation systems, the individual voltage amplifications of the two stages and the input conductance of the second stage are

$$A_{V1}(\omega) = \frac{V_2}{V_1} = \frac{-g_{21}}{g_{22} + G + G_{\text{in}2}} \tag{7.1}$$

$$A_{V2}(\omega) = \frac{V_{\text{II}}}{V_{\text{I}}} = \frac{-g_{21}}{g_{22} + G_L} \tag{7.2}$$

$$G_{\text{in}2} = \frac{V_{\text{I}}}{I_{\text{I}}} = \frac{\Delta_g + g_{11}G_L}{g_{22} + G_L} = \frac{\Delta_{g2}}{g_{22} + G_L} \tag{7.3}$$

Accordingly,

$$A_V(\omega) = A_{V1}(\omega)A_{V2}(\omega) = \frac{-g_{21}}{g_{22} + G + G_{\text{in}2}} \times \frac{-g_{21}}{g_{22} + G_L}$$

or

$$A_V(\omega) = \frac{{g_{21}}^2}{\Delta_{g1} + {g_{22}}^2 + (g_{11} + g_{22} + G)G_L} \tag{7.4}$$

where

$$\Delta_g = g_{11}g_{22} - g_{12}g_{21} \qquad \Delta_{g1} = \Delta_g + g_{22}G$$
$$\Delta_{g2} = \Delta_g + g_{11}G_L \tag{7.5}$$

(B) The result in Eq. 7.4 represents the desired single-stage amplifier. Denoting its parameters with capital letters, we may write

$$A_V(\omega) = \frac{-G_{21}}{G_{22} + G_L} = \frac{g_{21}{}^2/(g_{11} + g_{22} + G)}{(\Delta_{g1} + g_{22}{}^2)/(g_{11} + g_{22} + G) + G_L} \tag{7.6}$$

or

$$G_{21} = \frac{-g_{21}{}^2}{g_{11} + g_{22} + G} \tag{7.7}$$

$$G_{22} = G_{\text{out}} = \frac{\Delta_{g1} + g_{22}{}^2}{g_{11} + g_{22} + G} \tag{7.8}$$

The output conductance is here obtained in accordance with the Output Immittance Theorem.

(C) Since $G_{\text{out }1} = g_{22}$, it follows that we must lump $(g_{22} + G)$ into g_{11} of the second stage. The output conductance of a single stage, driven by a current generator, is, in general,

$$G_{\text{out}} = \frac{g_{11}g_{22} - g_{12}g_{21}}{g_{11}}$$

In this case,

$$G_{\text{out}} = \frac{(g_{11} + g_{22} + G)g_{22} - g_{12}g_{21}}{g_{11} + g_{22} + G} \tag{7.9}$$

which agrees with Eq. 7.8. This is a practical method for determining the output conductance of cascaded amplifiers.

(D) The correct application has been shown in part B. Applying the theorem to either fraction in the expressions that lead to Eq. 7.4 only gives us the output conductance for the chosen stage.

(E) For maximum output voltage, G_L should be zero and G should be as small as possible. Both G_L and G may have certain limiting values which cannot be exceeded because of bias and component considerations. For maximum output power, both G and G_L have optimum values, which can be determined through calculations. One prime consideration here is whether a design should be adopted with scarcely noticeable distortion, allowing linear network theory to be used, or whether nonlinearity should be acknowledged, say 10 per cent distortion, requiring special solution techniques.

(F) Lumping G into the second stage, we have a simple cascading, expressed by the matrix multiplication shown in Eq. 7.10, where $G_{11} = (g_{11} + G)$. Using this much quicker method, we disregard $G_{\text{out 1}}$ and $G_{\text{in 2}}$, and carry out the matrix manipulation in a mechanical fashion. We must, however, first change our g parameters into a parameters, using the matrix tables as follows:

$$\begin{vmatrix} \dfrac{-g_{22}}{g_{21}} & \dfrac{-1}{g_{21}} \\ \\ \dfrac{-\Delta g}{g_{21}} & \dfrac{-g_{11}}{g_{21}} \end{vmatrix} \begin{vmatrix} \dfrac{-g_{22}}{g_{21}} & \dfrac{-1}{g_{21}} \\ \\ \dfrac{-\Delta g_1}{g_{21}} & \dfrac{-G_{11}}{g_{21}} \end{vmatrix}$$

$$= \frac{1}{g_{21}{}^2} \times \begin{vmatrix} g_{22}{}^2 + \Delta g_1 & g_{22} + G_{11} \\ - & - \end{vmatrix} \qquad (7.10)$$

Using capitals for the a matrix, we read off directly

$$A_V(\omega) = \frac{1}{A_{11} + A_{12}G_L} = \frac{g_{21}{}^2}{g_{22}{}^2 + \Delta g_1 + (g_{22} + G_{11})G_L} \qquad (7.11)$$

$$G_{\text{out}} = \frac{A_{11}}{A_{12}} = \frac{g_{22}{}^2 + \Delta g_1}{g_{22} + G_{11}} \qquad (7.12)$$

These results agree with those given by Eqs. 7.4 and 7.8. G_{out} in Eq. 7.12 could alternatively have been written down from Eq. 7.11 by means of the Output Immittance Theorem, and in much shorter time than it takes the reader to look up the formula A_{11}/A_{12} and to copy the proper quantities from Eq. 7.10.

Conclusions to this solution

This was our first problem on a cascaded amplifier. The solution has forcefully brought out the simplicity of the matrix method in comparison with the stage-by-stage analysis method, in which we must determine at least one conductance in between the stages. Again, the Output Immittance Theorem offers the quickest way of determining the total amplifier output immittance, but care must be exercised so that the method is not applied merely to the second stage. The method of making a modified second stage represent the entire amplifier should be noted. The problem of finding the values of G and G_L when maximum output power is desired offers a challenge and is well suited as an extra assignment for the reader. Note that we determine only two of the four elements in matrix 7.10. Generally, we should only calculate what is required in the problem formulation.

PROBLEM 8

Three transistor amplifier stages are cascaded to form the complete amplifier shown in Fig. 8.1. The transistors are represented by simplified "model" transistors in order to reduce the computation work. Determine the following by numerical computation:

(A) The input conductances, $G_{in\,t}$ and $G_{in\,s}$.

(B) The amplifications, V_{2t}/V_{1t}, V_{2s}/V_{1s}, and V_2/V_1.

(C) The total amplification, V_{2t}/V_1.

(D) Using transmission a parameters, carry out matrix multiplication, and derive the network matrix for the complete amplifier.

(E) From the matrix obtained in part D, calculate the total amplification V_{2t}/V_1, and by matrix or other method, calculate the output conductance G_{out} of the complete amplifier.

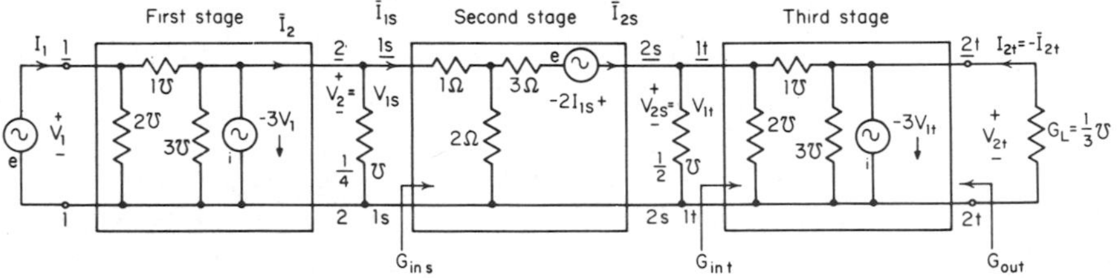

Fig. 8.1

Solution

(A) Starting with the last amplifier stage, we use the conventional formula, obtaining

$$G_{\text{in}\,t} = \frac{\Delta_{g2}}{G_{22}} = \frac{\Delta_g + g_{11}G_L}{g_{22} + G_L} \tag{8.1}$$

Since $(1/2 + G_{\text{in}\,t})$ is the load for the second stage, we obtain

$$G_{\text{in}\,s} = \frac{1 + r_{22}\,(1/2 + G_{\text{in}\,t})}{r_{11} + \Delta_r(1/2 + G_{\text{in}\,t})} \tag{8.2}$$

The following numerical values are calculated for the third stage in Fig. 8.1:

$g_{11t} = 3 \qquad g_{21t} = -4$

$g_{12t} = -1 \qquad g_{22t} = 4$

$g_{mt} = g_{21t} - g_{12t} = -3 \qquad \Delta_{gt} = 3 \times 4 - (-1)(-4) = 8$

$$G_{\text{in}\,t} = \frac{8 + 3 \times 1/3}{4 + 1/3} = \frac{27}{13} \doteq 2.08 \tag{8.3}$$

The following values are obtained for the second stage in Fig. 8.1:

$r_{11s} = 3 \qquad r_{21s} = 4$

$r_{12s} = 2 \qquad r_{22s} = 5$

$r_{ms} = r_{21s} - r_{12s} = 2 \qquad \Delta_{rs} = 3 \times 5 - 2 \times 4 = 7$

$$G_{\text{in}\,s} = \frac{1 + 5(\frac{1}{2} + \frac{27}{13})}{3 + 7(\frac{1}{2} + \frac{27}{13})} \doteq \frac{361}{547} = 0.66 \tag{8.4}$$

(B) We begin by calculating the voltage amplification in the last stage as follows:

$$\frac{V_{2t}}{V_{1t}} = \frac{-g_{21}}{g_{22} + G_L} = \frac{4}{4 + 1/3}$$

$$\frac{V_{2t}}{V_{1t}} = \frac{12}{13} \doteq 0.924 \tag{8.5}$$

The amplification in the middle stage is

$$\frac{V_{2S}}{V_{1S}} = \frac{r_{21}}{r_{11} + \Delta_r(1/2 + G_{\text{in}t})} = \frac{4}{3 + 7(67/26)}$$

$$\frac{V_{2S}}{V_{1S}} = \frac{104}{547} \doteq 0.190 \tag{8.6}$$

The amplification in the first stage is

$$\frac{V_2}{V_1} = \frac{-g_{21}}{g_{22} + (1/4 + G_{\text{in}\,S})} = \frac{4}{4 + (1/4 + 361/547)}$$

$$\frac{V_2}{V_1} = \frac{8752}{10743} = 0.815 \tag{8.7}$$

(C) The total voltage amplification is therefore

$$\frac{V_{2t}}{V_1} = \frac{V_{2t}}{V_{1t}} \times \frac{V_{2S}}{V_{1S}} \times \frac{V_2}{V_1} = 0.143 \tag{8.8}$$

Since we are using "model" transistors with small and simple numbers, and similarly port conductances which are simple numbers, large voltage amplifications do not obtain. On the contrary, we must deal with attenuations. From a pedagogical point of view, however, this is unimportant, since the purpose is to teach solution techniques.

(D) Since this amplifier has three stages, we shall use it for a demonstration of the detailed application of the matrix cascading method. The three a parameter equation systems are, with reference to Fig. 8.1, as follows:

$$V_1 = a_{11}V_2 + a_{12}\bar{I}_2 \tag{8.9}$$

$$I_1 = a_{21}V_2 + a_{22}\bar{I}_2 \tag{8.10}$$

$$V_{1S} = a_{11S}V_{2S} + a_{12S}\bar{I}_{2S} \tag{8.11}$$

$$I_{1S} = a_{21S}V_{2S} + a_{22S}\bar{I}_{2S} \tag{8.12}$$

$$V_{1t} = a_{11t}V_{2t} + a_{12t}\bar{I}_{2t} \tag{8.13}$$

$$I_{1t} = a_{21t}V_{2t} + a_{22t}\bar{I}_{2t} \tag{8.14}$$

The corresponding matrix equations are

$$\begin{vmatrix} V_1 \\ I_1 \end{vmatrix} = \begin{vmatrix} a_{11} & a_{12} \\ a_{21} & a_{22} \end{vmatrix} \begin{vmatrix} V_2 \\ \bar{I}_2 \end{vmatrix} \tag{8.15}$$

$$\begin{vmatrix} V_{1s} \\ I_{1s} \end{vmatrix} = \begin{vmatrix} a_{11s} & a_{12s} \\ a_{21s} & a_{22s} \end{vmatrix} \begin{vmatrix} V_{2s} \\ \bar{I}_{2s} \end{vmatrix} \tag{8.16}$$

$$\begin{vmatrix} V_{1t} \\ I_{1t} \end{vmatrix} = \begin{vmatrix} a_{11t} & a_{12t} \\ a_{21t} & a_{22t} \end{vmatrix} \begin{vmatrix} V_{2t} \\ \bar{I}_{2t} \end{vmatrix} \tag{8.17}$$

Combining Eqs. 8.16 and 8.17 we obtain

$$\begin{vmatrix} V_{1s} \\ I_{1s} \end{vmatrix} = \begin{vmatrix} a_{11s} & a_{12s} \\ a_{21s} & a_{22s} \end{vmatrix} \begin{vmatrix} a_{11t} & a_{12t} \\ a_{21t} & a_{22t} \end{vmatrix} \begin{vmatrix} V_{2t} \\ \bar{I}_{2t} \end{vmatrix} \tag{8.18}$$

Matrix multiplication now yields

$$\begin{vmatrix} V_{1s} \\ I_{1s} \end{vmatrix} = \begin{vmatrix} (a_{11s}a_{11t} + a_{12s}a_{21t}) & (a_{11s}a_{12t} + a_{12s}a_{22t}) \\ (a_{21s}a_{11t} + a_{22s}a_{21t}) & (a_{21s}a_{12t} + a_{22s}a_{22t}) \end{vmatrix} \begin{vmatrix} V_{2t} \\ \bar{I}_{2t} \end{vmatrix}$$

$$= \begin{vmatrix} A_{11} & A_{12} \\ A_{21} & A_{22} \end{vmatrix} \begin{vmatrix} V_{2t} \\ \bar{I}_{2t} \end{vmatrix} \tag{8.19}$$

Transforming to a parameters, we first lump the 1/2 mho coupling conductance into the third stage, and later lump the 1/4 mho coupling conductance into the first stage. Accordingly,

$$\begin{aligned} a_{11s} &= r_{11s}/r_{21s} = 3/4 & a_{11t} &= -g_{22t}/g_{21t} = -4/-4 \\ a_{12s} &= \Delta_{rs}/r_{21s} = 7/4 & a_{12t} &= -1/g_{21t} = -1/-4 \\ a_{21s} &= 1/r_{21s} = 1/4 & a_{21t} &= -\Delta_{gt}/g_{21t} = -10/-4 \end{aligned}$$

$$a_{22s} = r_{22s}/r_{21s} = 5/4 \tag{8.20}$$

$$a_{22t} = -g_{11}''/g_{21t} = -7/-8 \tag{8.21}$$

The elements in Eq. 8.19 are therefore

$$\begin{aligned} A_{11} &= 41/8 \doteq 5.12 & A_{21} &= 27/8 \doteq 3.38 \\ A_{12} &= 55/32 \doteq 1.72 & A_{22} &= 37/32 \doteq 1.16 \end{aligned}$$

Multiplying Eqs. 8.15 and 8.19, we obtain

$$\begin{vmatrix} a_{11} & a_{12} \\ a_{21} & a_{22} \end{vmatrix} \begin{vmatrix} A_{11} & A_{12} \\ A_{21} & A_{22} \end{vmatrix}$$

$$= \begin{vmatrix} (a_{11}A_{11}+a_{12}A_{21}) & (a_{11}A_{12}+a_{12}A_{22}) \\ (a_{21}A_{11}+a_{22}A_{21}) & (a_{21}A_{12}+a_{22}A_{22}) \end{vmatrix} = \begin{vmatrix} \bar{A}_{11} & \bar{A}_{12} \\ \bar{A}_{21} & \bar{A}_{22} \end{vmatrix} \quad (8.22)$$

The final matrix equation, governing the entire amplifier, is therefore

$$\begin{vmatrix} V_1 \\ I_1 \end{vmatrix} = \begin{vmatrix} \bar{A}_{11} & \bar{A}_{12} \\ \bar{A}_{21} & \bar{A}_{22} \end{vmatrix} \begin{vmatrix} V_{2t} \\ \bar{I}_{2t} \end{vmatrix} \quad (8.23)$$

The a parameters of the first stage are:

$$a_{11} = -g_{22}'/g_{21} = -17/-16 \qquad a_{12} = -1/g_{21} = -1/-4$$
$$a_{21} = -\Delta_g/g_{21} = -35/-16 \qquad a_{22} = -g_{11}/g_{21} = -3/-4 \quad (8.24)$$

The elements of Eq. 8.22 are therefore

$$\bar{A}_{11} = \frac{805}{128} \doteq 6.3 \qquad \bar{A}_{12} = \frac{1073}{512} \doteq 2.1 \qquad \bar{A}_{21} = - \qquad \bar{A}_{22} = - \quad (8.25)$$

(E) Calculating the total voltage amplification and the output conductance of the complete amplifier from Eq. 8.23, we obtain

$$\frac{V_{2t}}{V_1} = \frac{1}{\bar{A}_{11} + \bar{A}_{12}G_L} = \frac{1}{6.3 + 21(1/3)} \doteq 0.14 \quad (8.26)$$

$$G_{out} = \frac{\bar{A}_{11}}{\bar{A}_{12}} = \frac{6.3}{2.1} \doteq 3\,℧ \quad (8.27)$$

The answer in Eq. 8.26 agrees with that in Eq. 8.8. In Eq. 8.25 we did not bother to calculate $\bar{A}_{21}$ and $\bar{A}_{22}$, since they are not required for the final answers. The output conductance G_{out} in Eq. 8.27 could have been obtained more simply by application of the Output Immittance Theorem to Eq. 8.26.

Conclusions to this solution

This solution demonstrates in detail how the matrix method is applied. If the theory is left out, it is found that the matrix method is much quicker than the stage-by-stage analysis method used in part B. With some practice one can write the triple-multiplication matrix directly, although the saving in time scarcely justifies this procedure.

PROBLEM 9

The two-stage audio-frequency transistor amplifier shown in Fig. 9.1 utilizes a high-quality audio transformer as coupling element between the stages.

(A) With the turns ratio, n, of the transformer appearing in the answers, determine without use of matrix multiplication the mid-frequency voltage amplification, $A_V(\omega)$, of the total amplifier, and its output admittance, G_{out}. How many answers are available to these two questions? Assume $n = V_2/V_1'$.

(B) Give numerical answers to part A, when $n = 3$.

(C) Using the Sectional Network Matrix Technique, cut the network in sections in any manner you wish, and then determine the total amplification by means of matrix multiplication. (As an example, use three sections with transformer as middle section.)

(D) For each section, demonstrate how the matrix shows obedience to the Reciprocity Theorem, as the section is passivated.

(E) Replace the total amplifier by an equivalent single stage, give the network equivalent, and discuss whether it has physical existence.

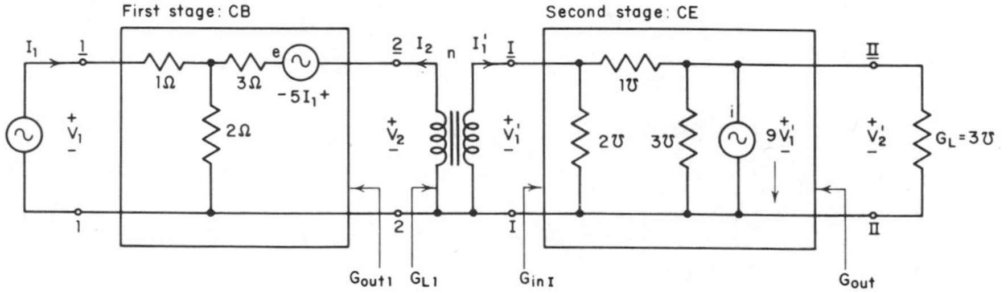

Fig. 9.1

(F) Produce an equivalent single-stage amplifier merely by network simplifications. How does this method compare with the one employed in (E)?

Solution

(A) The parameters for the two amplifier stages are:

$$\begin{aligned} r_{11} &= 3\,\Omega & g_{11}' &= 3\,\mho \\ r_{12} &= 2\,\Omega & g_{12}' &= -1\,\mho \\ r_{21} &= 5+2 = 7\,\Omega & g_{21}' &= 9-1 = 8\,\mho \\ r_{22} &= 5\,\Omega & g_{22}' &= 4\,\mho \\ \Delta_r &= 15-14 = 1\,\Omega^2 & \Delta_g' &= 12+8 = 20\,\mho^2 \end{aligned} \tag{9.1}$$

The formulas used in the following are easily derived from the proper long-hand equation systems. For the second stage

$$G_{\text{in}I} = \frac{I_1'}{V_1'} = \frac{\Delta_g' + g_{11}'G_L}{g_{22}' + G_L} = \frac{29}{7} = 4.14\,\mho \tag{9.2}$$

The looking-in conductance from the primary of the transformer is, in accordance with Fig. 9.1,

$$G_{L1} = G_{\text{in}I}/n^2 = 29/7n^2 \doteq 4.14/n^2\,\mho \tag{9.3}$$

The voltage amplification in the second stage is

$$A_{V2}(\omega) = \frac{V_2'}{V_1'} = \frac{-g_{21}'}{g_{22}' + G_L} = \frac{-8}{7} \doteq -1.14 \tag{9.4}$$

The voltage amplification in the first stage is

$$A_{V1}(\omega) = \frac{V_2}{V_1} = \frac{r_{21}}{r_{11} + \Delta_r G_L} = \frac{49n^2}{21n^2 + 29} \tag{9.5}$$

The total voltage amplification is, therefore,

$$A_V(\omega) = A_{V1}(\omega) \times \frac{1}{n} \times A_{V2}(\omega) = \frac{-56n}{21n^2 + 29} \tag{9.6}$$

If instead G_L is maintained throughout all of the calculations, we obtain

$$A_V(\omega) = \frac{-56n}{4(3n^2+5)+3(n^2+1)G_L} \tag{9.7}$$

Since the transformer may have a phase reversal of 180°, a second answer of $-A_V(\omega)$ exists for Eq. 9.7. G_{out} is calculated in part B.

(B) For $n = 3$ we obtain

$$G_{L1} = 29/63 \doteq 0.46 \tag{9.3a}$$

$$A_{V1} = 441/218 \doteq 2.0 \tag{9.5a}$$

$$A_V(\omega) = \frac{-84}{109} \doteq -0.77 \tag{9.6a}$$

$$A_V(\omega) = \frac{-84}{64+15G_L} \tag{9.7a}$$

The output conductance G_{out}, obtained by means of the Output Immittance Theorem from Eq. 9.7, is

$$G_{out} = \frac{4}{3} \times \frac{3n^2+5}{n^2+1} = \frac{64}{15} \doteq 4.3\,℧ \tag{9.8}$$

The same numerical result could have been obtained directly from Eq. 9.7a.

(C) If we make a middle section out of the transformer, its a matrix and long-hand equation system take the form

$$|a|_t = \begin{vmatrix} a_{11t} & a_{12t} \\ a_{21t} & a_{22t} \end{vmatrix} \tag{9.9}$$

$$V_2 = a_{11t}V_1' + a_{12t}I_1' \tag{9.10}$$

$$-I_2 = a_{21t}V_1' + a_{22t}I_1' \tag{9.11}$$

From this we formulate the definitions:

$$a_{11t} = \left.\frac{V_2}{V_1'}\right|_{I_1'=0} = n \qquad a_{12t} = \left.\frac{V_2}{I_1'}\right|_{V_1'=0} = 0$$

$$a_{21t} = \left.\frac{-I_2}{V_1'}\right|_{I_1'=0} = 0 \qquad a_{22t} = \left.\frac{-I_2}{I_1'}\right|_{V_1'=0} = \frac{1}{n} \tag{9.12}$$

The transformer matrix therefore becomes

$$|a|_t = \begin{vmatrix} n & 0 \\ 0 & 1/n \end{vmatrix} = \begin{vmatrix} 3 & 0 \\ 0 & 1/3 \end{vmatrix} \tag{9.13}$$

In evaluating the parameters in Eq. 9.12, we note that the signal transfer is from left to right. With open secondary winding, the voltage V_2 must yield an n times smaller voltage, thus $a_{11t} = n$. When the current $-I_2$ is impressed upon the primary side of the transformer, it encounters infinite impedance, since the impedance on the secondary side is infinite, and accordingly, $V_2 = \infty$ and therefore $V_1' = \infty$ so that $a_{21t} = 0$. For closed secondary winding, the applied voltage V_2 encounters a transformed zero impedance; thus $-I_2 = \infty$ and $I_1' = \infty$ so that $a_{12t} = 0$. For an applied current $-I_2$, the short-circuit current must be n times larger, so that $a_{22t} = 1/n$.

Writing the a matrices for the two amplifying stages directly from the matrix tables, we obtain

$$\begin{vmatrix} A_{11} & A_{12} \\ A_{21} & A_{22} \end{vmatrix} = \begin{vmatrix} 3/7 & 1/7 \\ 1/7 & 5/7 \end{vmatrix} \begin{vmatrix} n & 0 \\ 0 & 1/n \end{vmatrix} \begin{vmatrix} -1/2 & -1/8 \\ -5/2 & -3/8 \end{vmatrix}$$

$$= \begin{vmatrix} \frac{3n}{7} & \frac{1}{7n} \\ \frac{n}{7} & \frac{5}{7n} \end{vmatrix} \begin{vmatrix} \frac{-1}{2} & \frac{-1}{8} \\ \frac{-5}{2} & \frac{-3}{8} \end{vmatrix} = \begin{vmatrix} \frac{-(3n^2+5)}{14n} & \frac{-3(n^2+1)}{56n} \\ \frac{-(n^2+25)}{14n} & \frac{-(n^2+15)}{56n} \end{vmatrix}$$

$$= \begin{vmatrix} \frac{-16}{21} & \frac{-5}{28} \\ \frac{-17}{21} & \frac{-1}{7} \end{vmatrix} \tag{9.14}$$

Using conventional formulas, we write

$$A_V(\omega) = \frac{1}{A_{11} + A_{12}G_L} = \frac{-56n}{21n^2 + 29} \tag{9.6b}$$

$$G_{\text{out}} = \frac{A_{11}}{A_{12}} = \frac{4}{3} \times \frac{3n^2 + 5}{n^2 + 1} \tag{9.8a}$$

These results agree with those in Eqs. 9.6 and 9.8.

(D) For the middle section to represent a passive network, its a determinant must be 1. We find

$$\Delta_a = a_{11t}\, a_{22t} - a_{12t}\, a_{21t} = n(1/n) - 0 \times 0 = 1 \tag{9.15}$$

If we let the function sources vanish in the two amplifying stages, we obtain

$$\Delta_a = (3/2)(5/2) - (11/2)(1/2) = 1$$

$$\Delta_a{}' = (4/1)(3/1) - (1/1)(11/1) = 1 \tag{9.16}$$

Unity determinant proves obedience to the Reciprocity Theorem.

(E) We have already obtained a single matrix that represents the total amplifier (see Eq. 9.14). To be able to draw a conventional network equivalent, we may change to r parameters, writing

$$\begin{vmatrix} \dfrac{-(3n^2+5)}{14n} & \dfrac{-3(n^2+1)}{56n} \\ \\ \dfrac{-(n^2+25)}{14n} & \dfrac{-(n^2+15)}{56n} \end{vmatrix}_A \rightarrow \begin{vmatrix} \dfrac{3n^2+5}{n^2+25} & \dfrac{n}{2(n^2+25)} \\ \\ \dfrac{-14n}{n^2+25} & \dfrac{n^2+15}{4(n^2+25)} \end{vmatrix}_R$$

$$= \begin{vmatrix} 16/17 & (3/4)/17 \\ -21/17 & 3/17 \end{vmatrix}_{n=3} = \begin{vmatrix} R_{11} & R_{12} \\ R_{21} & R_{22} \end{vmatrix} \tag{9.17}$$

with the determinants

$$\Delta_A = A_{11}A_{22} - A_{12}A_{21} = (-1)/28$$

$$\Delta_R = R_{11}R_{22} - R_{12}R_{21} = \frac{3\,(n^2+1)}{4(n^2+25)} = \frac{15}{68}\Bigg|_{n=3} \tag{9.18}$$

Computing $R_{11} - R_{12}$, $R_{22} - R_{12}$, and $R_{21} - R_{12}$ from Eq. 9.17, we obtain the network equivalent shown in Fig. 9.2a. Using the conventional formulas, we obtain

$$A_V(\omega) = \frac{R_{21}}{R_{11} + \Delta_R G_L} = \frac{-1.24}{0.94 + 0.22 \times 3} \doteq -0.77$$

$$G_{\text{out}} = R_{11}/\Delta_R = 0.94/0.22 \doteq 4.3 \tag{9.19}$$

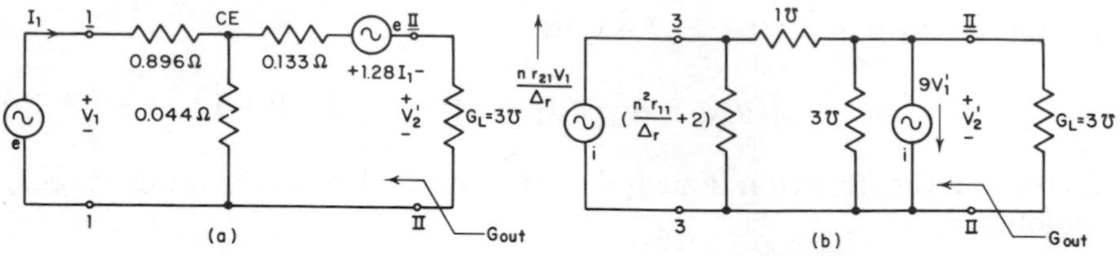

Fig. 9.2

Thus with the transformer contributing 0^0 phase shift, a CE-connected single transistor stage will replace the entire original amplifier. Whether such a single transistor exists is hard to determine when only "model" transistors are employed, but if real transistor data are inserted, one can usually tell whether the desired transistor is obtainable or not. The main requirement is that reasonable proportions exist between r_b', r_u', r_c', and r_m'. If one transformer winding is turned around, an entirely different proposition appears and the investigation must start all over again. If the restriction on full equivalence is lifted, so that, as an example, polarity is considered unimportant, or $A_V(\omega)$ important but G_{out} unimportant, etc., then it is much easier to find a single transistor stage that will replace the entire amplifier. But even so, we shall find it impossible in most cases and not a good idea in many of the rest.

(F) One method of approach here is to replace everything to the left of the transformer by a shunt-form generator. The output conductance of the first stage is r_{11}/Δ_r, and on the right side of the transformer this becomes $n^2 r_{11}/\Delta_r$, which we add to the 2-mho leg of the PI, as is shown in Fig. 9.2b. The shunt-form generator source is $r_{21}V_1/\Delta_r$, which on the right side of the transformer becomes $nr_{21}V_1/\Delta_r$, as is shown in Fig. 9.2b. The transformer has now vanished. Calculating $A_V(\omega)$ and G_{out} from the network equivalent in Fig. 9.2b, we obtain the correct values given by Eqs. 9.6a and 9.8. While this method of producing a single-stage equivalent is just as rigorous as the one used previously, it should be mentioned that the input differs from V_1 and that Fig. 9.2a shows the only complete network equivalent.

Conclusions to this solution

We note that whenever we talk about a high-quality audio transformer, we generally take the liberty to consider it ideal in the sense that voltages and currents transfer via n, whereas immittances transfer via n^2, at the same time as the winding inductances are considered infinite. A practical audio transformer does not allow these simplifications, and we must then introduce such quantities as coefficient of coupling, leakage immittance, and losses, in our calculations. In representing the transformer by its matrix, we make possible the treatment of the entire network by matrix methods, but the stage-by-stage-analysis method must not be forgotten, since it offers an excellent checking method. The problem of finding a single transistor stage equivalent to a multi-stage amplifier is often of academic interest only, but in the comparison of several multi-stage amplifiers, a certain clarity is often gained if each amplifier is replaced by its single-stage equivalent. The question as to whether the single-stage equivalent is realizable or not often invites reconsideration of assumptions made.

SOME FINAL THOUGHTS

This chapter brought up material from the previous chapters and gave us a first answer to the question: "Why connection-transformations?" The transformations to a parameters now appear important, since they allow us to use the mathematical tool of matrix multiplication. In this way we can calculate cascaded amplifiers much faster than by any other method, and particularly so if the "building blocks" are already presented in terms of a parameters.

We have laid the ground work for the idea of sectionalizing amplifiers. This technique permits us to redesign one section of an amplifier, at least to a certain extent, while keeping all preceding and following sections on ice, so to speak. By means of a matrix table for coupling networks, see Table 6, Appendix C, we can quickly introduce simple coupling networks in parameter form. The transistors proper are written in terms of a parameters with the aid of Tables 1 and 2 in the same Appendix. In many problems on cascaded transistor amplifiers, we can therefore write down the entire matrix chain without having to go through long calculations. Nevertheless, much time can be saved if we first carefully consider the various possibilities of breaking up the given network in sections, and of lumping certain network elements together to simplify the network. By reading off the tables in terms of transform variables and s-domain immittances, we can set up the problem solution in a general form, from which we can obtain both the periodic steady-state solution and the transient solution; in the latter case we must consider the initial conditions. The sectionalizing a matrix technique therefore fits the modern approach in the solution of active network problems.

5

Transistor Feedback Networks

We have already encountered one problem in which we discussed internal feedback in transistors (see Problem 4, Chapter 4). We shall now extend the treatment to external feedback, which is either applied or accidental. Together, internal and external feedback provide a "vice," squeezing the transistor amplifier into a specific performance, and it is our task to determine this performance analytically. If we were to apply external feedback and then turn the internal feedback into an equivalent external feedback, which can be done, it would become evident to us that a case exists in which the two "external" feedback actions cancel (a form of neutralization). In many of the following problems, an effort has been made to show the distinction between negative feedback, or degeneration, and positive feedback, or regeneration, the latter leading to the important concept of instability, which may give rise to oscillations, damped or undamped. The concept of instability has been given special consideration, and several different criteria have been developed to clarify the basic thoughts, and to show how one criterion can be turned into another. Later on, this technique has been extended to tunnel diodes in as much as a technique has been developed, by means of which a oneport can be portrayed as a twoport, to which one or more stability criteria may be applied.

PROBLEM 1

A passive network is encapsulated in such a manner that no part of it is accessible, except for a short piece of conductor. It was found that if this conductor is cut open at point x and stimulance injected, a considerable amount of stimulance is required before

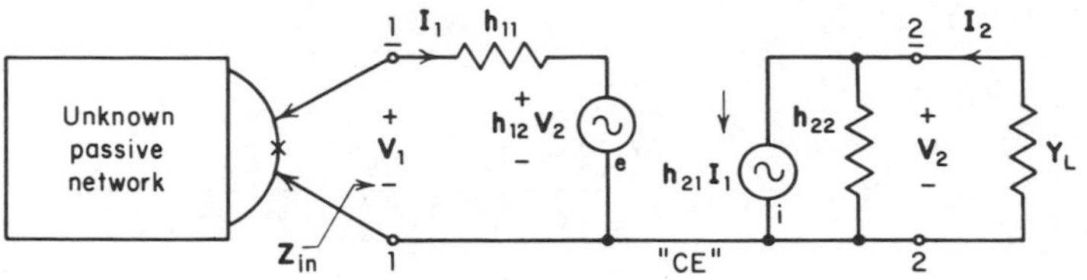

Fig. 1.1

the system becomes unstable. It was also found that the required stimulance could be obtained from the transistor, indicated to the right by its equivalent network (see Fig. 1.1). It should be noted that the transistor provides stimulance, although no arrangement for external feedback exists.[1]

(A) Derive a formula for the input impedance of the transistor network, and specify the real part

(B) Under what conditions does the transistor network provide a short-circuit at the point x?

(C) Give some thought to the design problem of providing maximum stimulance at point x, with particular reference to the proper load admittance $\mathbf{Y}_L$ to be used. Also give consideration to the question of how closely we can approach the point of instability in the system.

Solution

(A) From the twoport equation system we obtain the h parameters and input impedance as

$$\mathbf{h}_{11} = h_{11} + j\underline{h}_{11} \qquad \mathbf{h}_{22} = h_{22} + j\underline{h}_{22}$$

$$\mathbf{h}_{12}\mathbf{h}_{21} = h + j\underline{h} \qquad \mathbf{Y}_L = G_L + jB_L \tag{1.1}$$

We have here used a sub-bar to distinguish the j-part from the real part. The input impedance is now, from the long-hand equation system,

[1] For an excellent discussion of internal feedback conditions in transistor amplifiers, see R. F. Shea, *Transistor Circuit Engineering*, John Wiley and Sons, 1957, Chap. 6, Sec. 5.

$$\mathbf{Z}_{\text{in}} = \frac{\mathbf{V}_1}{\mathbf{I}_1} = \mathbf{h}_{11} - \frac{\mathbf{h}_{12}\mathbf{h}_{21}}{\mathbf{h}_{22} + \mathbf{Y}_L} \tag{1.2}$$

$$R_{\text{in}} = h_{11} - \frac{h(h_{22} + G_L) + \underline{h}(\underline{h}_{22} + B_L)}{(h_{22} + G_L)^2 + (\underline{h}_{22} + B_L)^2} \tag{1.3}$$

Here, generally, the real parts of all h parameters are positive, and h positive. We may also consider $\underline{h}$ positive, which calls for a capacitive load to make B_L positive, in order for the second term to override the first term, so that R_{in} becomes negative.

(B) Both the real part and the j-part of $\mathbf{Z}_{\text{in}}$ must be zero.

(C) A considerable amount of stimulance or negative resistance must be produced, and this is first of all a matter of choosing a transistor with suitable h parameters. As an example, the smaller h_{11} is, the more negative R_{in} becomes, provided nothing is changed in the right term in Eq. 1.3. G_L and B_L are likely to have optimum values, and the proper values may be found by further analysis, or often in a much simpler way, by measurements in the laboratory. How closely we can approach the point of instability before the system "takes off" depends upon a number of factors, such as constancy of the transistor parameters, constancy of bias to avoid Q-point movements, amount of nonlinearity (that should not be there) as the point of instability is approached, amount and kind of reactance in the system single-mesh or single-node-pair network, etc. It is most likely that the system will take a jump into the unstable mode of operation, and that a smooth threshold of regeneration will not be obtained unless specifically provided for.

Conclusions to this solution

This solution is of particular interest, since it demonstrates that instability can be obtained by internal feedback in a transistor amplifier without the need for externally applied feedback. This fact leads to many practical transistor applications, but generally it creates a nuisance, calling for neutralization measures. We learned that the magnitude and phase angle of the load has a great influence on the sign and magnitude of the input resistance, and that for a given load, one transistor may be stable where another is unstable. With reference to a smooth threshold of oscillation, we learned that this is unlikely to obtain just by itself; a rough threshold is more likely to obtain.

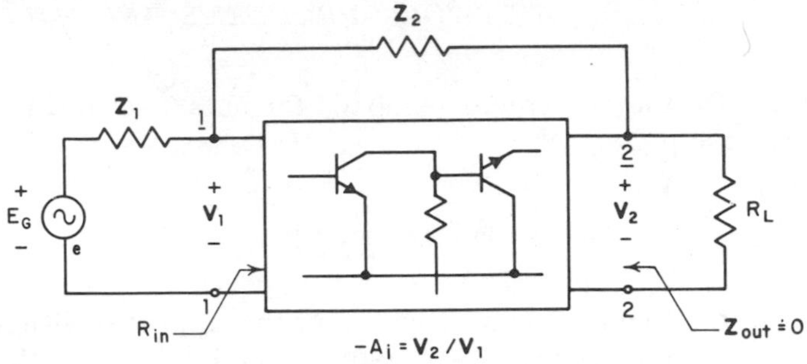

Fig. 2.1

PROBLEM 2

Figure 2.1 shows an "operational network," having a phase-reversing transistor amplifier with two stages: the first CE-connected and the second an emitter follower.[1] The cascaded stages may be represented by a total matrix $|R|$ in which R_{12} is considered sufficiently small to allow us to disregard the inherent feedback.

(A) Using Kirchhoff's laws, derive a formula for the voltage-transfer function $\mathbf{A} = \mathbf{V}_2/E_G$. R_{in} and A_i are known quantities, which are considered as constants.

(B) Using more than one method, derive a formula for the feedback-transfer function $\mathbf{H} = \mathbf{V}_{10}/\mathbf{V}_{20}$ and write $\mathbf{A} = f(A_i, \mathbf{H}, \mathbf{Z}_1, \mathbf{Z}_2)$, simulating the appearance of the classical feedback formula.

(C) Write a formula for the amplification $\mathbf{A}$ in terms of the matrix elements in $|R|$.

(D) The "operational network" is used for integration, with $\mathbf{Z}_1 = R_1 = 1/G_1$ and $\mathbf{Z}_2 = -j/\omega C$. Derive the transfer function used in part A, and state mathematically to what extent we have succeeded in making the output voltage represent an integral of the input voltage.

(E) Give some thought to the s-combine that would result in a transform approach if the matrix $|R|$ were made more realistic by the addition of capacitance in such a fashion that an upper cutoff frequency is produced.

[1]For a realistic discussion of operational networks, see J. K. Scully, Accuracy and Stability in Operational Amplifiers," *Electro-Technology*, August 1963.

NOTE: By the "classical feedback formula" we mean the general relationship

$$\mathbf{A} = \frac{\mathbf{A}_i}{1 - \mathbf{H}\mathbf{A}_i}$$

where $\mathbf{A}_i$ is the inherent amplification of the amplifier without feedback action, $\mathbf{H}$ the feedback-transfer function, and $\mathbf{A}$ the total, actual, or system amplification. The formula holds for a voltage-driven system with series injection of the feedback signal, meaning that both $\mathbf{A}_i$ and $\mathbf{H}$ are voltage ratios. The formula also holds for a current-driven system with shunt injection of the feedback signal, meaning that both $\mathbf{A}_i$ and $\mathbf{H}$ are current ratios. In this particular problem we encounter a crossbreed, and the simple case of fitting simple quantities into the classical feedback formula is not at hand. Nevertheless, if we can simulate this formula close enough to provide a denominator, the zero value of which creates a pole, we have established a stability criterion in the same manner as we established one employing the classical feedback formula. Note that in intricate feedback problems the criterion used above should be accompanied by an independent check that no roots appear on the right-hand side of the s-plane, which may jeopardize stability. (For a discussion of the s-plane see Fig. 5.3 and associated text.)

Solution

(A) Kirchhoff's current-sum law applied at port $1,\underline{1}$ yields, with $\mathbf{V}_1 = -\mathbf{V}_2/A_i$,

$$\mathbf{Y}_1(E_G - \mathbf{V}_1) + \mathbf{Y}_2(\mathbf{V}_2 - \mathbf{V}_1) - G_{\text{in}}\mathbf{V}_1 = 0 \tag{2.1}$$

Thus

$$\mathbf{A} = \mathbf{V}_2/E_G = -\mathbf{Y}_1 A_i/[G_{\text{in}} + \mathbf{Y}_1 + \mathbf{Y}_2(1 + A_i)] \tag{2.2}$$

(B) We may write Eq. 2.2 in the form

$$\mathbf{A} = \mathbf{Y}_1\mathbf{Z}_2 \frac{-A_i}{1 + \mathbf{Z}_2(G_{\text{in}} + \mathbf{Y}_1) + A_i} = \mathbf{Y}_1\mathbf{Z}_2\mathbf{H}\frac{-A_i/\mathbf{H}}{1/\mathbf{H} + A_i} \tag{2.3}$$

from which

$$\mathbf{A} = \mathbf{Y}_1\mathbf{Z}_2\mathbf{H}\frac{-A_i}{1 - \mathbf{H}(-A_i)} \tag{2.4}$$

$$\mathbf{H} = 1/[1 + \mathbf{Z}_2(G_{\text{in}} + \mathbf{Y}_1)] \tag{2.5}$$

Here Eq. 2.4 reminds us of the classical feedback formula. By equating the denominators in Eq. 2.3 we obtain $\mathbf{H}$ as given by Eq. 2.5. As another approach, we may consider $\mathbf{V}_2$ an applied voltage $\mathbf{V}_{20}$ and write, for $E_G = 0$,

$$\mathbf{V}_{10} = (\mathbf{Z}_1 /\!/ R_{\text{in}})\mathbf{V}_{20}/(\mathbf{Z}_2 + \mathbf{Z}_1 /\!/ R_{\text{in}})$$

or

$$\mathbf{H} = \mathbf{V}_{10}/\mathbf{V}_{20} = 1/[1 + \mathbf{Z}_2(G_{\text{in}} + \mathbf{Y}_1)] \tag{2.6}$$

which agrees with the result in Eq. 2.5.

(C) Although R_{12} is small, it does exist, so that we have a complete matrix. For the special but most unlikely case of a large load resistance, a simple derivation can be made, as follows

$$-A_i = \mathbf{V}_2/\mathbf{V}_1 = R_{21}/(R_{11} + \Delta_R G_L) \doteq R_{21}/R_{11} \tag{2.7}$$

where R_{21} has a negative numerical value. Using Eq. 2.2 we obtain

$$\mathbf{A} \doteq \mathbf{Y}_1 R_{21}/[R_{11}(G_{\text{in}} + \mathbf{Y}_1 + \mathbf{Y}_2) - R_{21}\mathbf{Y}_2] \tag{2.8}$$

If we do not allow the approximation $G_L \doteq 0$, the formula becomes

$$\mathbf{A} = \mathbf{Y}_1 R_{21}/[(R_{11} + \Delta_R G_L)(G_{\text{in}} + \mathbf{Y}_1 + \mathbf{Y}_2) - R_{21}\mathbf{Y}_2] \tag{2.9}$$

where we may set $R_{12} \doteq 0$, R_{12} being a part of Δ_R.

(D) Under specified conditions Eq. 2.2 yields, with $s = j\omega$,

$$\mathbf{A} = \frac{\mathbf{V}_2}{E_G} = \frac{-G_1 A_i}{C(1 + A_i)} \times \frac{1}{s + (G_1 + G_{\text{in}})/C(1 + A_i)} \tag{2.10}$$

For perfect integration, the second term in the denominator should vanish, which means that we should use a large series resistance R_1, a large capacitor C, and an amplifier having large input resistance R_{in} and large amplification A_i.

(E) Capacitances may appear in a number of different ways, and accordingly we may have a monotonous roll-off, yielding a cutoff frequency or a higher order curve. In the simplest case, the inherent amplification may be a function $A_I(\omega) = A_i(0)/(s + 1/T)$, where $A_i(\omega) = A_i(0)$ represents the amplification at low or mid-frequency, and where T is a specified time constant. If so, Eq. 2.10 will be of the second order in s, and perfect integration, requiring a 90° phase shift from the specified quantity, now will be more difficult to obtain.

Conclusions to this solution

This problem is representative of a large class of problems, in which the solution is accomplished by direct application of Kirchhoff's laws rather than the classical feedback theory. Many problems are solved better and faster this way. In part B, however, we do attempt to write the total or actual amplification in a way that resembles the classical feedback formula. By doing so, we are able to determine the feedback transfer function **H** by identification. The conventional method is to apply a voltage to the output of the network, since this voltage then becomes the input to the feedback path. The output voltage of the feedback path is then determined in a direct manner, whereupon **H** is calculated.

This problem is of special interest, since it deals with the device generally referred to as an "operational amplifier." We learn how the application of feedback to an amplifier in this case turns it into an integrator, although the achieved operation of integration is not perfect. We can come very close to the ideal, however, by following certain design criteria. The behavior of the integrator becomes more intricate to the extent that an upper cutoff frequency exists, caused by the influence of several storage elements inherent in different parts of the network.

PROBLEM 3

A CB-connected audio-frequency transistor amplifier is provided with positive feedback as shown in Fig. 3.1. The closed-port output current amplification of the inherent amplifier has the given value α, and r_u, r_b, and r_c are known. The critical value of H, yielding instability, is designated H_c.

(A) Derive the classical feedback formula, and discuss the conditions for instability, employing the Barkhausen-Nyquist criterion. Express H_c in terms of given network quantities.

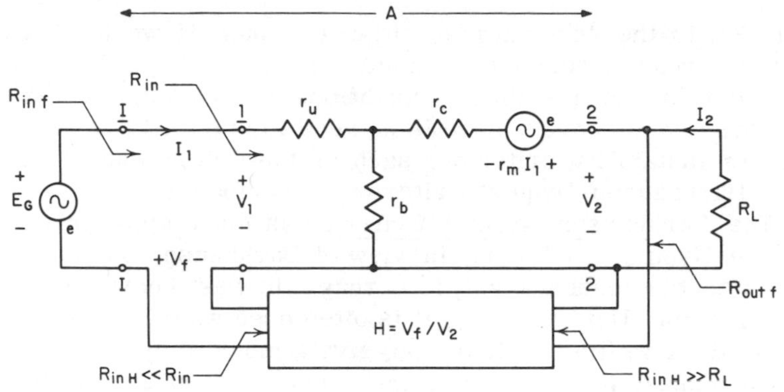

Fig. 3.1

(B) Obtain the instability conditions (B1) by deriving the matrix equation for the entire system and applying the Determinant Criterion. Now obtain these conditions by using the Immittance Criterion as applied to (B2) mesh 2, (B3) mesh 1, (B4) node 2,$\underline{2}$, (B5) node 1,$\underline{1}$.

(C) Discuss the variation of $R_{out\,f}$ as the positive feedback is gradually increased. Indicate roughly the shape of the curve $R_{out\,f} = f(H)$.

(D) Carry out a similar discussion for $R_{in\,f}$. Indicate roughly the shape of the curve $R_{in\,f} = f(H)$.

NOTE: The Determinant Criterion implies that we set the system determinant of the proper parameter, here the r parameter, equal to zero. The Criterion may be proven by means of Cramer's Rule, implying an output for zero input when the determinant is zero. Note that the system determinant is the twoport determinant with both external port immittances lumped into it. The Immittance Criterion states that the total impedance of the system mesh must be zero or that the total admittance of the system node-pair must be zero. To obtain the system mesh and the system node-pair, we must lump both the generator immittance and the load immittance into the mesh or node-pair provided by the amplifier proper. (In this case the generator resistance is zero.) A very useful application of this criterion is at hand if we place a cut across the signal transfer path anywhere at all in the total network, but particularly at the input port or at the output port. In the latter case, we see $\mathbf{Y}_L$ as the load, and we therefore write the instability equation as $\mathbf{Y}_{out} = -\mathbf{Y}_L$ Similarly, at the input port, we write $\mathbf{Y}_{in} = -\mathbf{Y}_G$, where $\mathbf{Y}_G$ is the generator admittance. Thus, if we have already for some reason derived a formula for $\mathbf{Y}_{\text{out}}$ or $\mathbf{Y}_{\text{in}}$, all we have to do to obtain the instability conditions is to complete one of the equations given above. There is no need to start all over again and apply an instability criterion, such as the Determinant Criterion, or the Barkhausen-Nyquist Criterion, described next.

The Barkhausen-Nyquist Criterion, a more appropriate name than the Nyquist Criterion, in view of Barkhausen's early contributions to the feedback art, is perhaps the best known of all feedback criteria. Unfortunately, it is often used where other criteria, such as the Immittance Criterion, give a much simpler solution. In specific cases, however, the Barkhausen-Nyquist Criterion, $\mathbf{H}_c\mathbf{A}_i = 1$, is not only the fastest criterion but also fits into an approach using the very powerful mathematical tool referred to as the Nyquist Diagram or Nyquist Plot. Although not required in a number of simple transistor amplifier feedback problems, a check of the positive half of the s-plane for possible solutions should be undertaken for a complete analysis of the stability conditions.

Solution

(A) The classical feedback formula is a generalized statement of the equation in the point of linear mixing (of the voltages E_G and V_f), which is

$$E_G + V_f - V_1 = E_G + HV_2 - V_1 = 0$$

Dividing by V_2 and inserting $A = V_2/E_G$ and $A_i = V_2/V_1$ we obtain

$$A = \frac{A_i}{1 - HA_i} \tag{3.1}$$

which is the classical feedback formula. Instability occurs when

$$HA_i = H_cA_i = 1$$

$$H_c = 1/A_i \tag{3.2}$$

To express H_c in network quantities, we note that $\alpha \doteq r_m/r_c$ = constant, so that $r_m \doteq \alpha r_c$ is known. We can now write:

$$r_{11} = r_u + r_b \qquad r_{21} = r_m + r_b \qquad r_u = r_{11} - r_{12} \qquad r_m = r_{21} - r_{12}$$

$$r_{12} = r_b \qquad r_{22} = r_c + r_b \qquad r_b = r_{12} \qquad r_c = r_{22} - r_{12} \tag{3.3}$$

The twoport long-hand equation systems are, with $V_2 = -R_L I_2$ and $V_f = -HR_L I_2$,

$$\left.\begin{aligned} V_1 &= r_{11}I_1 + r_{12}I_2 \\ V_2 &= r_{21}I_1 + r_{22}I_2 \end{aligned}\right\} \qquad \begin{aligned}(3.4)\\(3.5)\end{aligned}$$

$$\left.\begin{aligned} E_g &= r_{11}I_1 + (r_{12} + HR_L)I_2 \\ V_2 &= r_{21}I_1 + \qquad\qquad r_{22}I_2 \end{aligned}\right\} \qquad \begin{aligned}(3.6)\\(3.7)\end{aligned}$$

From this, the inherent amplification A_i and the critical value H_c of H become

$$A_i = \frac{V_2}{V_1} = \frac{r_{21}}{r_{11} + \Delta_r G_L} \tag{3.8}$$

$$H_c = \frac{1}{A_i} = \frac{r_{11} + \Delta_r G_L}{r_{21}} \tag{3.9}$$

(B1) The system-matrix equation follows from Eqs. 3.6 and 3.7 and is shown in Eqs. 3.10 and 3.11, with V_2 transferred to the right-hand side:

$$\begin{vmatrix} E_g \\ V_2 \end{vmatrix} = \begin{vmatrix} r_{11} & (r_{12} + HR_L) \\ r_{21} & r_{22} \end{vmatrix} \begin{vmatrix} I_1 \\ I_2 \end{vmatrix} \tag{3.10}$$

$$\begin{vmatrix} E_G \\ 0 \end{vmatrix} = \begin{vmatrix} r_{11} & (r_{12} + HR_L) \\ r_{21} & (r_{22} + R_L) \end{vmatrix} \begin{vmatrix} I_1 \\ I_2 \end{vmatrix} \tag{3.11}$$

Setting the determinant of (11) equal to zero, the system becomes self-sustained with E_G vanishing, thus:

$$r_{11}(r_{22} + R_L) - (r_{12} + H_c R_L)r_{21} = 0 \tag{3.12}$$

from which we obtain Eq. 3.9 by solving for H_c.

(B2) Eliminating I_1 in Eqs. 3.6 and 3.7 we obtain

$$r_{21}E_G = (-\Delta_r - r_{11}R_L + HR_L r_{21})I_2 \tag{3.13}$$

For vanishing E_G, the parenthesis must be zero. Solving for $H = H_c$, we again obtain Eq. 3.9.

(B3) Again using Eqs. 3.6 and 3.7, this time eliminating I_2, we obtain

$$(r_{22} + R_L)E_G = (\Delta_r + r_{11}R_L - HR_L r_{21})I_1 \tag{3.14}$$

For vanishing E_G, the parenthesis must be zero, and again we obtain H_c in Eq. 3.9.

(B4) Inserting Eq. 3.8 in Eq. 3.1 we obtain the system amplification as

$$A = V_2/E_G = r_{21}R_L/(\Delta_r + r_{11}R_L - HR_L r_{21}) \tag{3.15}$$

The output resistance is then in accordance with the Output Immittance Theorem

$$R_{\text{out}\,f} = \Delta_r/(r_{11} - Hr_{21}) \tag{3.16}$$

Placing a cut at node 2,<u>2</u> and applying the Immittance Criterion, we set $R_{\text{out}\,f} = -R_L$, yielding $\Delta_r = -r_{11}R_L + H_c r_{21}R_L$, from which we again obtain the result in Eq. 3.9. As an alternative, we may solve for $R_{\text{out}\,f} = -V_{20}/I_{20}$ in Eqs. 3.6 and 3.7, thus obtaining R_{out} as a function of R_L:

$$R_{\text{out}\,f} = (\Delta_r - HR_L r_{21})/r_{11} \tag{3.17}$$

This special case is acceptable here, however, since we are going to put $R_{\text{out}\,f} = -R_L$ anyhow. Accordingly, we obtain an equation which again yields Eq. 3.9.

(B5) The input conductance at port 1,<u>1</u> is, from Eqs. 3.4 and 3.5,

$$G_{\text{in}} = I_1/V_1 = (r_{22} + R_L)/(r_{11}R_L + \Delta_r) \tag{3.18}$$

Using the Compensation Theorem to express V_f as a resistance R_f, we write:

$$R_f = -V_f/I_1 = -H\,V_2/I_1 = HR_L I_2/I_1 = -HR_L r_{21}/(r_{22} + R_L) \tag{3.19}$$

The conductance-balance equation is now, with $E_G = 0$,

$$(r_{22} + R_L)/(r_{11}R_L + \Delta_r) = (r_{22} + R_L)/(H_cR_Lr_{21}) \qquad (3.20)$$

which again yields the result in Eq. 3.9. If instead we had considered the port I,I we would have calculated the input conductance G_{inf}, and since the conductance on the left side of the port is infinite, our equation would have taken the form

$$1/0 = G_{inf} = (r_{22} + R_L)/(\Delta_r + r_{11}R_L - H_cR_Lr_{21}) \qquad (3.21)$$

which again yields Eq. 3.9.

(C) $R_{out\,f}$ as function of H is given by Eq. 3.16. We note that for $H = 0$ we obtain the output resistance of the twoport proper, Δ_r/r_{11}. To find which way the curve goes, we seek the slope of the curve for small values of H, writing

$$k = dR_{out\,f}/dH = d/dH\left[\Delta_r/(r_{11} - Hr_{21})\right] = \Delta_r r_{21}/(r_{11} - Hr_{21})^2$$
$$= \text{positive} \qquad (3.22)$$

This curve is plotted in Fig. 3.2a. At $H = r_{11}/r_{21}$, the curve reaches $+\infty$, and then continues from $-\infty$, with the system entirely stable. It is not until $H = H_c$, yielding $R_{out} = -R_L$, that the system takes off, which means that the curve in Fig. 3.2a cannot be traced any further. If we insert $H = H_c$ from Eq. 3.9 in Eq. 3.16, we obtain as verification, $R_{out} = -R_L$.

(D) The input resistance R_{inf} curve is obtained in a similar fashion and is shown in Fig. 3.2b. The input resistance is in accordance with Eq. 3.21:

$$R_{in\,f} = \frac{\Delta_r + r_{11}R_L}{r_{22} + R_L} - \frac{r_{21}R_L}{r_{22} + R_L}H = R_{in} + cH \qquad (3.23)$$

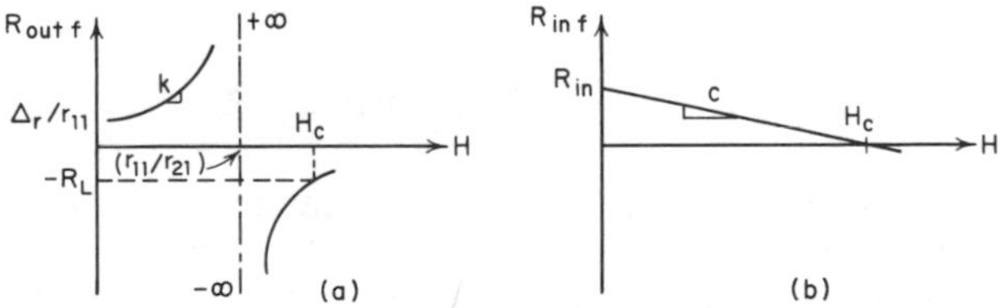

Fig. 3.2

This is the equation of a straight line having the ordinate R_{in} for $H = 0$, and a slope c, which has the negative value, $-r_{21}R_L/(r_{22}+R_L)$.

Conclusions to this solution

In this solution we used several different stability criteria and found that all of them gave the same result. While the problem formulation particularly invited the use of the Barkhausen-Nyquist Criterion, we realize that if the solution approach uses the matrix equation for the system, the Determinant Criterion would be the quickest one to use. It is important here to note that the first column matrix must be zero, achieved by moving V_2 away from the column matrix, and letting E_G vanish. The Immittance Criterion is always inviting, and particularly when we use it by placing a cut at a port. Often we have derived the input and/or the output immittance, and by simply setting it equal to the external port immittance with negative sign, we directly obtain the instability conditions. The art of placing cuts in a system should be cultivated by the student. We learned how helpful it is to plot curves indicating how port immittances vary as functions of the applied feedback. An extension is to plot curves for both signs of H including negative feedback.

Generally, problems on negative feedback are easier to solve than problems on positive feedback. For one thing, the latter are treacherous, since we occasionally and erroneously may carry out calculations on an active network that does not exist; that is, the take-off point may already have been passed. Consequently, we may think we are making linear-network-theory calculations on an amplifier when in reality we are applying linear-network theory to an oscillator, already operating nonlinearly.

PROBLEM 4

Given is the two-stage transistor amplifier shown in Fig. 4.1, which has a very much lower output resistance than input resistance. The transistors are identical, and their CB-connection r parameters are known.

Part I Negative feedback, $R_u = 0$

(A) Determine the voltage amplification, the output conductance, and the input conductance of the inherent amplifier. Formulate the network matrix, and extend it to the total network, including feedback, to obtain the system matrix.

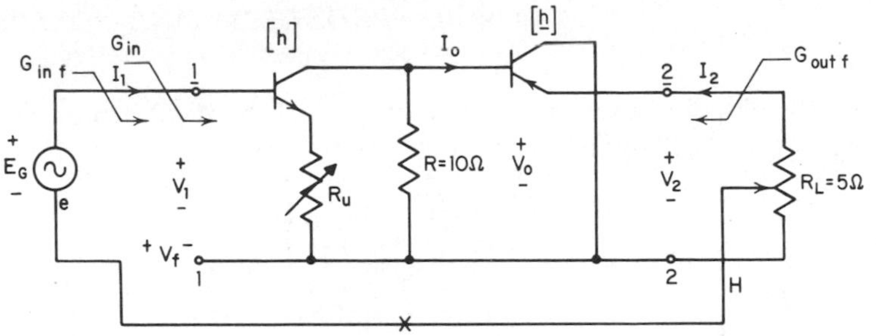

Fig. 4.1

(B) Determine the voltage amplification, the output conductance, and the input conductance of the total network, including feedback.

(C) State the above quantities under the condition that the tap on the load potentiometer has been raised sufficiently to give a total amplification of $1/H$.

(D) If each transistor in CB-connection has r_{11} = 5 ohm, r_{12} = 4 ohm, r_{21} = 23 ohm, and r_{22} = 24 ohm, what are the matrices $|h|$ and $|\underline{h}|$, and what is the h matrix for the total network, that is, the system h matrix.

(E) Obtain numerical answers for all previously calculated quantities. Discuss the approximation in part C.

Part II Positive feedback, $R_u = 0$ *(except in part H)*

It is assumed that a 180° phase shift is provided at point x.

(F) Write the general formulas for the total voltage amplification, output conductance, and input conductance.

(G) Write the instability conditions in terms of (1) the Barkhausen-Nyquist Criterion, (2) the Determinant Criterion, (3) the Immittance Criterion, applied to a suitable mesh, (4) the Immittance Criterion, applied to a suitable node-pair (place a cut at the chosen node).

(H) The resistance $R_u = r_u$ is now inserted. Find the change in positive feedback necessary to bring the new system to the point of instability (assume r_m to remain unchanged).

Solution

(A) The inherent amplifier is located between ports 1 and 2.

We lump the conductance, $G = 1/R$, into h_{22} of the first stage, writing $h_{22}' = h_{22} + G$. The equation systems are

$$\left.\begin{aligned} V_1 &= h_{11}I_1 + h_{12}V_0 \\ -I_0 &= h_{21}I_1 + h_{22}'V_0 \end{aligned}\right\} \quad \begin{aligned} (4.1) \\ (4.2) \end{aligned}$$

$$\left.\begin{aligned} V_0 &= \underline{h}_{11}I_0 + \underline{h}_{12}V_2 \\ I_2 &= \underline{h}_{21}I_0 + \underline{h}_{22}V_2 \end{aligned}\right\} \quad \begin{aligned} (4.3) \\ (4.4) \end{aligned}$$

The input conductance of the second stage is

$$G_0 = \frac{I_0}{V_0} = \frac{\underline{h}_{22} + G_L}{\underline{\Delta}_h + \underline{h}_{11}G_L} \tag{4.5}$$

$$\underline{\Delta}_h = \underline{h}_{11}\underline{h}_{22} - \underline{h}_{12}\underline{h}_{21} \tag{4.6}$$

The voltage amplification of the first stage is therefore

$$A_1 = \frac{V_0}{V_1} = \frac{-h_{21}}{\Delta_h + h_{11}G_0} \tag{4.7}$$

$$\Delta_h = h_{11}h_{22}' - h_{12}h_{21} \tag{4.7a}$$

Similarly the voltage amplification of the second stage is

$$A_2 = V_2/V_0 = -\underline{h}_{21}/(\underline{\Delta}_h + \underline{h}_{11}G_L) \tag{4.8}$$

The total voltage amplification of the inherent amplifier is therefore

$$A_i = A_1A_2 = h_{21}\underline{h}_{21}/(\Delta_h + h_{11}G_0)(\underline{\Delta}_h + \underline{h}_{11}G_L) \tag{4.9}$$

where G_0 is given by Eq. 4.5. To find the output conductance, we first determine the output resistance of the first stage, which is h_{11}/Δ_h. Adding this to $\underline{h}_{11}$, we obtain $\underline{\Delta}_h' = (\underline{h}_{11} + h_{11}/\Delta_h)\underline{h}_{22} - \underline{h}_{12}\underline{h}_{21}$, and accordingly

$$G_{out} = \frac{\underline{\Delta}_h'}{\underline{h}_{11} + h_{11}/\Delta_h} = \frac{h_{11}\underline{h}_{22} + \Delta_h\underline{\Delta}_h}{h_{11} + \underline{h}_{11}\Delta_h} \tag{4.10}$$

The input conductance is from equation systems (4.1) (4.2) and (4.3) (4.4):

$$G_{in} = \frac{I_1}{V_1} = \frac{\underline{h}_{22} + h_{22}'(\underline{\Delta}_h + \underline{h}_{11}G_L) + G_L}{h_{11}\underline{h}_{22} + (h_{11} + \underline{h}_{11}\Delta_h)G_L + \Delta_h\underline{\Delta}_h} \tag{4.11}$$

Designating the h parameters of the two stages constituting the inherent amplifier by capital letters, we can obtain these parameters from Eqs. 4.1 to 4.4 by combinations and eliminations, obtaining the matrix equation and network matrix

$$\begin{vmatrix} V_1 \\ I_2 \end{vmatrix} = \begin{vmatrix} H_{11} & H_{12} \\ H_{21} & H_{22} \end{vmatrix} \begin{vmatrix} I_1 \\ V_2 \end{vmatrix} \tag{4.12}$$

$$|H| = \begin{vmatrix} H_{11} & H_{12} \\ H_{21} & H_{22} \end{vmatrix} \tag{4.13}$$

where

$$H_{11} = K(h_{11} + \underline{h}_{11}\Delta_h) \qquad H_{22} = K(\underline{h}_{22} + h_{22}'\underline{\Delta_h})$$

$$H_{12} = K h_{12}\underline{h}_{12} \qquad \Delta_H = H_{11}H_{22} - H_{12}H_{21}$$

$$H_{21} = -K h_{21}\underline{h}_{21} \qquad K = \frac{1}{1 + h_{22}'\underline{h}_{11}} \tag{4.14}$$

We can now write Eqs. 4.9, 4.10, and 4.11 in terms of H parameters, obtaining

$$A_i = \frac{-H_{21}}{\Delta_H + H_{11}G_L} \tag{4.15}$$

$$G_{\text{out}} = \frac{\Delta_H}{H_{11}} \tag{4.16}$$

$$G_{\text{in}} = \frac{H_{22} + G_L}{\Delta_H + H_{11}G_L} \tag{4.17}$$

To extend the matrix to the system, including feedback, we merely extend V_1 in the first column matrix in Eq. 4.12 to E_G by setting $V_1 = E_G + V_f = E_G + HV_2$, whereupon we move HV_2 to the right-hand side, leaving E_G alone in the first column matrix. Since the first stage is CE-connected and the second stage an emitter follower, it is apparent that the feedback must be negative, A_i in Eq. 4.15 being produced as a negative number. The feedback network matrix takes the form, with its determinant,

$$|H| = \begin{vmatrix} H_{11} & (H_{12} - H) \\ H_{21} & H_{22} \end{vmatrix} \tag{4.18}$$

$$\Delta_{Hf} = \Delta_H + HH_{21} \tag{4.19}$$

(B) The system voltage amplification is obtained from the classical feedback formula as

$$A = \frac{A_i}{1 - HA_i} = \frac{-H_{21}}{\Delta_{Hf} + H_{11}G_L} \tag{4.20}$$

The system output conductance is in accordance with the Output Immittance Theorem, from Eq. 4.20

$$G_{\text{out}\,f} = \frac{\Delta_{Hf}}{H_{11}} \tag{4.21}$$

The system input conductance is, from an extension of Eq. 4.17,

$$G_{\text{in}f} = \frac{H_{22} + G_L}{\Delta_{Hf} + H_{11}G_L} \tag{4.22}$$

(C) The approximation follows from

$$A = \frac{A_i}{1 - HA_i} \doteq -\frac{1}{H} \tag{4.23}$$

As we raise the tap on R_L, H becomes larger, thus $|HA_i|$ becomes larger, and finally $|HA_i| \gg 1$. This condition will be discussed with reference to numerical values.

(D) Employing the transformation techniques used in problem 10 in Chapter 3 we obtain

$$\begin{vmatrix} 5 & 4 \\ 23 & 24 \end{vmatrix}_{r\,\text{CB}} \rightarrow \begin{vmatrix} 5 & 1 \\ -18 & 2 \end{vmatrix}_{r\,\text{CE}} \rightarrow \begin{vmatrix} 14 & \frac{1}{2} \\ 9 & \frac{1}{2} \end{vmatrix}_{h\,\text{CE}}$$

$$\Delta_r = 28 \qquad \Delta_r = 28 \qquad \Delta_h = 5/2$$

$$\begin{vmatrix} h_{11} & h_{12} \\ h_{21} & h_{22}' \end{vmatrix} = \begin{vmatrix} 14 & \frac{1}{2} \\ 9 & 0.6 \end{vmatrix} \qquad \Delta_h = 3.90 \tag{4.24}$$

For the second stage we obtain

$$\begin{vmatrix} 5 & 4 \\ 23 & 24 \end{vmatrix}_{r\,\text{CB}} \rightarrow \begin{vmatrix} 24 & 1 \\ 20 & 2 \end{vmatrix}_{r\,\text{CC}} \rightarrow \begin{vmatrix} 14 & \frac{1}{2} \\ -10 & \frac{1}{2} \end{vmatrix}_{h\,\text{CC}}$$

$$\Delta_r = 28 \qquad \Delta_r = 28 \qquad \Delta_h = 12$$

$$\begin{vmatrix} \underline{h}_{11} & \underline{h}_{12} \\ \underline{h}_{21} & \underline{h}_{22} \end{vmatrix} = \begin{vmatrix} 14 & 0.5 \\ -10 & 0.5 \end{vmatrix} \qquad (4.25)$$

The numbers for the matrices of the inherent amplifier, and the total amplifier or system are, with $K = 0.1064$,

$$|H| = \begin{vmatrix} 7.29 & .0266 \\ 9.58 & .820 \end{vmatrix} \qquad |H|_f = \begin{vmatrix} 7.29 & (0.0266-H) \\ 9.58 & 0.820 \end{vmatrix}$$

$$\Delta_H = 5.72 \qquad \Delta_{Hf} = 5.72 + 9.58H \qquad (4.26)$$

(E) Inserting numerical values in all previously calculated quantities, we obtain from Eqs. 4.7 to 4.11, 4.15 to 4.17, and 4.20 to 4.22,

$$A_1 = -1.97 \qquad A_2 = 0.675 \qquad A_i = -1.33$$

$$G_{in} = 0.141\,\mho \qquad G_{out} = 0.785\,\mho \qquad G_{out\,f\,(H=1)} = 2.1\,\mho$$

$$A_{H=1} = -0.57 \qquad G_{in f\,(H-1)} = 0.061\,\mho \qquad (4.27)$$

The first five quantities here pertain to the feedback-free system. The last three to the condition of negative feedback. The system values are calculated for the arbitrary value $H = 1$. We note that this turns the amplifier into an attenuator, since we have very low inherent amplification to start with, but it shows that negative feedback of the voltage controlled type increases the output conductance and decreases the input conductance. For $H - 1$ we obtain $|HA_i| = 1 \times 1.33$, which is not large in comparison with 1, and the approximation called for in part C is therefore not possible.

(F) To treat positive feedback we set $H = -H_1$ and thus obtain from Eqs. 4.19 to 4.22 and from 4.26

$$\Delta_{Hf} = 5.72 - 9.58H_1 \qquad A = -9.58/(7.18 - 9.58H_1)$$

$$G_{out\,f} = (5.72 - 9.58H_1)/7.29 \qquad G_{in f} = 1.02/(7.18 - 9.58H_1) \qquad (4.28)$$

(G1) In accordance with the Barkhausen-Nyquist Criterion we set $-H_{1c}A_i = 1$ and thus obtain $H_{1c} = -1/A_i = 1/1.33 \doteq 0.75$.

(G2) Using the Determinant Criterion, we write the network matrix in Eq. 4.18, the load admittance being lumped into the fourth element as follows:

$$\left|H\right|_f = \begin{vmatrix} H_{11} & (H_{12}+H_1) \\ H_{21} & (H_{22}+G_L) \end{vmatrix} = \begin{vmatrix} 7.29 & (0.0266+H_1) \\ 9.58 & 1.02 \end{vmatrix}$$

thus obtaining

$$\Delta_{Hf\,2} = 7.29 \times 1.02 - (0.0266 + H_{1c}) \times 9.58 = 0$$

$$H_{1c} \doteq 0.75 \tag{4.29}$$

(G3) If we consider the input mesh and turn V_f into an impedance by means of the Compensation Theorem, we obtain

$$-V_f/I_1 = -HV_2/I_1 = H_1 V_2\, R_{\text{in}}/I_1 R_{\text{in}} = H_1 A_i R_{\text{in}}$$

A summation of all the resistance in the mesh yields

$$H_{1c} A_i R_{\text{in}} + R_{\text{in}} = 0 \tag{4.30}$$

from which we again obtain $H_{1c} \doteq 0.75$.

(G4) Placing a cut in the input port $1,\underline{1}$, we write

$$G_{\text{in}}/H_{1c}A_i + G_{\text{in}} = 0 \tag{4.31}$$

and here again we obtain $H_{1c} \doteq 0.75$.

(H) The second matrix in Eq. 4.24 tells us that doubling the resistance in the emitter lead produces the new matrix

$$\begin{vmatrix} \bar{r}_{11} & \bar{r}_{12} \\ \bar{r}_{21} & \bar{r}_{22} \end{vmatrix}_{\text{CE}} = \begin{vmatrix} 6 & 2 \\ -17 & 3 \end{vmatrix}_{\text{CE}}$$

$$\bar{\Delta}_r = 52\,\Omega^2 \tag{4.32}$$

The value of the third element is obtained as follows: we interpret r_m in the problem formulation to refer to the CE-connection, and its unchanged value is therefore $r_m = r_{21} - r_{12} = -18 - 1 = -19 = \bar{r}_{21} - 2$, or $\overline{r}_{21} = -17$. The amplification of the first degenerated stage is now

$$A_{1\,\text{dgn}} = \frac{\overline{r}_{21}}{\overline{r}_{11} + \overline{\Delta}_r \overline{G}_L} = \frac{-17}{6 + 52(0.1 + 0.048)} \doteq -1.24 \qquad (4.33)$$

Since in this case the inherent amplification is $-1.24 \times 0.675 = -0.84$, we no longer have actual amplification, and even the top position on the potentiometer cannot bring the system to the point of instability. If we could go outside the potentiometer, which implies amplification in the feedback path, we would find that instability would be achieved for $H_{1C\,\text{dgn}} = 1/0.84 = 1.19$.

Extending the scope of the problem somewhat, we may ask what performance the positive feedback amplifier would give with $R_u = 0$ but with $H_1 < H_{1C}$. A suitable value may be $H_1 = 0.70$. For this value Eq. 4.28 yields

$$A = -19 \qquad G_{\text{out}\,f} = -0.134\ \mho \qquad G_{\text{in}\,f} = 2.14\ \mho \qquad (4.34)$$

Thus the system amplification has been raised from -1.33 to -19, a considerable increase. The output conductance is now negative, but it has not yet reached the value -0.20, which would cause instability. The positive feedback has increased the input conductance from 0.14 mho to 2.14 mho, a very large increase. This fits well into the requirement that at the point of instability, the input resistance must go to zero (since the generator resistance is zero).

Conclusions to this solution

This problem can be solved in many different ways. The solution presented above reviews previous material. Since we are not obliged to use h parameters, a different solution would be obtained if we worked everything in r parameters all the time. We observed the particular effects on amplification and port immittances of negative feedback, and also of positive feedback. It was found that the different methods employed agreed completely. We should get used to the idea of working problems more than one way, time permitting.

PROBLEM 5

Consider the feedback conditions pertaining to a transistor amplifier in general.

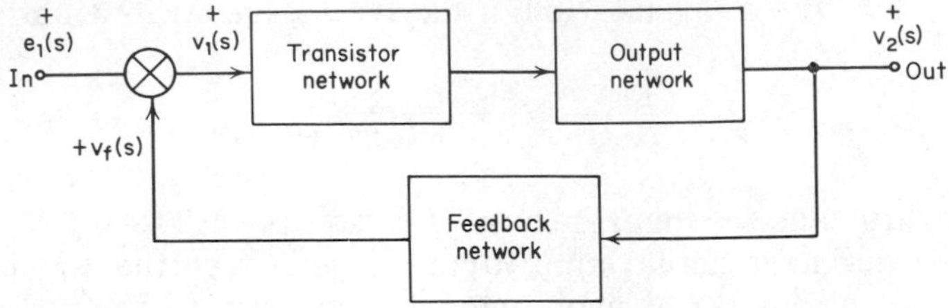

Fig. 5.1

Part I

(A) By defining the quantities $A(s)$, $A_i(s)$, $H(s)$, $F(s)$, and $K(s)$ with reference to the block diagram in Fig. 5.1.

(B) Formulate polynomial ratios for the quantities in part A, using ascending or descending powers of the s-variable relating to the system parameters, and also give factorial root expressions.

(C) What may be concluded from a comparison between the poles of $F(s)$ and those of $K(s)$? What about the zeros?

(D) Examine $K(s)$ and discuss the instability conditions with reference to its roots.

Part II

Answer the following questions dealing with the transistor amplifier in Fig. 5.2, shown without supply sources, and carry out the

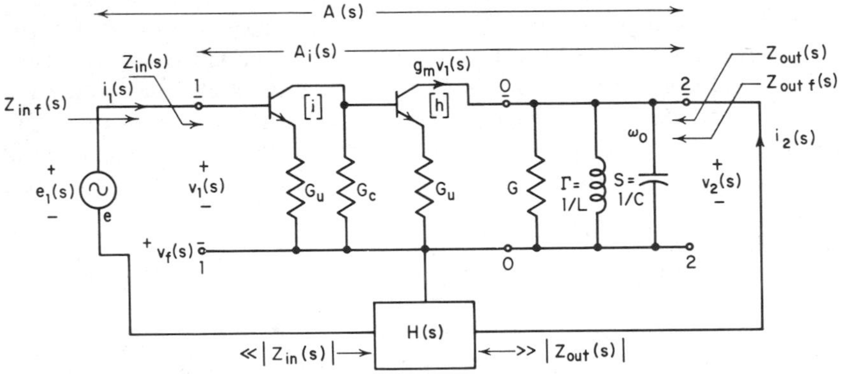

Fig. 5.2

given assignments. The design is such that we are at liberty to assume that $g_m v_1(s)$ represents the current from a current generator. For the sake of simplicity, we shall also make the assumption that $H(s) = H^0$.

(E) Discuss the feedback conditions in the amplifier.

(F) Derive polynomial ratios in terms of system parameters for significant quantities in part A, and determine $A(s)$ under the resonance condition $\omega_0^2 = 1/CL$.

(G) Determine in the frequency domain the roots pertaining to the total feedback system, and discuss the meaning of the sign for the real term of $s = \sigma_f + j\Omega_f$.

(H) Using the classical heuristic integro-differential equation method, derive the roots from the time domain, and show that they are identical with those obtained in part G.

(I) Repeat part H using the Laplace Transform.

(K) In the analysis of a more elaborate transistor amplifier of this kind, how do the classical integro-differential equation method and the Laplace Transform method compare? If both transient conditions and periodic steady-state conditions are requested, how would you rate the following methods in a proposed analysis: (1) the Classical Integro-Differential Equation Method, (2) the Laplace Transform Method, and (3) the Symbolic Method?

(L) Provide a root-locus plot in the s-plane, showing zeros and poles for the amplifier under discussion. Answer the following questions: (1) Is there such a thing as negative frequency? Is there such a thing as negative angular velocity? Discuss and explain. (2) Explain the symbols on the vertical axis. (3) How do we produce a pole by super-resonance? (4) Discuss how changing the frequency and the Q of a tuned network is reflected by movements of the twin-poles. What about poles on the right-hand side? (5) Derive the "arm"-formula and show how amplifier transmission and phase conditions may be determined from it.

(M) Is it a rigorous procedure to determine roots in the time domain, for example, by employing the heuristic Classical Integro-Differential Equation Solution, and to insert and use these roots in a frequency-domain operational equation?

Part III

(N) Discuss the following instability criteria, and apply each one by suitable network analysis to the amplifier given in Part II (assume resonance as in part G): (1) the Energy Conservation Criterion; (2) the Immittance Criterion; (3) the Barkhausen-Nyquist Criterion; (4) the Determinant Criterion; (5) the Root Criterion.

(O) If you were asked to summarize the message contained in all these criteria, how would you formulate a brief and concise answer?

Solution

(A) The listed quantities are defined as the following voltage ratios:

$$A(s) = v_2(s)/e_1(s) \qquad A_i(s) = v_2(s)/v_1(s) \qquad H(s) = v_f(s)/v_2(s)$$

$$F(s) = v_f(s)/v_1(s) \qquad K(s) = e_1(s)v_1(s) \tag{5.1}$$

Here $A(s)$ is the actual, or total, or system amplification; $A_i(s)$ the inherent amplification; $H(s)$ the feedback transfer function; $F(s)$ the open-loop transfer function; and $K(s)$ the denominator of the actual amplification formula, thus the quantity that determines the system poles. As an alternative, we may write the s-symbols as bar symbols, thus write $\bar{A}$ rather than $A(s)$.

(B) The required polynomial ratios are

$$A_i(s) = A_i^\circ \frac{N(s)}{D(s)} = A_i^\circ \frac{1 + N_1 s_D + N_2 s_D^2 + \dots}{1 + D_1 s_D + D_2 s_D^2 + \dots} \tag{5.2}$$

$$H(s) = H^\circ \frac{n(s)}{d(s)} = H^\circ \frac{1 + n_1 s_D + n_2 s_D^2 + \dots}{1 + d_1 s_D + d_2 s_D^2 + \dots} \tag{5.3}$$

Alternatively, these polynomials may be written in terms of descending powers of s. In the above formulas, we consider the applied signal to come from a physical driving signal generator for which $s = s_D = j\omega_D$. Combining Eqs. 5.2 and 5.3 we can now write

$$F(s) = H(s)A_i(s) = H^\circ A_i^\circ \frac{n(s)}{d(s)} \times \frac{N(s)}{D(s)} = F^\circ \frac{\mathcal{N}(s)}{\mathcal{D}(s)} \tag{5.4}$$

$$K(s) = 1 - F(s) = \frac{d(s)D(s) - H^\circ A_i{}^\circ n(s)N(s)}{d(s)D(s)} = \frac{\mathscr{D}(s) - F^\circ \mathscr{N}(s)}{\mathscr{D}(s)} \tag{5.5}$$

$$A(s) = \frac{A_i(s)}{K(s)} = A_i{}^\circ \frac{d(s)N(s)}{d(s)D(s) - H^\circ A_i{}^\circ n(s)N(s)}$$

$$= A_i{}^\circ \frac{\mathscr{D}(s)N(s)}{D(s)\mathscr{D}(s) - F^\circ D(s)\mathscr{N}(s)} \tag{5.6}$$

Anyone of the polynomials in a numerator or in a denominator above may be expressed by its roots in terms of a factorial expression. An example of factorization will be shown in part D. We shall here only make use of the factorized form for two sequences of roots, $s_{n1}, s_{n2}, \ldots\ldots,$ and $s_{d1}, s_{d2}, \ldots\ldots,$ writing for $A_i(s)$

$$A_i(s) = A_i{}^\circ \frac{N(s)}{D(s)} = A_i{}^\circ \frac{(s_D - s_{n1})(s_D - s_{n2})(s_D - s_{n3})\ldots}{(s_D - s_{d1})(s_D - s_{d2})(s_D - s_{d3})\ldots} \tag{5.7}$$

or in short-hand form

$$A_i(s) = A_i{}^\circ \prod_{p=1}^{P} (s_D - s_{np}) \Big/ \prod_{q=1}^{Q} (s_D - s_{dq}) \tag{5.8}$$

where, in general, for an index sequence from o to O,

$$\prod_{o=1}^{O} (s_D - s_o) = (s_D - s_1)(s_D - s_2)\ldots(s_D - s_O) \tag{5.9}$$

Note that in these formulas the driving j-angular velocity is denoted by a subscript D, while the s-quantities determined by network parameters do not employ the subscript D. In this way we are able to keep the two apart to avoid misunderstandings.

(C) We note from Eqs. 5.4 and 5.5 that $F(s)$ and $K(s)$ have the same denominator, thus the same poles. Since the numerators differ, however, the zeros are different.

(D) In determining the roots of a polynomial, we set the polynomial equal to zero, in this way obtaining an equation. The root of an equation is defined as a quantity which, when substituted for the unknown in the equation, reduces it to an identity. This is a significant statement. The root of an equation is a quantity that satisfies the equation. If $K(s)$ (or any other one of the polynomials) is a second order s-function, $f(s)$, we obtain the necessary equation by setting $f(s)$ equal to zero, writing

$$K(s) = f(s) = s^2 + s2a + b^2 = 0 \tag{5.10}$$

We shall find that this equation has a complex double-root, or two twin-roots, one of which is a complex conjugate of the other. *Whereas one root has a negative angular velocity, both roots represent a system of positive frequency only, since there is no such thing as a negative frequency,* The negative angular velocity is a very peculiar negative angular velocity, since it only appears if its twin appears simultaneously. Accordingly, we will not acknowledge the existence of a negative angular velocity, and instead we shall talk about the *negative-twin angular velocity.*

In accordance with this terminology, therefore, only one positive angular velocity and one positive frequency exist in the system, and these quantities characterize, and originate from, the driving generator. One positive-twin angular velocity and one positive-twin frequency exist due to system self-behavior (mode). In addition, one negative-twin angular velocity and one negative-twin frequency exist, also due to system self-behavior (mode). Nowhere in the system is there any "negative" frequency, for the simple reason that "negative" frequency does not exist.[1]

Solving for s in Eq. 5.10, we obtain, with $\Omega^2 = b^2 - a^2$,

$$(-s_1, -\bar{s}_1) = -a \pm j\sqrt{b^2 - a^2} = -a \pm j\Omega \tag{5.11}$$

which is the double-root or combination of two twin-roots. The factorized expression for $f(s)$ takes the form

$$K(s) = f(s) = (s + s_1)(s + \bar{s}_1) \tag{5.12}$$

If we insert the roots for s either in Eq. 5.10 or 5.12, the original definition of root holds, and we accomplish the identity, $0 = 0$. If we insert the roots for s_1 and $\bar{s}_1$ in Eq. 5.12 we merely obtain Eq. 5.10. We note that in Eq. 5.10 we are dealing with the self-behavior of the network.

There are many possible numerical values for a and b in Eq. 5.10, but only certain values will make $K(s) = 0$. When this equality occurs, $A(s)$ experiences a pole. To review the proper terminology, we shall consider a simple polynomial, $x = (z + z_1)$, where $-z_1$ is

[1]See Stockman, H. E., "On Angular Velocity," *Proceedings of the IRE*, vol. 45, No. 3, p. 368, March 1957.

a root. The zero of the polynomial is the value $-z_1$ of the variable z, making the polynomial vanish. Thus the thing we call zero is a value of z, more particularly the value, $-z_1$. The parenthesis $(z + z_1)$ is not a zero; it merely becomes zero. A zero of x is a root of $x = 0$. If z and z_1 are real quantities, we may define the zero as the value of the variable z for which the graph of the polynomial x crosses the s-axis. If we provide the function, $y = 1/x = 1/(z + z_1)$, nothing has been changed in the previous statement that x becomes a zero. When this happens, however, y becomes infinitely large, and as a plot on the z-axis it looks like a "pole," going towards infinity. In daily parlance, we then say that y experiences a pole, or even has a pole, or is a pole. We may also say that $z = -z_1$ yields a pole, and it is also correct to say that the pole occurs at $z = -z_1$. One occasionally finds the statement that $z = -z_1$ is a pole. Mathematically, we write a function y as follows:

$$y = f(z) = \frac{f_n(z)}{(z + z_1)}\,\nu \qquad (5.13)$$

where z provides a zero if equal to $-z_1$, and where y then is a pole, unless we extend our terminology to the extent of allowing $z = -z_1$ to be a zero and a pole at one and the same time. It is all a matter of which specific quantity we are talking about—the quantity or its inverse.

In Eq. 5.13, $z = -z_1$ represents a (nonessential) isolated singular point, with ν a positive integer (any of the numbers 1, 2, 3,...), and with $f_n(z)$ analytic at $z = -z_1$, and $f_n(-z_1) = 0$. The integer ν is the order of the pole. It follows that if $K(s)$ in Eq. 5.12 provides the denominator under stated conditions, there are two basic ways of providing a pole, i.e., to produce $K(s) = 0$. One (academic) way is to vary s_D, but we must then provide one real and one j-quantity of s_D, so that we can cover both parts of the root. Assuming that we get rid of j-quantities by the use of resonance, a real component from a fictitious "spiral" generator will then truly accomplish the zero, and we talk about superresonance, to be discussed further in part L3. Going the other way, using a physical signal generator (a circle generator) of frequency $\omega_D/2\pi$, and applying tuning, we then have no other choice for pole generation than to kill off the real part of the roots by regeneration, brought to the point of instability.

Part II

(E) Each stage provided a phase shift of 180°, so that the total amplifier provides positive feedback via the $H(s)$ network. At sufficient feedback coupling the amplifier will oscillate at a frequency determined by the inductance L and capacitance C.

(F) The output voltage is, in accordance with Ohm's Law, with $S = 1/C$ and $\Gamma = 1/L$,

$$v_2(s) = g_m v_1(s)/(G + s_D C + \Gamma/s_D)$$

or

$$A_i(s) = \frac{v_2(s)}{v_1(s)} = g_m S \frac{s_D}{s_D^2 + s_D GS + \Gamma S} = 2k \frac{s_D}{s_D^2 + s_D 2a + \omega_0^2} \tag{5.14}$$

where $GS = 2a$, $1/CL = b^2 = \omega_0^2$, and $g_m S = 2k$. Solving for the roots in the denominator, we obtain, as in Eqs. 5.11 and 5.12,

$$A_i(s) = 2k \frac{s_D}{(s_D + s_1)(s_D + \bar{s}_1)} \tag{5.15}$$

This equation is of the same type as Eq. 5.7. The ensuing formulas for $F(s)$, $K(s)$, and $A(s)$ now become, with $H(s) = H°$,

$$F(s) = H(s)A_i(s) = 2kH^{\circ} \frac{s_D}{s_D^2 + s_D 2a + \omega_0^2} \tag{5.16}$$

$$K(s) = 1 - F(s) = \frac{s_D^2 + s_D 2c + \omega_0^2}{s_D^2 + s_D 2a + \omega_0^2} \tag{5.17}$$

so that

$$A(s) = \frac{A_i(s)}{K(s)} = 2k \frac{s_D}{s_D^2 + s_D 2c + \omega_0^2} \tag{5.18}$$

where

$$c = a - kH^{\circ} \tag{5.19}$$

We can here see how, step by step, the expression for the actual amplification is made to include the feedback action. When the network is tuned, the first and last term in the denominator cancel, so that we obtain

$$A(s)_{\text{res}} = 2k \frac{s_D}{s_D 2c} = \frac{k}{c} = \frac{g_m}{G - H^{\circ} g_m} \tag{5.20}$$

(G) The roots of the total system are the roots of the denominator $K(s)$ in Eq. 5.18 given by Eq. 5.11 with a replaced by c, thus:

$$(-s_{1f}, -\bar{s}_{1f}) = -c \pm j\sqrt{b^2 - c^2} = c_f \pm j\Omega_f \qquad (5.21)$$

The real term here must remain negative for the system to be stable. The limiting case yields $c = 0$, so that the instability condition becomes, from Eq. 5.19, with $H°$ replaced by $H*$

$$c = a - kH* = 0 \qquad H* = a/k = G/g_m \qquad (5.22)$$

(H) The integro-differential equation for the CLR network becomes

$$g_m v_1(t) = C\frac{dv_2(t)}{dt} + Gv_2(t) + \Gamma \int v_2(t)\, dt \qquad (5.23)$$

Here $v_1(t)$ and $v_2(t)$ are linked via the feedback path, so that we may write

$$E_1(t) + H° v_2(t) - v_1(t) = 0 \qquad (5.23a)$$

or

$$\frac{C}{g_m}\,\frac{dv_2(t)}{dt} + \left(\frac{G}{g_m} - H°\right) v_2(t) + \frac{\Gamma}{g_m}\int v_2(t)\, dt = E_1(t) \qquad (5.24)$$

Recognizing the coefficients here in terms of previously used symbols, we may write

$$\frac{d^2 v_2(t)}{dt^2} + 2c\,\frac{dv_2(t)}{dt} + b^2 v_2(t) = 0 \qquad (5.25)$$

Following the classical heuristic method, we guess at the solution, Ve^{pt}, which we differentiate twice and insert in Eq. 5.25. The result of this is the characteristic equation, which in principle is the denominator of Eq. 5.18. Therefore, the roots are here the same as those derived from this denominator (see Eq. 5.21).

(I) Using the Laplace Transform method, and employing the already available Eq. 5.25, we insert proper s-transforms, obtaining

$$s^2 v_2(s) + s2cv_2(s) + b^2 v_2(s) = f(s) \qquad (5.26)$$

$$v_2(s) = \frac{f(s)}{s^2 + s2c + \omega_0{}^2} \tag{5.27}$$

Thus we have obtained an s-combine with a denominator identical to the one previously calculated, which may be written in factorized form. One advantage of Eq. 5.27 is that we may use a transform table to obtain not only the instantaneous output voltage of any driving periodic voltage, but in addition the transient of whatever driving transform $f(s)$ we apply. In the latter case, we must consider the initial conditions.

(K) The Laplace Transform Method is faster to use in engineering than the classical heuristic method as it allows us to avoid the labor of determining constants and also has "built-in" initial conditions. Both methods solve the entire problem, both for transients and for the steady-state. The Symbolic Method only handles the periodic steady-state.[1]

(L) The desired root-locus plot is shown in Fig. 5.3. We are here using the roots in Eq. 5.21, and we factor Eq. 5.18 thusly

$$A(s) = 2k\frac{(s_D + 0)}{(s_D + s_{1f})(s_D + \bar{s}_{1f})} = 2k\,\frac{\mathbf{r}_0}{\mathbf{r}_1\mathbf{r}_2} = 2k\,\frac{r_0}{r_1 r_2}\,\underline{\left|\frac{\pi}{2} - \phi_1 - \phi_2\right.} \tag{5.28}$$

Before entering into a discussion of this formula with reference to Fig. 5.3, we shall consider some of the questions in part L.

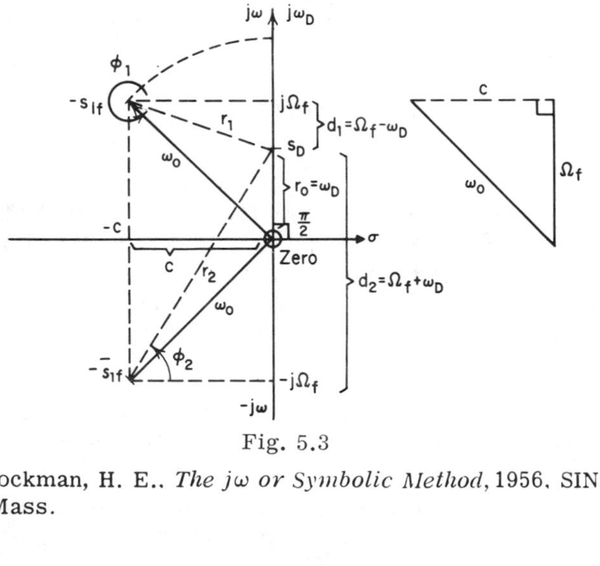

Fig. 5.3

[1] See Stockman, H. E., *The jω or Symbolic Method*, 1956, SINE-SER Co., Arlington, Mass.

(L1) Frequency is defined as the number of repetitions of a periodic process per unit time (that is, the inverse of the period). Since this quantity cannot be negative, there is no such thing as negative frequency. As mentioned previously, there is such a thing as negative angular velocity in system self-behavior, but it is recommended that it be referred to as negative-*twin* angular velocity.

(L2) The $j\omega$-scale goes up and down from the origin because of the existence of negative-twin angular velocity. The $j\omega_D$-scale goes only in positive direction, since this angular velocity represents that of a physical driving signal generator.

(L3) If the network is frozen, we can only change the driving conditions. Thus we tune the signal generator until resonance is obtained, eliminating the j-angular velocity of the root. We then replace the physical signal generator by a fictitious one of variable amplitude, a spiral generator of diminishing amplitude, used until the signal disappears in noise. We must therefore start out at very large voltage and current, almost burning out the network, or the time for the experiment will be too short. The generated complex angular velocity applied to the network is of the form, $s_D = \sigma_D + j\omega_D$, where σ_D is negative. The applied real part will cancel the network real part, so that the denominator becomes zero, with a pole as result (superresonance).

(L4) As we vary the coordinates of the twin poles, using a physical driving signal generator, the changed performance of the network is truly reflected by the constructions in Fig. 5.3. If the parallel resistance is increased, so that the losses are reduced, the Q of the network increases, indicated by the distance c being made shorter and shorter. The limit is encountered for $c = 0$, since poles cannot appear on the right-hand side with the network still stable. If the network is frozen and the applied frequency $\omega/2\pi$ is changed, the poles remain in fixed positions, but the point s_D slides along the positive vertical axis. As will be shown, the arms r_0, r_1, and r_2 describe the transfer function, and, with the angles also taken into account, the description becomes extended to include the phase conditions.

(L5) It is seen from Eq. 5.28 that the "arm-formula" is merely another expression for the actual amplification $A(s)$. We shall now verify the corresponding quantities. The magnitude of the numerator in Eq. 5.28 is $r_0 = \omega_D$, and the phase angle of this arm is 90°. The arms r_1 and r_2 are determined from respective triangles in accordance with the formulas

$$r_1 = \sqrt{c^2 + (\Omega_f - \omega_D)^2} \tag{5.29}$$

$$r_2 = \sqrt{c^2 + (\Omega_f + \omega_D)^2} \tag{5.30}$$

We note that r_1 and r_2 represent the two parentheses in the numerator of $A(s)$; as an example, the first one has the magnitude, from Eq. 5.21,

$$|(s_D + s_{1f})| = |+c - j(\Omega_f - \omega_D)| = \sqrt{c^2 + (\Omega_f - \omega_D)^2}$$

which agrees with the result we obtained in Eq. 5.29 by construction in the s-plane. Thus the magnitude of $A(s)$ is described by the arm-formula as shown. With reference to the phase angles of r_1 and r_2, they are indicated as ϕ_1 and ϕ_2 in Fig. A. Analytically we obtain

$$(s_D + s_{1f}) = c - j(\Omega_f - \omega_D)$$

$$\underline{|(s_D + s_{1f})} = \phi_1 = tan^{-1}[-(\Omega_f - \omega_D)]/c \tag{5.31}$$

and

$$(s_D + \bar{s}_{1f}) = c + j(\Omega_f + \omega_D)$$

$$\underline{|(s_D + \bar{s}_{1f})} = \phi_2 = tan^{-1}(\Omega_f + \omega_D)/c \tag{5.32}$$

which results agree with the symbols and the construction in Fig. 5.3. Thus, by taking a sequence of s_D-points on the vertical axis, from the origin to a point of frequency $2\Omega/2\pi$, or higher, we can plot both the frequency response and the phase function of the system.[1] Another way of doing the same thing, of course, is to use Eq. 5.14 without any reference to the s-plane.

(M) In part H above, we wrote an integro-differential equation, from which we obtain the roots. That this is a rigorous procedure in the solution of the problem follows from the fact that, in principle, the obtained characteristic equation is Eq. 5.10, and we therefore conclude that the roots must be identical.

Further clarification may be needed with reference to the use

[1] Stockman, H. E.. *Introduction to Distributed Amplification*, 1956. SINE-SER Co., Arlington, Mass.

of roots in calculations pertaining to a stable system. We wish to make clear that roots obtained in the time domain not only permit determination of instability in the frequency domain, but also make possible calculations we may wish to carry out otherwise, including those relating to positive and negative feedback conditions. To verify this, we shall take a simple example, setting, with reference to part C in Eq. 5.19, $g_m = 4$, $a = 1$, $b^2 = 3$, and $S = 1/C = 1$, thus obtaining $c = 1 - 2H$. Arbitrarily, we shall set $H = 0.1$, thus obtaining positive feedback with $c = 0.8$. If we further assume a driving generator that yields $s_D = j\omega_D = j1$, we obtain from Eq. 5.18

$$A(s) = 2k \frac{s_D}{s_D{}^2 + s_D 2c + \omega_0{}^2} = 4 \frac{j}{-1 + j1.6 + 3} = \frac{j4}{2 + j1.6} \qquad (5.33)$$

The magnitude of $A(s)$ is 1.56, a slight increase due to regeneration over the feedback-free value 1.41.

The roots obtained in part H from the time domain are, from Eq. 5.21, $-0.8 \pm j\sqrt{3 - 0.64} = 0.8 \pm j\sqrt{2.36}$. Inserting this result in Eq. 5.28, we obtain

$$A(s) = 2k \frac{(s_D - 0)}{(s_D + s_{1f})(s_D + \bar{s}_{1f})}$$

$$= 4 \frac{j}{[j - (-0.8 + j\sqrt{2.36})][j - (-0.8 - j\sqrt{2.36})]} = \frac{j4}{2 + j1.6} \qquad (5.34)$$

which is precisely the same result as in Eq. 5.33. These root calculations hold for all values of the driving angular velocity, including the one for which resonance is obtained, $s_D = j\omega_D = j\sqrt{3}$. Using Eq. 5.18 to determine $|A(s)|$ at resonance, we get

$$|A(s)| = 2k \left| \frac{s_D}{s_D^2 + s_D 2c + \omega_0{}^2} \right| = 4 \left| \frac{j\sqrt{3}}{-3 - j1.6\sqrt{3} + 3} \right| = 2.5 \qquad (5.35)$$

Using Eq. 5.28 instead, we obtain

$$A(s) = 2k \left| \frac{(s_D - 0)}{(s_D - s_{1f})(s_D - \bar{s}_{1f})} \right|$$

$$= 4 \left| \frac{j\sqrt{3}}{[j\sqrt{3} - (-0.8 + j\sqrt{2.36})][j\sqrt{3} - (-0.8 - j\sqrt{2.36})]} \right| = 2.5 \qquad (5.36)$$

which agrees with the previous result.

We may again consider the two basic methods of producing a pole—the unrealistic one of using a spiral generator and the realistic one of using a circle generator. Employing the latter, we increase regeneration until the point of instability is reached, with $c = 0$. In the case of the former, we allow the system to remain lossy, retaining $H = 0.8$, and use a spiral generator that cancels both terms in the root $(-0.8 + j\sqrt{2.36})$. To do this, the inwards spiraling generator must have the s-form, $(-0.8 + j\sqrt{2.36})$. Using Eq. 5.18, we find that the denominator becomes

$$(-0.8 + j\sqrt{2.36})^2 + (-0.8 + j\sqrt{2.36})(2)(0.8) + 3 = 0 \qquad (5.37)$$

Thus we have produced a pole by super-resonance.

We may review the calculations in Eqs. 5.33 and 5.34 using negative feedback instead of positive feedback, in which case $c = 1.2$ and $A(s)$ is reduced to 1.28. Thus, we find that the roots may be used in negative-feedback calculations as well.

Part III

(N1) The Power Criterion is perhaps the most basic of all criteria since it employs the energy-conservation principle. It may be stated in this form: the power injected in the system must equal the power dissipated in the system for steady-state conditions to be maintained. In practical use, however, this criterion is the same as the Immittance Criterion to be described below, since we merely turn immittance into power by means of voltage or current squared. As an example, if a current appears in a mesh where there is no applied voltage but a series stimulance R_N, then, if the total loss resistance is R, the Immittance Criterion yields

$$0 = R_N I + RI \qquad -R_N = R$$

whereas the Power Criterion yields

$$0 = R_N I^2 + RI^2 \qquad -R_N = R$$

Therefore, either one may be used.

(N2) Using the Immittance Criterion, we may as an example first consider the input mesh with $E_1(s) = 0$, assuming the system to be self-sustained. Changing the feedback source into an impedance by means of the Compensation Theorem, we then write an equation stating that the total impedance must be zero, thus

$$-[H(s)A_i(s)v_1(s)]/i_1(s) + Z_{in}(s) = 0 \qquad (5.38)$$

or, since

$$Z_{in}(s) = v_1(s)/i_1(s)$$
$$C - H(s)A_i(s) + 1 = 0 \qquad (5.39)$$

which is the Barkhausen-Nyquist criterion, to be discussed next. Thus, in this case, the Immittance Criterion turns into the same thing as the Barkhausen-Nyquist Criterion. This is to be expected, since the Barkhausen-Nyquist formula is derived by the application of Kirchhoff's Voltage-Sum Law to the input mesh.

As a variation, we shall next apply the Immittance Criterion to the node (1,$\underline{1}$), this time turning the feedback-source impedance into a conductance, and requesting that the total node conductance must be zero for instability. Thus we obtain

$$-i_1(s)/H(s)A_i(s)v_1(s) + Y_{in}(s) = 0 \qquad (5.40)$$

which similarly yields the Barkhausen-Nyquist Criterion. When we place a cut in a network, we see certain immittances to the right and to the left. The immittance seen one way is the same as the immittance seen the other way, except for the sign. To show that the Immittance Criterion holds even at the extreme port, where the source $E(s)$ appears, we claim

$$\text{Conductance seen to the right} = \frac{1}{-\dfrac{H(s)A_i(s)v_1(s)}{i_1(s)} + Z_{in}(s)} = \infty \qquad (5.41)$$

where the denominator must be zero, and, accordingly, we are returned to the statement of Eq. 5.38. As a variation of this, we may say that if we insert the critical value for $H(s)$, which is $H^* = G/g_m$, and note from Eq. 5.37 that $A_i(s) = g_m/G$, we obtain

$$\text{Resistance seen to the right} = -\frac{GA_i(s)v_1(s)}{g_m i_1(s)} + \frac{v_1(s)}{i_1(s)} = Z_{in}(s)(-1 + 1) = 0 \qquad (5.42)$$

which is the correct result.

As a final application of this criterion, we may examine the nodes 0 and $\underline{0}$, cutting the network in Fig. 5.2 at this point. Looking left, then, we should see the conductance $-G$. If the current $g_m v_1(s)$ had been constant, we would see infinite impedance looking left, but since $g_m v_1(s)$ is a function source, we see a finite value. We determine this value by means of the Applied Source Method, setting $E_1(s)$ equal to zero, and applying the source $v_{20}(s)$ to the port $(0, \underline{0})$, maintaining the total system as is. The result will be a current $i_{20}(s) = -g_m v_1(s)$, so that in accordance with Ohm's law, the conductance looking left from port $(0, \underline{0})$ becomes

$$\frac{i_{20}(s)}{v_{20}(s)} = \frac{-g_m v_1(s)}{v_{20}(s)} = \frac{-g_m}{g_m/G} = -G \tag{5.43}$$

which is the correct result for instability.

(N3) By referring to the Nyquist Criterion as the Barkhausen-Nyquist Criterion, we make it cover all the earlier applications of the Barkhausen Criterion, which was especially formulated for tube amplifiers. The two criteria are linked by the following expression, employing Barkhausen's original quantity k, here written $k(s)$,

$$k(s) = -\left(\frac{1}{g_m Z_L(s)} + \frac{1}{\mu}\right) = \frac{1}{A_i(s)} = H(s) \tag{5.44}$$

In accordance with the Barkhausen-Nyquist Criterion, $H(s)A_i(s) = 1$, so that we may write, with the help of Eq. 5.14, at resonance,

$$H(s) = H^* = \frac{1}{A_i(s)} = \frac{1}{2ks_D}(-\omega_0^2 + s_D 2a + \omega_0^2) = \frac{G}{g_m} \tag{5.45}$$

which agrees with the previous result.

(N4) The Determinant Criterion is obtained from the network matrix for the system, when its determinant is set equal to zero. The proof of the procedure lies in Cramer's Rule. Using Eqs. 5.23 and 5.23a in the frequency domain, we obtain

$$\left.\begin{aligned} 0 &= -g_m v_1(s) + G v_2(s) \\ E_1(s) &= v_1(s) - H^0 v_2(s) \end{aligned}\right\} \qquad \begin{vmatrix} -g_m & G \\ 1 & -H^0 \end{vmatrix} \tag{5.46}$$

which has the zeroed symbol for the determinant, and the determinant proper,

$$\begin{vmatrix} -g_m & G \\ 1 & -H^* \end{vmatrix} = 0 \qquad g_m H^* - G = 0 \tag{5.47}$$

from which $H^* = G/g_m$ as before.

(N5) We have already used this method in Eq. 5.22, finding as a result the critical value of $H(s)$ to be $H^* = G/g_m$.

(O) Correctly interpreted, all feedback criteria give one and the same result, represent one and the same fundamental truth. They all have the common message that operation in accordance with the principle of energy conservation is stable operation, whereas if the system yields more power than that dissipated in the system, instability, and possibly oscillations, result.

Conclusions to this solution

In this solution we have written polynomial ratios for all quantities in the classical feedback formula and referred them back to the parameters of the feedback system. This indicates under which conditions poles can be produced by design changes of these parameters. In the latter part of the problem, we learn how we may fictitiously generate poles in a frozen system, merely by replacing the physical driving generator by a spiral generator, spiraling into noise. We have learned how to formulate roots in the time domain and then use them in the frequency domain, whether we have no feedback, positive feedback, or negative feedback. Thus a certain amount of fictitious-generator spiraling may be combined with an arbitrary amount of feedback, with a pole as result. We have compared various solution methods, including the Laplace Transform method. The twin roots have been discussed with reference to the s- plane construction, and two different ways of arriving at frequency response and phase function for the entire system have been considered: analytical computation and s-plane construction. The latter method is of great general importance, since it involves the mathematical tool we may have to employ anyhow: the s-plane. Finally, we have analyzed a number of instability criteria and calculated the critical value H^* from each one. As has been stated previously, a final check of possible solutions in the right-half plane should be made in intricate problems.

PROBLEM 6

Given is the Colpitt oscillator in Fig. 6.1a, using an rf transistor. The transistor is known through its h parameters, which are considered to be real. When the bias sources are neglected, a preliminary form of the equivalent network may take the appearance shown in Fig. 6.1b. In this particular case, special biasing justifies the assumption, $Z_{in} \gg Z_{out}'$.

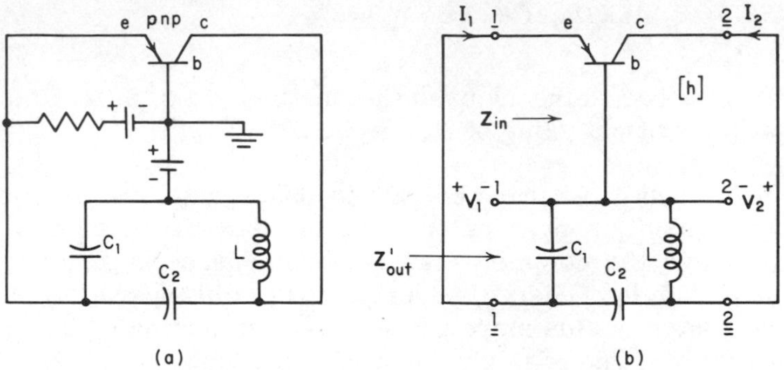

Fig. 6.1

(A) Draw and label a full equivalent of the system, showing one or more function sources.

(B) Analyze the system with respect to its stability conditions, using (1) the Determinant Criterion, (2) the Immittance Criterion, (3) the Barkhausen-Nyquist Criterion.

(C) Analyze the system with respect to its stability conditions, employing cascade connection and a matrix solution.

Solution

(A) The most fundamental equivalent network is that using the double-source transistor equivalent (see Fig. 6.2a). To understand the approximation made, we assume that some kind of an isolator is inserted between the output of the feedback network and the input to the inherent amplifier. Thus the feedback voltage $\mathbf{V}_f$ (see Fig.

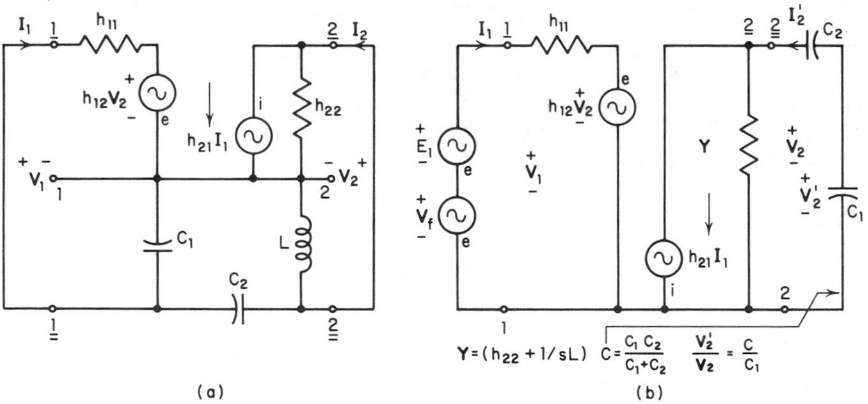

Fig. 6.2

6.2b) can be represented by a voltage source, which in series with an assumed input voltage E_1 feeds the input port $1, \underline{1}$. We lump the inductance L into the admittance h_{22}, obtaining the admittance **Y**. In part A we do not acknowledge the equality, $\mathbf{V}_f = \mathbf{V}_1$. Instead, we consider the problem of an oscillator as if it were a problem of a regenerative amplifier, which gives us a greater choice of solution methods.

(B1) The twoport equation system is as follows:

$$\left.\begin{aligned} E_1 + \mathbf{V}_f &= h_{11}\mathbf{I}_1 + h_{12}\mathbf{V}_2 \qquad (6.1) \\ \mathbf{I}_2' &= h_{21}\mathbf{I}_1 + \mathbf{Y}\mathbf{V}_2 \qquad (6.2) \end{aligned}\right\}$$

$$\left.\begin{aligned} 0 &= h_{11}\mathbf{I}_1 + (h_{12} - C/C_1)\mathbf{V}_2 \qquad (6.3) \\ 0 &= h_{21}\mathbf{I}_1 + (\mathbf{Y} + sC)\mathbf{V}_2 \qquad (6.4) \end{aligned}\right\}$$

In Eq. 6.3 we have acknowledged that $E_1 = 0$ and $\mathbf{V}_f = \mathbf{V}_2' = \mathbf{V}_1$. The matrix equation and the determinant now become

$$\begin{vmatrix} 0 \\ 0 \end{vmatrix} = \begin{vmatrix} h_{11} & (h_{12} - C/C_1) \\ h_{21} & (\mathbf{Y} + sC) \end{vmatrix} \begin{vmatrix} \mathbf{I}_1 \\ \mathbf{V}_2 \end{vmatrix} \qquad (6.5)$$

$$\mathbf{\Delta}_{hs} = h_{11}(\mathbf{Y} + sC) - (h_{12} - C/C_1)h_{21} \qquad (6.6)$$

The Determinant Criterion yields

$$\mathbf{\Delta}_{hs} = 0 \qquad h_{11}(h_{22} + 1/sL + sC) = (h_{12} - C/C_1)h_{21}$$

from which

$$s^2 + s\,\frac{C_1\Delta_h + Ch_{21}}{CC_1h_{11}} + \frac{1}{CL} = s^2 + s2a + b^2 = 0 \qquad (6.7)$$

where

$$a = \frac{C_1\Delta_h + Ch_{21}}{2CC_1h_{11}} \qquad \Delta_h = h_{11}h_{22} - h_{12}h_{21} \qquad b^2 = \frac{1}{CL} \qquad (6.8)$$

Here, Eq. 6.7 represents the second-order equation which governs the instability condition. In general terms of the s-domain, a must be zero, since this is the limiting case between a wave that increases in amplitude and one that decreases in amplitude, and b is the angular velocity of the oscillation produced. In terms of the $j\omega$-domain, precisely the same result obtains, as is evident if we write

$$-\omega_0^2 + j\omega_0 2a + b^2 = 0 \quad \begin{cases} -\omega_0^2 + b^2 = 0 \\ \omega_0 2a = 0 \end{cases} \quad \begin{cases} b^2 = \omega_0^2 \\ a = 0 \end{cases} \tag{6.9}$$

The instability conditions are therefore

$$\frac{C_1 + C_2}{C_2} = \frac{-h_{21}}{\Delta_h} \tag{6.10}$$

$$\omega_0 = 1/\sqrt{CL} \tag{6.11}$$

Note that in the CB-connection used, $-h_{21}$ is a positive quantity.

(B2) Setting the admittance at port $2.\underline{2}$ equal to zero, we first transform the source $h_{21}\mathbf{I}_1$ into an admittance, as follows, with $E_1 = 0$ and $\mathbf{V}_f = \mathbf{V}_1$,

$$\frac{h_{21}\mathbf{I}_1}{\mathbf{V}_2} = h_{21}\frac{\mathbf{V}_1 - h_{12}\mathbf{V}_2}{\mathbf{V}_2 h_{11}} = h_{21}(C/C_1 - h_{12})/h_{11} \tag{6.12}$$

The Criterion now yields

$$h_{21}(C/C_1 - h_{12})/h_{11} + \mathbf{Y} + sC = 0 \tag{6.13}$$

which is the same result as that derived from Eq. 6.7.

(B3) Applying the Barkhausen-Nyquist Criterion, we may consider the capacitive network as the feedback network, obtaining $H = C/C_1$. The inherent amplification is, from Eqs. 6.1 and 6.2,

$$\mathbf{A}_i = -h_{21}/(sCh_{11} + \mathbf{Y}h_{11} - h_{12}h_{21}) \tag{6.14}$$

The Criterion then yields

$$H\mathbf{A}_i = \frac{C}{C_1} \times \frac{-h_{21}}{sCh_{11} + \mathbf{Y}h_{11} - h_{12}h_{21}} = 1 \tag{6.15}$$

which again gives the result in Eq. 6.7.

(C) We formulate one amplifying a matrix (6.16) for the amplifier in Fig. 6.2a, and one coupling a matrix (6.17) for the capacitive section. Accordingly, we write

$$\begin{vmatrix} h_{11} & h_{12} \\ h_{21} & \mathbf{Y} \end{vmatrix}_h \rightarrow \begin{vmatrix} -\mathbf{\Delta}_h/h_{21} & -h_{11}/h_{21} \\ -h_{22}/h_{21} & -1/h_{21} \end{vmatrix}_a \tag{6.16}$$

$$\begin{vmatrix} (1+C_1/C_2) & 1/sC_2 \\ sC_1 & 1 \end{vmatrix}_a \tag{6.17}$$

$$\mathbf{\Delta}_h = h_{11}\mathbf{Y} - h_{12}h_{21} = \Delta_h + h_{11}/sL \tag{6.18}$$

In developing the system a matrix by matrix multiplication, we need only the very first element, $\mathbf{A}_{11}$, since $\mathbf{A}_{11}$ is the ratio between the system input and output voltages, which are equal. Accordingly, $\mathbf{A}_{11} = 1$, so that

$$\mathbf{A}_{11} = \frac{\mathbf{V}_1}{\mathbf{V}_2'} = 1 = \frac{-\mathbf{\Delta}_h}{h_{21}}\left(1 + \frac{C_1}{C_2}\right) - \frac{h_{11}}{h_{21}} sC_1 \tag{6.19}$$

which directly yields Eq. 6.7. Thus all four calculation methods give exactly the same result.

Matrix 6.17 was obtained with the assistance of Table 6 in Appendix C.

Conclusions to this solution

We learn from this solution how extremely important it is that we do not start right in and begin to write Kirchoff's laws, obtaining perhaps a third-order matrix. Instead, we stop and think, contemplating the possibility of arriving at a simpler network equivalent, before we write any equations at all. In this way we may solve the problem with a minimum of calculations, making back-checking easy. Among the four methods used, the choice of method depends almost entirely upon existing conditions. As an example, if this amplifier were part of a total network expressed by a matrices, we might use the last method, but otherwise we would probably prefer another method. If we are using z or h matrices anyhow, the first method is likely to be more suitable. If there is no preference for any particular method, we would probably use the almost always attractive Immittance Criterion method. If, on the other hand, we go by habit and custom, we would probably employ the Barkhausen-Nyquist Criterion. Note previous statements about the desirability of a final stability check.

SOME FINAL THOUGHTS

The preceding solutions have given us a great deal of practice in the handling of both negative and positive feedback. As we start out to solve a problem, we have to make a choice between direct application of Kirchhoff's laws and the use of the classical feedback formula, $\mathbf{A} = \mathbf{A}_i/(1 - \mathbf{H}\mathbf{A}_i)$. Occasionally, the two methods require the same solution time, but usually one approach is much faster than the other. In case of positive feedback, leading to instability, a greater variation of solution methods is at hand, and, there are a number of instability criteria from which to choose. Many students use the Barkhausen-Nyquist Criterion as a cure-all, only to find themselves by-passed by others who have availed themselves of additional techniques. If one method is to be mentioned, it is the Immittance Criterion Method, which sometimes gives strikingly simple solutions. It is not uncommon to find a student who derives formulas for input and output immittance and then proceeds, perhaps through lengthy calculations, to derive a formula for the feedback-transfer function in order to apply the Barkhausen-Nyquist Criterion. If he had set the obtained immittance equal to zero, infinity, or some specified quantity, as the case may be, instead, the student could have written expressions for the instability conditions almost instantly. On the other hand, there are cases where the Barkhausen-Nyquist solution does not represent the simplest approach but is preferred for some specific reason—the most common one being that we need the Nyquist plot in the continued part of the problem solution.

6
Tunnel Diode Amplifiers

The conventional transistor may be described as the combination of two diodes, and a specific transistor junction may be analyzed as a diode, and actually used as a diode. It may, for example, contribute detection in a radio receiver using the transistor proper as an amplifier. In addition, separate diodes are used in many transistor devices. Diode networks are therefore natural subjects in a course on transistors, and diodes are treated both in this chapter and in the following one. We are particularly interested in two aspects of diode performance: (1) the negative slope of the current-voltage characteristic, and (2) its nonlinear behavior. In this chapter, we are concerned only with the former aspect. Negative resistance, or stimulance, may be secured in semiconductor devices in several different ways: (1) by the use of the third-quadrant negative slope of the germanium diode, (2) by the use of multiple np-devices, and (3) by the use of the amazing tunnel diode. As long as the device, in one connection or another, can be represented as a diode displaying negative slope in its current-voltage characteristic, much of the following theory can be applied to it. To be specific, we have chosen the best known device, the tunnel diode, to illustrate how the stimulance property is treated mathematically. Initially, we shall discuss the high-frequency network equivalent and then investigate the characteristics of the series and shunt amplifier.

PROBLEM 1

A tunnel diode is known by its equivalent network shown in Fig. 1.1, where R_N represents the tunnel-diode negative resistance or stimulance. Define and calculate:

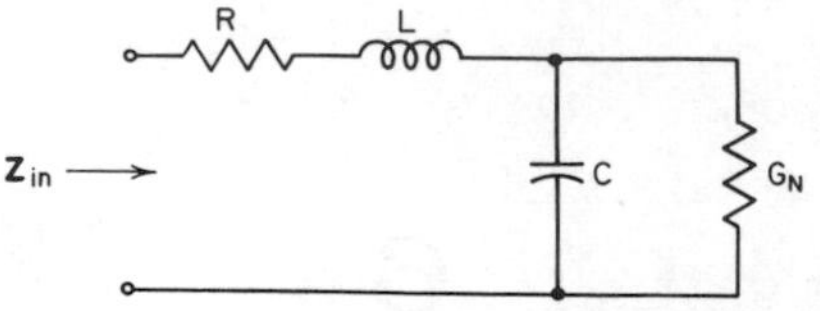

R = 1Ω, L = 10 mμh, C = 8 μμf, $R_N = 1/G_N = -80\Omega$.

Fig. 1.1

(A) The self-resonance frequency $\omega_0/2\pi$, using $\mathbf{Z}_{\text{in}}$, and state the condition for oscillation.

(B) The zero-loss cutoff frequency $\omega_c/2\pi$ and its maximum value $\omega_{c\,\max}/2\pi$, using $\mathbf{Z}_{\text{in}}$.

(C) The series resistance R_N' and series capitance C' obtained when the shunt combination C, R_N is interpreted as the impedance, $R_N' + 1/j\omega C'$.

(D) Insert numerical values in the results obtained in parts A, B, and C and determine $R_{N\,\text{in}}$, when the frequency has the value 100 Mcps. Also determine the CR_N- product of the diode.

(E) Plot a curve for $R_{N\,\text{in}}$ as the frequency is varied from 100 Mcps to 100,000 Mcps.

Solution

(A) The self-resonance frequency is defined as the frequency at which $J(\mathbf{Z}_{\text{in}})$ vanishes. We write

$$\mathbf{Z}_{\text{in}} = R + j\omega L + 1/(G_N + j\omega C) \tag{1.1}$$

$$J(\mathbf{Z}_{\text{in}}) = \omega_0(G_N{}^2L + \omega_0{}^2C^2L - C)/(G_N{}^2 + \omega_0{}^2C^2) = 0 \tag{1.2}$$

from which

$$f_0 = \frac{\omega_0}{2\pi} = \frac{1}{2\pi C}\sqrt{\frac{C - G_N{}^2L}{L}} = \frac{1}{2\pi\sqrt{CL}}\Bigg|_{G_N=0} \tag{1.3}$$

Note that f_0 would have been the same if G_N had represented a positive conductance. At $G_N = \sqrt{C/L}$, Eq. 1.3 ceases to give a real value of f_0.

(B) The zero-loss cutoff frequency is defined as the frequency at which the resistance in the single-mesh equivalent network goes to zero. The input impedance $\mathbf{Z}_{\text{in}}$ describes the desired single mesh; thus, from Eq. 1.1,

$$R_e(\mathbf{Z}_{\text{in}}) = R_e[R + j\omega L + 1/(G_N + j\omega C)]$$
$$= (G_N{}^2R + G_N + \omega_c{}^2C^2R)/(G_N{}^2 + \omega_c{}^2C^2) = 0 \qquad (1.4)$$

from which the stimulance or cutoff frequency is obtained,

$$f_c = \omega_c/2\pi = \sqrt{-(G_N{}^2R + G_N)/C^2R}/2\pi \qquad (1.5)$$

Since G_N represents a negative numerical value, we prefer to write this as

$$f_c = \omega_c/2\pi = \sqrt{[(-G_N) - G_N{}^2R]/R}/2\pi C \qquad (1.6)$$

Here $(-G_N)$ represents a positive quantity, usually much smaller than 1. Thus, for practical purposes, f_c has a positive value, and usually a very large positive value. We may note, however, that in case R is unusually large, and the diode exceedingly poor with regard to negative resistance R_N, then $R = R_N$ is a theoretical possibility, or $G = G_N$. Equation 1.6 then yields: $f_c = 0$. To find out how high f_c may rise as G_N is varied and R maintained constant, we proceed from Eq. 1.6 as follows. Since f_c is a maximum when its square is a maximum, we write

$$\frac{df_c{}^2}{dG_N} = \frac{d}{dG_N}\left\{\frac{1}{(2\pi C)^2R}[-G_N - G_N{}^2R]\right\} = \frac{1}{(2\pi C)^2R}[-1 - 2G_NR] = 0 \qquad (1.7)$$

from which $-G_N = 1/2R$, and thus, from Eq. 1.6,

$$f_{c\,\max} = \frac{1}{4\pi CR} \qquad (1.8)$$

(C) We obtain from the third term in Eq. 1.1 the series resistance and capacitance:

$$R_N' = \frac{G_N}{G_N{}^2 + \omega^2C^2} = \frac{R_N}{1 + \omega^2C^2R_N{}^2} \qquad (1.9)$$

$$C' = \frac{G_N{}^2 + \omega^2C^2}{\omega^2C} = \frac{1 + \omega^2C^2R_N{}^2}{\omega^2CR_N{}^2} \qquad (1.10)$$

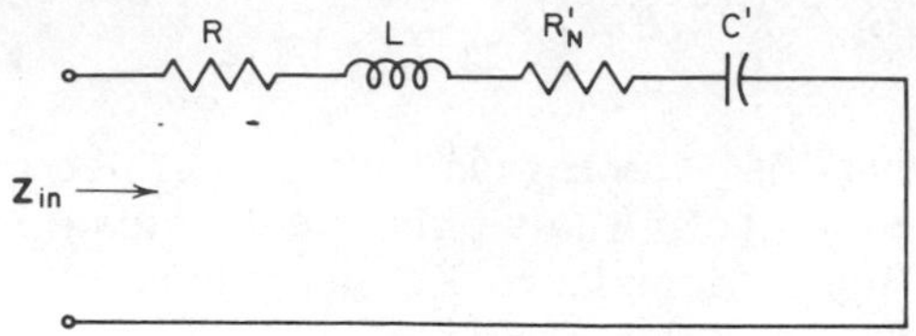

Fig. 1.2

The tunnel-diode network equivalent now takes the form shown in Fig. 1.2. Using this circuit to obtain the results in Eqs. 1.3 and 1.6, we write

$$\omega_0 L - \frac{1}{\omega_0 C'} = 0 \tag{1.11}$$

$$(R + R_N')\Big|_{\omega=\omega_c} = 0 \tag{1.12}$$

The values obtained for ω_0 and ω_c agree with those calculated from Eqs. 1.3 and 1.6. It is seen from Eq. 1.3 that high self-resonance frequency is obtained for a large value of R_N at given inductance L, so that $G_N{}^2L$ becomes small. It is seen from Eq. 1.6 that a high cutoff frequency also is obtained for a large value of R_N at given resistance R, so that $G_N{}^2R$ becomes small. Thus we are looking for diodes with high negative resistance value. Actually, it is the amount of negative resistance available at the port we are interested in, but unfortunately, this resistance R_N' falls off with frequency, as is shown by Eq. 1.9, and R subtracts from it all the time. Accordingly, we never secure enough negative resistance at the port.

(D) Inserting numerical values, we obtain

$$f_0 = \frac{1}{2\pi 8 \times 10^{-12}} \sqrt{\frac{8 \times 10^{-12} - (1/-80)^2 \times 10^{-8}}{10^{-8}}} \doteq 507 \text{ Mcps} \tag{1.13}$$

$$f_c = \sqrt{[1/80 - (1/80)^2]}/2\pi 8 \times 10^{-12} \doteq 2{,}220 \text{ Mcps} \tag{1.14}$$

$$f_{c\,\max} = \frac{1}{4\pi 8 \times 10^{-12}} \doteq 10{,}000 \text{ Mcps} \tag{1.15}$$

$$R_N' = \frac{-80}{1 + (2\pi 10^8)^2(8 \times 10^{-12})^2(-80)^2} \doteq -69\Omega \tag{1.16}$$

$$C' = \frac{1 + (2\pi 10^8)^2(8 \times 10^{-12})^2(-80)^2}{(2\pi 10^8)^2(8 \times 10^{-12})(-80)^2} \doteq 52\mu\mu f \tag{1.17}$$

$$R_{N\,\text{in}} = R + R_N' = 1\,\Omega - 69\,\Omega = -68\,\Omega \tag{1.18}$$

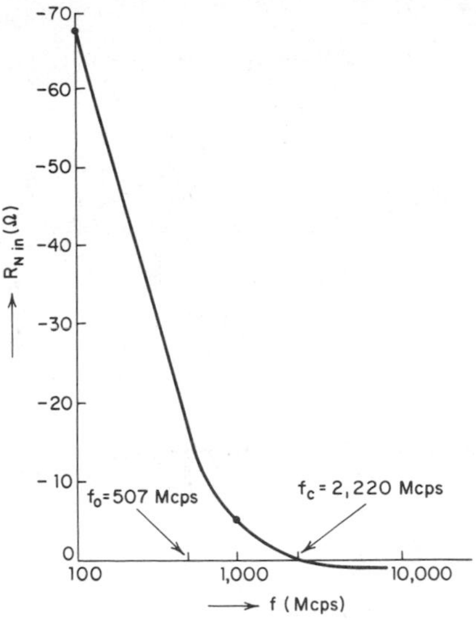

Fig. 1.3

$$|CR_N| = 8 \times 10^{-12} \times 80 = 64 \times 10^{-11} \text{ second} \qquad (1.19)$$

(E) The curve in Fig. 1.3 has been plotted from a few calculated points. It shows how drastically the negative resistance available at the port falls off as the frequency is increased.

Conclusions to this solution

The general procedure of calculation with stimulance diodes is outlined. We let R_N represent a negative value, but often we introduce $-R_N$ in formulas where we prefer to have positive values. The very practical single-mesh diode circuit is derived, and it is shown how we can calculate both the self-resonance frequency and the cutoff frequency from it, and in addition the negative resistance available at the port. This is one of the most important characteristics of the diode, and the plotted curve shows how difficult it is to make a tunnel diode that produces a sufficiently high negative resistance at the port as the frequency is increased. The network equivalent in Fig. 1.1 is occasionally criticized as being over-simplified for practical needs.

PROBLEM 2

Given is a tunnel diode with the idealized characteristic shown

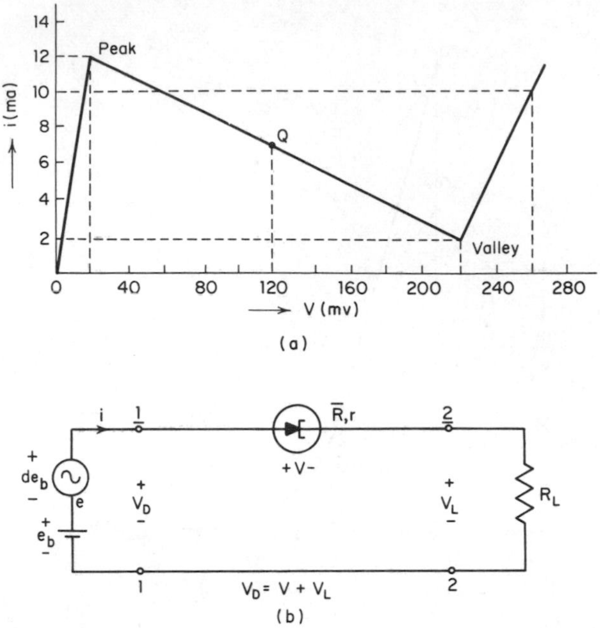

Fig. 2.1

in Fig. 2.1a and connected as shown in Fig. 2.1b. The tunnel diode is connected in series with a bias source, e_b, a signal voltage source, de_b, and a load resistance, R_L. Unless otherwise stated, R_L = 30 ohm. Initially, de_b in Fig. 1.1b is set equal to zero.[1]

(A) Plot a curve for the direct-current resistance $\overline{R}$ as obtained graphically from the given characteristic. Is this resistance linear? Does Ohm's law pertaining to $\overline{R}$ represent a linear function?

(B) In the same axes system, plot a curve for the variational resistance r as obtained graphically from the given characteristic. Is this resistance r linear? Does Ohm's law pertaining to r represent a linear function?

(C) Consider the load resistance R_L as an extension of the diode resistances and plot the dynamic characteristic for the combination. (Redraw the diode characteristic in a new axes system.) Discuss the importance and meaning of the dynamic characteristic.

[1]See Gentile, S. P., *Basic Theory and Applications of Tunnel Diodes*, Van Nostrand, 1962. Also see Chang, K. K. N., *Parametric and Tunnel Diodes*, Prentice-Hall, 1964.

(D) Discuss the phenomenon of voltage amplification, clarifying the role played by the negative-slope characteristic of the diode.

(E) Consider particularly the operation of the network when the diode is replaced by a positive resistance $\overline{R}_{Q1}$, equal to the diode direct-current resistance in the Q-point. If the input voltage is $e(t) = E \cos \omega t$, what is the output voltage across the load?

(F) With the true diode reinserted in the circuit, assume the input voltage maximum amplitude to be $E = 40\ mv$, and carry out constructions in a specified axes system, by means of which an approximate value for the output voltage V_L can be obtained. Then follow through with analytical reasoning, verifying the previously obtained value of the voltage V_L.

(G) Draw an equivalent network, and discuss voltage, current, and power amplification of the series amplifier.

(H) Plot a curve showing how the voltage amplification varies as R_L is reduced from its 30-ohm value. Discuss stability. Calculate the input resistance of the tunnel diode amplifier, and plot a curve to show how it varies as R_L is reduced from its 30-ohm value. Also calculate the output resistance.

(I) Derive the formula for amplification in accordance with the classical feedback theory, and apply the Barkhausen-Nyquist stability criterion. Also verify previously obtained values for input and output resistance.

Solution

(A) The construction line 0Q in Fig. 2.2a has the voltage coordinate 120 mv and the current coordinate 7 ma, so that the dc resistance $\overline{R}_Q$ in the Q-point becomes $\overline{R}_Q = 120/7 = 17.2$ ohm. All other points on the dynamic characteristic are obtained in the same fashion, and then the curve shown in Fig. 2.2b is constructed. The plot is linear up to the point 20mv, 12 ma, whereupon it becomes nonlinear (since a further doubling of the voltage does not yield a doubling of the current). Ohm's law pertaining to $\overline{R}$ does not represent a linear function for $v > 20$ mv.

(B) The variational resistance $r = 1/g$ is defined as the inverse slope g of each one of the three branches of the curve. The slopes are respectively

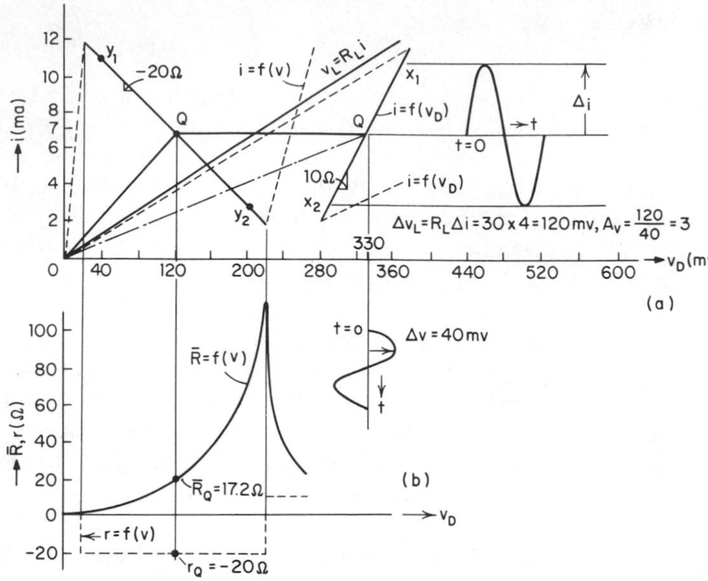

Fig. 2.2

$$g = i/v = 12/20 = 3/5 \text{ mho} \qquad g = i/v = -10/200 = -1/20 \text{ mho}$$
$$r = 1/g = 5/3 \text{ ohm} \qquad r = 1/g = -20 \text{ ohm}$$
$$g = i/v = 8/40 = 1/5 \text{ mho}$$
$$r = 1/g = 5 \text{ ohm} \tag{2.1}$$

The curve for r is shown in Fig. 2.2b by means of a dotted line. Note the simultaneous existence of the positive resistance, $\bar{R}_Q = 17.2$ ohm and the variational negative resistance $r_Q = -20$ ohm, both describing the diode in the Q-point. It is merely a question of looking upon one side of the coin or the other; all the time it is one and the same coin. Ohm's law pertaining to r represents independently a linear function for each one of the three branches of the curve, as the Q-point is sequentially positioned on the three branches.

(C) The dynamic characteristic is the curve, $i = f(v_D)$, pertaining to the combination of the diode and its load resistance. This characteristic is obtained with the aid of the load line, $v_L = R_L i$ and constructed by means of the component addition, $v_D = v + v_L$. The original characteristic has an inverse slope in the Q-point of -20 ohm, and adding to this 30 ohm in the load, we end up with 10 ohm, which is precisely the inverse slope of the dynamic characteristic (see Fig. 2.2a). Like magic, the characteristic has changed from having a negative-resistance middle branch to having a positive-resistance middle branch. The current in the Q-point remains the same, 7 ma, but the voltage is now $120 + 30 \times 7 = 330$ mv. Accordingly, the required bias supply is $e_b = 330$ mv. The direct-current resistance of the extended diode is $\overline{R}_D = 330/7 = 47.2$ ohm or, in another way, $30 + 17.2 = 47.2$ ohm. By using the dynamic characteristic, we simplify certain calculations and provide a simpler equivalent network.

(D) The net resistance in the diode circuit is always positive. Thus during the first part of the positive half-cycle of an applied sine wave, the current i must increase. The current is our common variable for the diode and its load. Our starting point is therefore a rising current, and the diode characteristic then tells us that the diode voltage v diminishes. This is the key to the discussion of voltage amplification, since it means that the load voltage experiences an extra increase—the sum of the diode voltage and load voltage equaling the applied voltage. The operation is therefore the same as if the diode shifted some of its voltage over to the load. The up-swing in the output voltage is therefore greater than it would be if the diode had a constant resistance. If we next consider the negative half-cycle of an applied sine wave, our starting point will be a falling current, and the diode characteristic then tells us that the diode voltage v increases. Thus there is a smaller portion of the applied voltage left across the load, which is just another way of saying that the down-swing of the output voltage will be greater. Two important facts come out of this reasoning: the device is able to produce voltage amplification, and the output voltage is in phase with the input voltage. Another thing that we learn is that two independent methods for the calculation of voltage amplification evolve: (1) using biasing conditions, that is, direct current and direct voltages only, and (2) using variational and load resistance, together with signal voltages and currents only. Both methods give precisely the same result, and the student should make a point of being able to perform tunnel-diode calculations in accordance with method 1 as well as method 2. Most engineers use method 2.

To grasp the phenomenon of voltage amplification, the student may think of the diode as a "pump," performing a pumping action that always supplies the load with some extra voltage the way the swing goes.

(E) If the diode were to have a positive resistance $\overline{R}_{Q1}$, the entire diode characteristic would become a straight line, with equal direct-current and variational resistance. If the finite variational voltage Δe_b is now applied, causing the variational output voltage Δv_L, the formula for voltage amplification becomes

$$\frac{\Delta v_L}{\Delta e_b} = \frac{R_L}{\overline{R}_{Q1} + R_L} \tag{2.2}$$

Equation 2.2 is obtained by direct application of the Voltage Proportioning Method. No amplification is obtained in this case. For the given instantaneous voltage input, the output voltage becomes

$$v_L(t) = \frac{R_L}{\overline{R}_{Q1} + R_L} E \cos \omega t \tag{2.3}$$

Note that the system is free from distortion.

(F) We carry out the construction shown in Fig. 2.2a with an input sine-wave voltage amplitude of 40 mv, obtaining an output-current swing of 4 ma. As indicated, the voltage amplification is therefore 3 times. There is no distortion. For the specified applied sine-wave voltage, the output voltage would be the true replica

$$v_L(t) = R_L i_L(t) = 30 \times 4 \cos \omega t = 120 \cos \omega t \tag{2.4}$$

Linearity follows directly from the geometrical construction in Fig. 2.2a. But Fig. 2.2b informs us about the perhaps startling phenomenon that to enjoy a linear voltage amplification, we must put up with a nonlinear direct-current diode-resistance variation. Another way of saying this is, that if the diode had a straight-line direct-current resistance variation, distortion-free voltage amplification would be impossible.

We shall now carry through a complete direct-current calculation of voltage amplification. We begin by determining the diode direct-current resistances at the extreme points of the swings. The extreme current values are only known to us after we have made the geometrical construction in Fig. 2.2a, but if we for simplicity take the values at points x_1 and x_2, we find that they are 3 and 11 ma Having located the points y_1 and y_2 on the diode characteristic, we can now find the two values $\overline{R}_1$ and $\overline{R}_2$ on the curve $\overline{R} = f(v_D)$ in Fig. 2.2b. On a large-scale plot, these values were determined as $\overline{R}_1 \doteq 3$ ohm and $\overline{R}_2 \doteq 67$ ohm. This method is not practical, and it is only included here to bring out the fact that these two specific resistance values exist on the $\overline{R} = f(v)$ curve. Employing a different method to find the two resistances, we may note that the extreme voltages across the diode-load combination are 330 + 40 = 370mv and 330 − 40 = 290mv. Inserting the respective currents and subtracting the load resistance, we obtain

$$\bar{R}_1 = 370/11 - 30 = 3.07 \text{ ohm}$$
$$\bar{R}_2 = 290/3 - 30 = 66.7 \text{ ohm} \qquad (2.5)$$

We may now write, proportioning the d-c resistances as in Eq. 2.2,

$$v_{L1} = 30(330 + 40)/(3.07 + 30) = 336 \text{ mv} \qquad (2.6)$$

$$v_{L2} = 30(330 - 40)/(66.7 + 30) = 90 \text{ mv} \qquad (2.7)$$

Accordingly,

$$v_{L2} - v_{L1} = 336 - 90 = 246 \text{ mv} \qquad \Delta v_L = 246/2 = 123 \text{mv} \qquad (2.8)$$

This result agrees reasonably well with that of 120 mv previously obtained. In using this somewhat academic method, we obtain a deeper insight into the true diode operation. Also, the method is of value for checking purposes. In the following, however, we shall employ the commonly used variational-resistance method.

(G) The equivalent network is shown in Fig. 2.3a, from which the voltage amplification is $R_L/(r + R_L)$. The same result may be obtained from an application of the conventionally used definition of tunnel-diode amplification: the ratio of V_L/E_1 with the tunnel diode in the circuit to V_L/E_1 when the tunnel diode is removed. Accordingly,

$$A_V = (V_L/E_1)/(V_L/E_{1,r=0}) = R_L/(r_Q + R_L) = 30/(-20 + 30) = 3 \qquad (2.9)$$

We are here using capital letters to designate signal quantities by

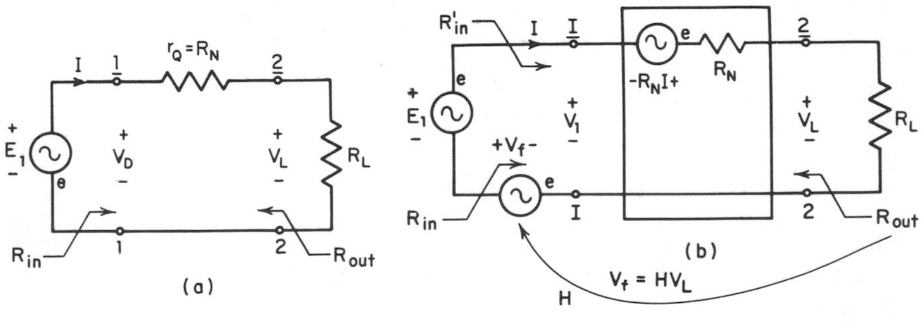

Fig. 2.3

means of sinors. Since no phase angles are involved, the sinors are maximum amplitudes of sine waves.

This result agrees with that obtained earlier. Since the output current is the same as the input current, the current amplification is $A_I = 1$. The gain is therefore, with $r_Q = R_N$,

$$G = A_V A_I = R_L/(R_N + R_L) \tag{2.10}$$

Thus voltage amplification and gain are one and the same thing.

(H) The curve is plotted from Table 2.1, which also shows the input resistance $R_{in} = R_N + R_L$.

TABLE 2.1

R_L	A_V	R_{in}	R_L	A_V	R_{in}
30	3	10	22	11	2
28	3.5	8	21	21	1
26	4.3	6	20	∞	0
24	6	4			

The desired curves are shown in Fig. 2.4. It is seen how, at the point of instability, the voltage amplification becomes infinitely

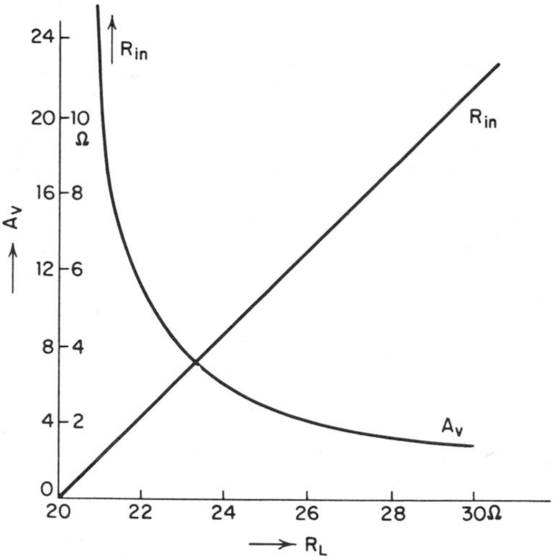

Fig. 2.4

large, while the input resistance becomes zero. The output resistance is $R_{\text{out}} = R_N$.

The following technique has been developed by the author to make possible the application of the Barkhausen-Nyquist stability criterion to diodes possessing stimulance. First of all, we make the amplifier stable by cancelling the diode negative resistance by means of a positive resistance, $-R_N$, in series, introducing this quantity via the Compensation Theorem as the voltage source, $R_N I$, with the signs shown in Fig. 2.3b. Since we are not allowed to change the system, we must cancel this source by another source and thus introduce the source $V_f = -R_N I$ in such a manner that the pattern for the classical feedback formula results. The inherent amplification is $A_{Vi} = R_L/(0 + R_L) = 1$, and the feedback transfer function becomes $H = V_f/V_L = -R_N I/R_L I = -R_N/R_L$. Accordingly,

$$A_V = A_{Vi}/(1 - HA_{Vi}) = 1/[1 - (-R_N/R_L)(1)] = R_L/(R_N + R_L) \qquad (2.11)$$

which agrees with the result we obtained in (9). The Barkhausen-Nyquist stability criterion yields

$$H_c A_{Vi} = 1 \qquad (-R_N/R_L)(1) = 1 \qquad R_L = -R_N \qquad (2.12)$$

Finally, the input and output resistances (with the latter determined from the classical feedback formula in Eq. 2.11 by means of the Output Immittance Theorem) are as follows:

$$R_{\text{in}} = V_1/I - V_f/I = R_L - (-R_N I)/I = R_L + R_N \qquad R_{\text{out}} = R_N \qquad (2.13)$$

Thus the classical feedback theory substantiates previously obtained results.

Conclusions to this solution

In the initial part of this solution we are concerned with the static and dynamic characteristics of the tunnel diode network. We note that we can readily calculate amplification and gain with the aid of variational quantities, and this method, making use of the signal equivalent network, is the conventional method. We also learn, however, that much of these calculations may be duplicated by bias voltage considerations, since Kirchhoff's laws for direct currents and voltages must hold simultaneously with Kirchhoff's laws for signal currents and voltages. As has already been stated, the diode d-c and a-c behavior is like the two sides of a coin. It is one and the same coin. We can do business with either side of the coin up. The phenomenon of voltage amplification has been discussed, and we have learned to look upon the diode as a pumping or parametric device. This viewpoint will be very helpful in future study of parametric devices involving storage elements. Finally, we have learned a method of extending the diode-network equivalent so that the classical feedback theory can be applied, and we find that all the answers so obtained agree with previous ones.

PROBLEM 3

Given is a tunnel diode with the simplified characteristic shown in Problem 2. The diode is connected, as shown in Fig. 3.1, in parallel with the load resistance R_L. Unless otherwise stated, $R_L = 10$ ohm. In series with the voltage supply, e_b is connected at signal source de_b, which initially has the value zero. Also shown is a relatively large series resistance, r_b, for simulation of the often used current-generator drive.

(A) Plot a curve for the direct-current resistance, $\overline{R}$, or the direct-current conductance, $1/\overline{R}$, as obtained graphically from the given characteristic. Is resistance $\overline{R}$ linear? Does Ohm's law pertaining to $\overline{R}$ represent a linear function?

(B) In the same axes system, plot a curve for the variational resistance, r, or the variational conductance, $1/r$, as obtained graphically from the given characteristic. Is this resistance r linear? Does Ohm's law pertaining to r represent a linear function?

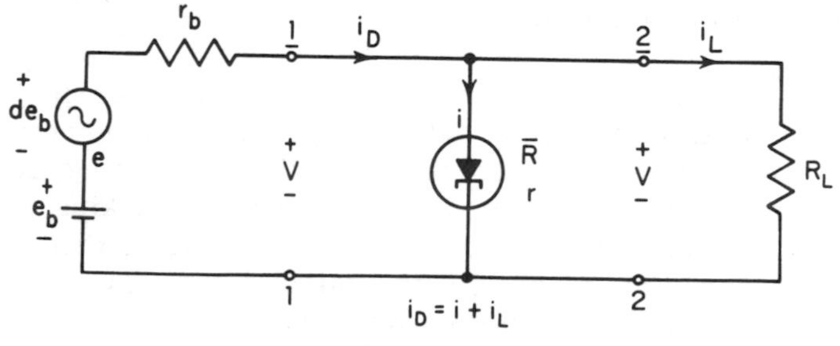

Fig. 3.1

(C) Consider the load resistance R_L as part of the diode resistance, and plot the dynamic characteristic for the combination. (Redraw the diode characteristic in a new axes system.) Discuss the importance and meaning of the dynamic characteristic.

(D) Discuss the phenomenon of current amplification, clarifying the role played by the negative-slope characteristic of the tunnel diode.

(E) Consider particularly the operation of the network when the diode is replaced by a positive resistance $\overline{R}_{Q1}$, equal to the diode direct-current resistance in the Q-point. If the input current is $i(t) = I \cos \omega t$, what is the output current in the load?

(F) With the true diode reinserted in the network, assume the input voltage maximum amplitude to be $E = 40$ mv, and carry out constructions in a specified axes system by means of which an approximate value for the output current amplitude I_L can be obtained. Then follow through with analytical reasoning, verifying the previously obtained value of I_L.

(G) Draw an equivalent network, discuss voltage, current, and power amplification of the shunt amplifier.

(H) Plot a curve showing how the current amplification varies as R_L is increased from its 10-ohm value. Discuss stability. Calculate the input conductance of the tunnel-diode amplifier, and plot a curve to show how it varies as R_L is increased from its 10-ohm value.

(I) Derive the formula for amplification in accordance with the classical feedback theory, and apply the Barkhausen-Nyquist stability criterion. Also verify previously obtained values for input and output conductance.

Solution

(A) This solution is in many respects similar to that given in connection with problem 2 in this chapter. The diode current-voltage characteristic is the same. Whereas in the series amplifier a bias voltage, e_b, of 330 mv was required to produce the required Q-point at $v = 120$ mv, precisely 120 mv is needed here. Whereas the values, $R_L > |R_N|$, $R_L = 30$ ohm, and $R_N = -20$ ohm, were required for stability in the series amplifier, the values, $R_L <$

$|R_N|$, R_L =10 ohm, and $R_N = -20$ ohm, are required here. Furthermore, no current amplification could be obtained in the series amplifier, but it is voltage amplification that cannot be produced in the shunt amplifier. There was considerable voltage amplification in the series amplifier, and we shall find that a large current amplification may be obtained in the shunt amplifier.

The direct-current resistance, $\overline{R}$, is a property of the diode, and the resulting curve is therefore the same as the one shown in the previous problem solution.

(B) The answer is the same as that given in the previous problem solution.

(C) The dynamic characteristic is here the current-voltage characteristic, $i_D = i + i_L = f(v)$. With $R_L = 10$ ohm, it follows that at all times $i_L = G_L v = 0.1v$, and this straight-line equation has been plotted to yield the load line shown in Fig. 3.2. The sum $(i + i_L)$ has been determined for several points on the tunnel-diode characteristic, and thus the dynamic characteristic is obtained as shown in Fig. 3.2. We note that the dynamic characteristic has an all-positive slope. With $R_N = -20$ ohm and $R_L = 10$ ohm, we expect the dynamic characteristic around the Q-point to have the slope $(-20)(10/-20) + 10 = 20$ ohm, and a check verifies that this is truly the positive slope of the plotted curve. The new bias current is read off as 19 ma, and full agreement exists; to the diode current of 7 ma we have added the load current of 12 ma. The d-c resistance of the diode alone is as before, $\overline{R}_Q = 17.2$ ohm, and the d-c resistance of the combination of the diode and the load is $(17.2 \times 10)/(17.2 + 10) = 6.33$ ohm. If we check the slope of the dot-dash line from the origin of the axes system through the new Q-point, positioned on the dynamic characteristic, we shall find that it verifies the value 6.33 ohm $(120/19 = 6.33)$.

(D) Just like the series amplifier, the shunt amplifier provides an all-positive signal-input resistance, as well as an all-positive d-c resistance. Thus, as the input direct current increases, the input direct voltage also increases, and vice versa. Since an increase in diode voltage means a decrease in diode current, the unavoidable conclusion is that an extra large increase in load current results. Similarly, a decrease in input current makes for an extra large decrease in load current because the diode now takes more current. The diode performance here is very similar to that in the series amplifier. It provides a pumping action that manages to add some load current during intervals of increased

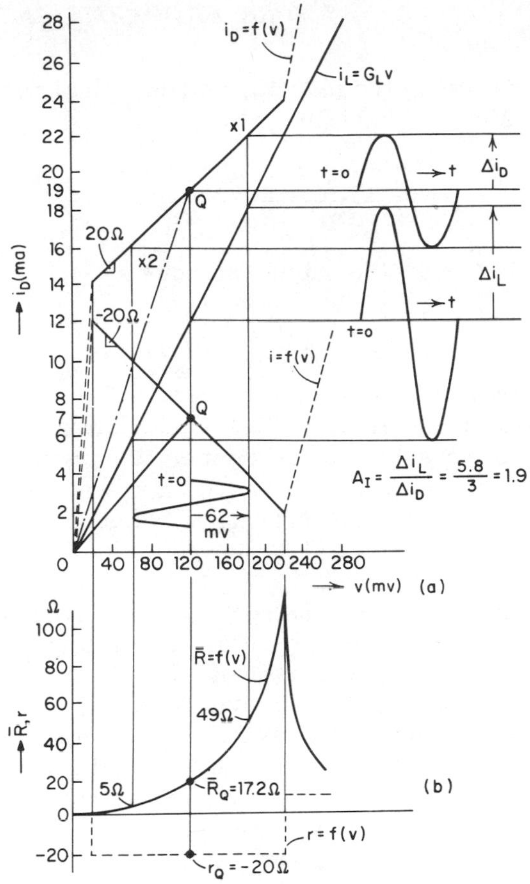

Fig. 3.2

input current, and to take away some load current during intervals of decreased input current, thereby increasing the swing of the output current by a current-shifting process. Accordingly, considerable current amplification may be obtained. We note that the output-current swing is in phase with the input current swing; the shunt amplifier does not have a 180° phase shift. Just as we did for the series amplifier, we can reason here by means of direct-current quantities or by means of variational-current quantities. Again, we have the proposition of the two sides of a coin remaining one and the same coin whichever way we look at it.

(E) Just as we did for the series amplifier, we write a basic equation for changes in the direct quantities, employing the Current Proportioning Method to obtain

$$\frac{\Delta i_L}{\Delta i_D} = \frac{\overline{R}_{Q1}}{\overline{R}_{Q1} + R_L} \tag{3.1}$$

For the specified input, the output becomes

$$i_L(t) = \frac{\overline{R}_{Q1}}{\overline{R}_{Q1} + R_L} I \cos \omega t \tag{3.2}$$

No amplification is obtained in this case, since the arrangement is merely that of a passive current divider. We are using the direct-current symbol $\overline{R}_{Q1}$ in Eqs. 3.1 and 3.2, but we could equally well have employed a variational-current symbol, since in this particular case the two are the same.

(F) The details of the construction of the dynamic characteristic in Fig. 3.2a are as follows. For each voltage value, we read off the diode-current coordinate and the load-line current coordinate and add the two. This provides us with a series of points on the dynamic characteristic. We note how the negative slope of the diode characteristic is turned into an equal positive slope (−20 ohm is turned into 20 ohm). If a sine wave current of maximum amplitude $\Delta i_D = 3$ ma was applied about the Q-point, we would swing between points x_1 and x_2 on the dynamic characteristic. The geometrical construction indicates that at point x_1 we have a voltage $v \doteq 182$ mv. The d-c resistance of the total network is 182/22 $\doteq 8.3$ ohm. Since the load resistance is 10 ohm, a simple calculation shows that the diode d-c resistance is 49 ohm, and very correctly, this is the value encountered on the curve $\overline{R} = f(v)$. A similar reasoning may be carried out with reference to the point x_2. Here the voltage is 58 mv, the total d-c resistance 3.6 ohm, the diode d-c resistance 5.6 ohm, and the value read off from the $\overline{R} = f(v)$ curve roughly the same. The maximum amplitude of the voltage swing is $182 - 120 = 120 - 58 = 62$ mv, and the sine-wave voltage across the load resistance is therefore $\widetilde{v} = 62 \sin \omega t$. The load or output current is accordingly

$$i_L(t) = I_L \sin \omega t = 6.2 \sin \omega t \tag{3.3}$$

since in accordance with Ohm's law, $62/10 = 6.2$. The geometrical construction on the load line yields the extreme values, 18.2 ma and 5.5 ma, so that the maximum amplitude becomes $18.2 - 12 = 12$

− 5.8 = 6.2 ma, in full agreement with the value calculated in Eq. 3.3. The current amplification of the shunt amplifier is $\Delta i_L/\Delta i_D = 6.2/3 \doteq 2.1$. There is no distortion.

(G) The equivalent network is shown in Fig. 3.3a, from which the current amplification becomes

$$A_I = \frac{I_L}{I_D} = \frac{R_N}{R_N + R_L} = \frac{-20}{-20+10} = 2 \tag{3.4}$$

where, as in the previous solution, capital letters indicate sinors. This value agrees quite well with that obtained through graphical construction in part F. The result also agrees with that obtained if we apply the often used relationship for tunnel diodes, which compares the output current when the diode is included in the network with the output current when the diode is not included, thus

$$A_I = \frac{\dfrac{R_N I_D}{R_N + R_L}}{I_D} = \frac{R_N}{R_N + R_L} \tag{3.5}$$

The voltage amplification is unity, and the power amplification the same as the current amplification.

(H) The required curves are plotted from Table 3.1, in which the input conductance has been calculated from the formula

$$G_{in} = G_N + G_L \tag{3.6}$$

The plotted curves are shown in Fig. 3.4. It is seen that the current

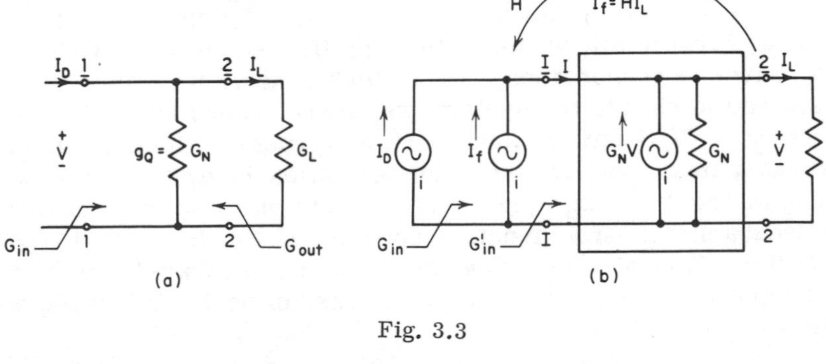

Fig. 3.3

amplification increases sharply, as the critical load-resistance value 20 ohm is approached. At this point the input resistance goes to infinity.

TABLE 3.1

R_L	A_I	G_{in}	R_L	A_I	G_{in}
10	2	0.05	18	10	0.006
12	2.5	0.034	19	20	0.003
14	3.3	0.022	20	∞	0.0
16	5	0.013			

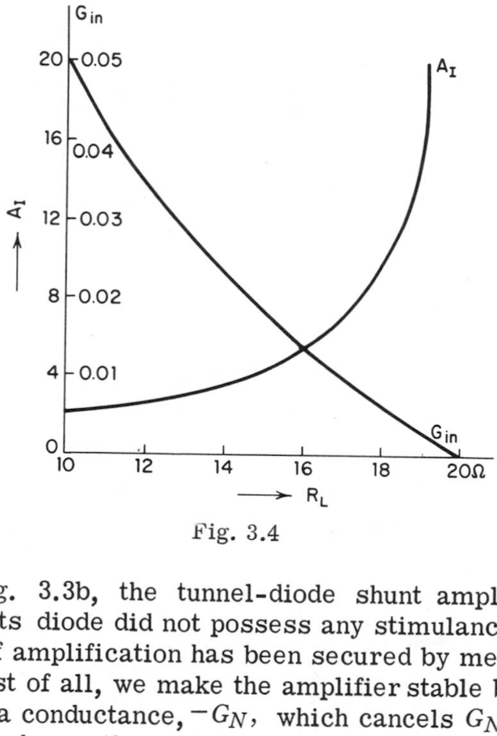

Fig. 3.4

(I) In Fig. 3.3b, the tunnel-diode shunt amplifier has been shown as if its diode did not possess any stimulance, and instead, the feature of amplification has been secured by means of positive feedback. First of all, we make the amplifier stable by introducing, as a source, a conductance, $-G_N$, which cancels G_N. Since we are not allowed to change the system, we insert a cancellation feedback source, $I_f = -G_N V$, at the input port, and proceed to identify significant quantities. The inherent amplification is $A_i = 1$, since with nothing inside the "box," the output current equals the input current. The feedback transfer function becomes $H = I_f/I_L = -G_N V/G_L V = -G_N/G_L$. Formally deriving the classical feedback formula for shunt injection, we proceed as in the case of series injection, and write

$$\frac{I_D}{I_L} = \frac{I}{I_L} + \frac{-I_f}{I_L} \tag{3.7}$$

$$\frac{1}{A} = \frac{1}{A_i} + (-H), \quad \text{or} \quad A = \frac{A_i}{1 - HA_i} \tag{3.8}$$

Inserting derived quantities, we obtain

$$A_I = \frac{1}{1 - (-G_N/G_L)} = \frac{G_L}{G_N + G_L} = \frac{R_N}{R_N + R_L} \tag{3.9}$$

which agrees with the result in Eq. 3.5. The instability condition is obtained for

$$HA_i = 1 \qquad -\frac{G_N}{G_L} \times 1 = 1 \qquad \text{or} \qquad G_L = -G_N \tag{3.10}$$

The input conductance may be derived from Eq. 3.7 in the form

$$G_{\text{in}} = -HG_L + G_{\text{in}}' = -\left(\frac{-G_N}{G_L}\right)G_L + G_{\text{in}}' = G_N + G_L \tag{3.11}$$

which result agrees with that in Eq. 3.6. The output conductance, from the Output Immittance Theorem applied to Eq. 3.9, is $G_{\text{out}} = G_N$. Thus the classical feedback theory substantiates all previously obtained results.

Conclusions to this solution

This solution runs parallel to that given for the series amplifier, but we should note the difference in construction of the dynamic characteristic. We may prefer to turn the shunt-amplifier diagram around, and plot $v = f(i)$, which leads to the plot, $i_L = f(i_D)$ —perhaps a more logical plot for a current amplifier. If so, the tunnel diode proper appears in a diagram with reversed axes, and one must not lose sight of which quantity is the dependent one and which is the independent one.

The phenomenon of current amplification is clarified by the constructions in the diagram as well as considered from an analytical point of view. By representing the oneport diode as a twoport device, we have succeeded in applying the classical feedback theory to the shunt amplifier in the same manner as we applied it to the series amplifier. We found that all the results obtained by means of classical feedback theory agreed with the previous results.

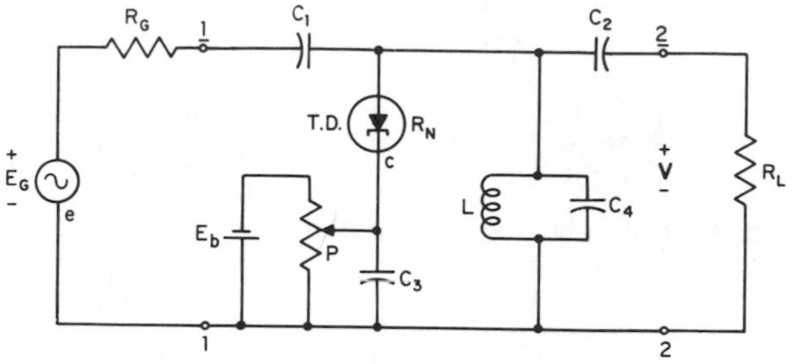

Fig. 4.1

PROBLEM 4

Given is the shunt-form tunnel-diode tuned rf amplifier shown in Fig. 4.1 in which the resistance variation introduced by the potentiometer P may be disregarded so far as the equivalent network is concerned.

(A) Draw the equivalent network. (Note that at least the tunnel diode capacitance c must be included.)

(B) For $R_G = 60\,\Omega$, $R_N = -50$ ohm, $c = 10\,\mu\mu f$, $L = 100\,\mu h$, $C = 100\,pf$, and R_L set 5 per cent below the value required for stability, calculate and plot the frequency response curve with reference to the output voltage V. Repeat with R_L set only 2 per cent below the value required for stability.

(C) Determine the take-off condition and the frequency of oscillation if R_L is accidentally given such a value that instability occurs.

Solution

(A) The radio-frequency network equivalent of the given amplifier is shown in Fig. 4.2a. We have here replaced the series-form driving generator by a shunt-form generator and made the assumption that the series capacitors C_1 and C_2 in Fig. 4.1 have zero impedance. Fig. 4.2b shows a further simplification of the network equivalent.

(B) We must first find the critical value G_{Lc} of G_L required for take-off. For zero resulting conductance, we write

$$G = G_G + G_N + G_{Lc} = 0 \tag{4.1}$$

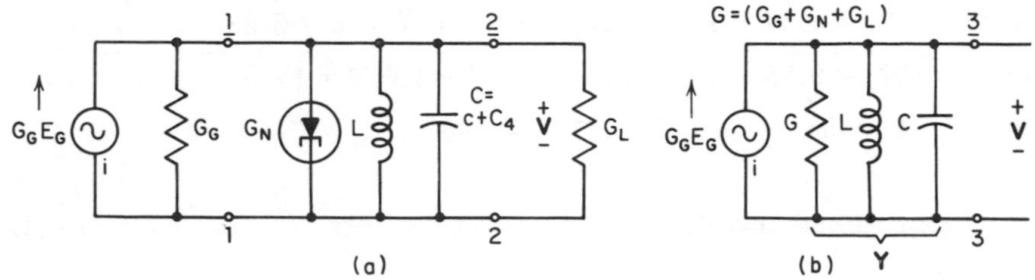

Fig. 4.2

$$G_{Lc} = -G_G - G_N = -\frac{1}{60} + \frac{1}{50} = 0.00333 \text{ mho} \tag{4.2}$$

For R_L set to $R_{L1} = 0.95\ (1/0.00333) \doteq 285$ ohm, the amplifier is stable. Similarly, for R_L set to $R_{L2} = 0.98\ (1/0.00333) \doteq 295$ ohm, the amplifier is also stable. With $s = j\omega$, $1/CL = \omega_0^2$, and $\omega/\omega_0 = x$, the voltage amplification is

$$\frac{\mathbf{V}}{E_G} = \frac{G_G}{\mathbf{Y}} = \frac{G_G}{G + sC + 1/sL} = \frac{G_G}{G + j\omega_0 C\left(\dfrac{x^2-1}{x}\right)} \tag{4.3}$$

Designating $\omega_0 CR = \omega_0 C/G = Q$ as a quality factor of the network, we write

$$\frac{\mathbf{V}}{E_G} = \frac{RG_G}{1 + jQ\left(\dfrac{x^2-1}{x}\right)} \tag{4.4}$$

$$\frac{V}{E_G} = \frac{RG_G}{\sqrt{1 + Q^2\left(\dfrac{x^2-1}{x}\right)^2}} \tag{4.5}$$

Here, R takes on first the value R_1 for $R_L = R_{L1}$, and then the value R_2 for $R_L = R_{L2}$. Equation 4.5 allows us to plot the requested curves. The following quantities are calculated:

$G_1 = G_G + G_N + G_{L1} = 1/60 - 1/50 + 1/285 \doteq 18 \times 10^{-5}$ ℧, $R_1 \doteq 5{,}560\,\Omega$

$G_2 = G_G + G_N + G_{L2} = 1/60 - 1/50 + 1/295 \doteq 6 \times 10^{-5}$ ℧, $R_2 \doteq 16{,}700\,\Omega$

$\omega_0^2 = 1/CL = 1/110 \times 10^{-12} \times 100 \times 10^{-6} \doteq 91 \times 10^{12}\ (\text{rad/sec})^2$

$\omega_0 = 10^6\sqrt{91} \doteq 9.55 \times 10^6$ rad/sec, $f_0 \doteq \omega_0/2\pi \doteq 1.52$ Mcps

$$Q_1 = \omega_0 C R_1 = 9.55 \times 10^6 \times 110 \times 10^{-12} \times 10^5/18 = 5.83$$

$$Q_2 = \omega_0 C R_2 = 9.55 \times 10^6 \times 110 \times 10^{-12} \times 10^5/6 = 17.5$$

$$Q_1^2 = 5.83^2 \doteq 34 \qquad Q_2^2 = 17.5^2 \doteq 306 \tag{4.6}$$

Using these quantities, we now complete Tables 4.1 and 4.2.

TABLE 4.1 $R_L = R_{L1}$, $Q = Q_1$

x	x^2	$(x^2-1)^2$	$\left(\frac{x^2-1}{x}\right)^2 = a$	$1+Q^2a$	$\sqrt{1+Q^2a} = b$	$\frac{1}{b}$	$\frac{G_G'}{b}$	$\frac{V}{E_G}$
1.4	1.96	0.92	0.47	17.0	4.13	0.242	0.0040	22
1.2	1.44	0.194	0.135	5.58	2.36	0.424	0.0071	39
1.1	1.21	0.044	0.036	2.22	1.49	0.671	0.011	61
1.0	1.00	0.0	0.0	1.00	1.00	1.00	0.0167	93
0.9	0.81	0.036	0.045	2.53	1.59	0.629	0.0105	58
0.8	0.64	0.13	0.203	7.89	2.81	0.356	0.0060	33
0.6	0.36	0.41	1.14	39.7	6.30	0.159	0.0027	15

TABLE 4.2 $R_L = R_{L2}$, $Q = Q_2$

1.2	1.44	0.194	0.135	42.3	6.50	0.154	0.0026	43
1.1	1.21	0.044	0.036	12.0	3.46	0.289	0.0048	80
1.05	1.10	0.010	0.009	3.76	1.94	0.515	0.0086	143
1.0	1.00	0.000	0.000	1.00	1.00	1.000	0.0167	278
0.95	0.90	0.010	0.011	4.36	2.09	0.479	0.0080	132
0.9	0.81	0.036	0.045	14.8	3.85	0.260	0.0043	72
0.8	0.64	0.130	0.203	63.1	7.86	0.127	0.0021	35

The resulting frequency-response curves are shown in Fig. 4.3. With high damping, $R_L = R_{L1}$, a rather flat resonance curve results, but as the damping is reduced, for the case $R_L = R_{L2}$, the resonance curve becomes sharply peaked, indicating a more selective amplifier. The width of the bottom curve at the half-power point is $\Delta x_1 \doteq 0.16$, and the width of the top curve at the half-power point is $\Delta x_2 \doteq 0.07$. Being read off from the diagram in Fig. 4.3, these values are naturally quite rough. The corresponding bandwidths are $\Delta f_1 = \omega_0 \Delta x_1/2\pi \doteq 0.24$ Mcps and $\Delta f_2 = \omega_0 \Delta x_2/2\pi \doteq 0.11$ Mcps, respectively. Due to the low Q-values, we cannot

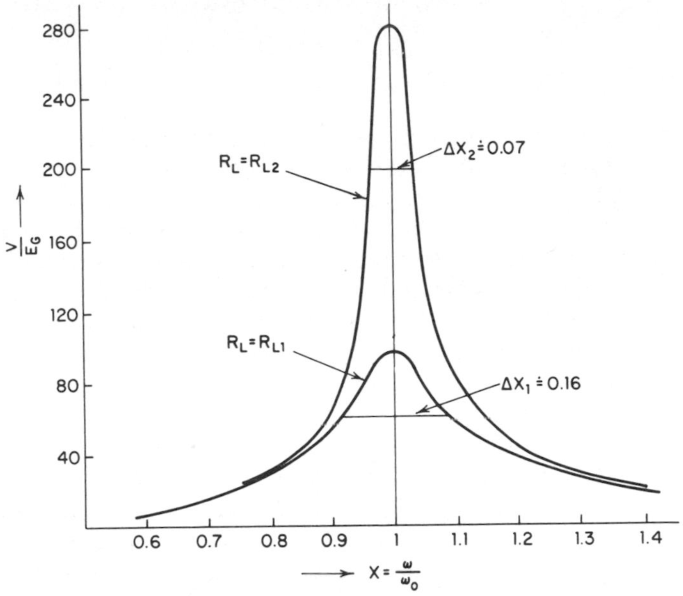

Fig. 4.3

very well use the approximations, $\Delta\omega_1 \doteq \omega_0/Q_1$ and $\Delta\omega_2 \doteq \omega_0/Q_2$, but if we do this, nevertheless, we obtain the values, 0.26 Mcps and 0.09 Mcps, respectively.

To obtain the cutoff values analytically, we write, from Eq. 4.5,

$$\frac{RG_G}{\sqrt{1 + Q^2\left(\dfrac{x^2 - 1}{x}\right)^2}} = \frac{RG_G}{\sqrt{2}} \tag{4.7}$$

$$Q\left(\frac{x^2 - 1}{x}\right) = \pm 1 \tag{4.8}$$

Solving the second-degree equation in Eq. 4.8 (and approximating the roots still further by setting the square root equal to 1, which means that we assume the reasonance curves to be symmetrical), we obtain the values 0.085 and 0.03. These quantities represent half the bandwidth in the variable x and accordingly our answers become $\Delta x_1 \doteq 0.17$ and $\Delta x_2 \doteq 0.06$. These values agree reasonably well with the graphically obtained ones, $\Delta x_1 \doteq 0.16$ and $\Delta x_2 \doteq 0.07$ respectively.

(C) The critical value, $R = R_{Lc}$, for take-off has already been determined in Eq. 4.2 and is $1/0.00333 \doteq 300$ ohm. The frequency of oscillation is given by Eq. 4.6, where $f_0 \doteq 1.52$ Mcps.

Conclusions to this solution

In this solution, we have gone through the various steps in calculating a tunnel-diode radio-frequency amplifier, and we have learned to plot its frequency-response curves. Again, we have an example of the importance of lumping certain quantities together to form a fewer number of more important quantities, such as x and Q. In this manner, the tabulation of data can be made more concise and more generally useful. The plotted response curves show the effect of damping on voltage amplification and bandwidth. It should be noted that the resonance curves are not quite symmetrical, and the danger of using formulas too strongly approximated on the basis of curve symmetry is apparent. As the damping is further reduced, the voltage amplification increases from the already quite high value of 278 times and goes to infinity, while at the same time the bandwidth goes to zero. This condition cannot be obtained in physical devices because instability may occur even before the amplification has reached twice the indicated value. The tunnel-diode amplifier then becomes a tunnel-diode oscillator, and although the take-off conditions for this oscillator have been calculated in the solution, we cannot proceed to use linear network theory to calculate the final condition at which the oscillation voltage will cease to increase.

Although we chose the load resistance as our variable in this problem, we might equally well have kept it constant and assumed the use of two different tunnel diodes, one with higher stimulance than the other. As an alternative, we may have assumed two different bias values on the same diode, producing two values of stimulance. The resulting frequency-response curves would have been similar to those shown in Fig. 4.3.

SOME FINAL THOUGHTS

The calculations on tunnel diodes we have just been through set a pattern for many diode networks involving stimulance. Many of the construction details pertaining to the dynamic characteristic are the same, independent of the type of stimulance device used. Port-immittance curves and frequency-response curves may vary little from device to device, provided the basic integro-differential equations are similar. Somewhere in the device there exists stimulance, expressed by a negative slope in a current-voltage (or voltage-current) characteristic, and somewhere we specify an output port, which also has a current-voltage (or voltage-current) characteristic. We may lump the entire system into this port. If the device is to work as a stable amplifier, only a limited amount of stimulance must appear at the output port, but if we want the device to work as an oscillator, sufficient stimulance must be provided, not only to cause instability but also to bring the oscillation amplitude to required value for a continuous wave or a recurrent-pulse output. Sometimes we portray the stability conditions by means of a dynamic characteristic, imposing certain restrictions on its slope, and sometimes we treat the problem analytically. In principle it makes no difference whether the negative slope of a dynamic characteristic is produced by a stimulance device, such as a tunnel diode, or by the use of a transistor free of stimulance and provided with external positive feedback. Certainly we can use the difference in the network arrangement for the purpose of classifying the devices, but in a mathematical analysis we have a free hand to treat a stimulance device as a nonstimulance device provided with positive feedback, and to treat a positive feedback amplifier as a nonfeedback amplifier employing an otherwise positive-slope characteristic, turned into a negative-slope characteristic. Largely, it is the same thing. We have in this chapter developed a technique for portraying a oneport as a twoport, so that we can apply the powerful classical feedback theory and make use of the Barkhausen-Nyquist stability criterion.

7
Nonlinear Semiconductor Networks

In the previous chapter we were dealing with a specific characteristic of certain diodes: the negative-slope characteristic. In this chapter we shall learn how to analyze mathematically the positive-slope diode characteristic, employing a technique that can be automatically extended to cover negative-slope regions as well. The technique borders on the powerful method of analysis often referred to as "curve fitting," and the treatment given here may serve as an introduction to this kind of analysis.

In the following discussion, we may distinguish between two approaches, which really portray one and the same thing. One approach is to use the originally supplied equation for the diode characteristic, the other to employ the single-variable Taylor series. To some extent, one method may be used as a check on the other. The tremendous importance and power of the Taylor series as a mathematical tool must not be overlooked. It is one of the cleverest mathematical tools ever devised, and some of the results that can be achieved may even appear uncanny. The reader should fully familiarize himself with this method, which is easily extended from oneports to twoports by substituting the double-variable Taylor series.

PROBLEM 1

The current-voltage characteristic of a certain semiconductor diode resembles a square-law curve sufficiently well to allow us to replace the characteristic by the parabola branch shown in Fig. 1.1. Carry out the following assignments and give numerical answers whenever possible:

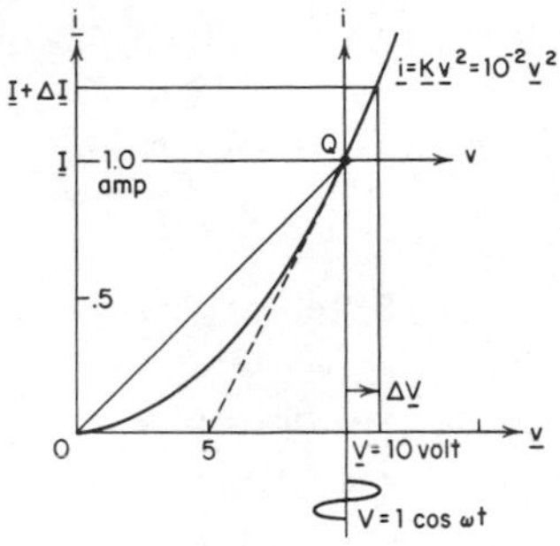

Fig. 1.1

(A) Apply a change, $\Delta \underline{V}$, in the bias voltage $\underline{V}$ and derive the "parabolic signal equation" in terms of the signal variables, $\Delta \underline{V} = \underline{v}$ and $\Delta \underline{I} = \underline{i}$. Define the constants.

(B) Show that Taylor's series for one variable gives the same result as that obtained in part A.

(C) Show by means of a graph how the direct-current conductance varies as we slide the Q-point by increasing the value of the bias voltage from zero value.

(D) Show by means of a graph how the variational immittance varies under the same conditions.

(E) In the expansion obtained in part A or B, specify the term used in: (1) the a-c voltmeter (diode plus direct-current movement), and (2) the frequency-doubler operation.

Solution

(A) Inserting the current and voltage changes in the given equation for the parabola, we obtain

$$\underline{I} + \Delta \underline{I} = \underline{K}(\underline{V} + \Delta \underline{V})^2 = \underline{K}\underline{V}^2 + 2\underline{K}\underline{V}\,\Delta \underline{V} + \underline{K}(\Delta \underline{V})^2 \qquad (1.1)$$

Since $\underline{I} = \underline{K}\underline{V}^2$, we may write the change in current as

$$\Delta \underline{I} = 2\underline{K}\underline{V}\,\Delta \underline{V} + \underline{K}(\Delta \underline{V})^2 \qquad (1.2)$$

or with

$$K = 2\underline{K}\underline{V} \qquad (1.3)$$

$$\Delta \underline{I} = K\Delta \underline{V} + \underline{K}(\Delta \underline{V})^2, \quad \text{or} \quad i = Kv + \underline{K}v^2 \tag{1.4}$$

In the Q-point, $\underline{V} = 10$ volt, $K = 2\underline{KV} = 0.2$ (from Eq. 1.3), and therefore

$$i = 0.2v + 10^{-2}v^2 \tag{1.5}$$

Differentiating Eq. 1.4 twice, we obtain

$$di/dv = K + 2\underline{K}v = K\,\Big|_Q = g_Q = 1/r_Q \tag{1.6}$$

$$\frac{d^2i}{dv^2} = 2\underline{K}$$

$$\underline{K} = \frac{1}{2}\frac{d^2i}{dv^2} \tag{1.7}$$

Above we have analytically found expressions for the two constants in terms of derivatives. The slope of the curve in the Q-point is the conductance $g_Q = K = 1/r_Q$. If the voltage deviation is caused by the indicated cosine wave, we obtain from Eq. 1.4

$$\begin{aligned} i &= K \cos \omega t + \underline{K} \cos^2 \omega t \\ &= K \cos \omega t + \frac{\underline{K}}{2} + \frac{\underline{K}}{2} \cos 2\omega t \\ &= 0.2 \cos \omega t + 0.005 + 0.005 \cos 2\omega t \text{ amp} \end{aligned} \tag{1.8}$$

As an alternative, we could have started from the equation for the parabola given in Fig. 1.1 and inserted $v = 10 + \cos \omega t$. The answer would exceed that in Eq. 1.8 by 1, which is the bias-current value. Note that the parabolic signal equation in Eqs. 1.4 and 1.5 only gives the current from the Q-point. The total current also includes the bias value, here 1 amp. Note that the derivatives can be determined either from the given curve or from the signal equation.

(B) The Taylor series for one variable yields

$$i = \sum_{n=1}^{\infty} \frac{1}{n!}\left(\frac{\partial}{\partial v} v\right)^n i = \frac{1}{1}\frac{di}{dv} v + \frac{1}{2}\frac{d^2i}{dv^2} v^2 = Kv + \underline{K}v^2 \tag{1.9}$$

and thus represents the parabolic signal equation, the third derivative being zero. Note the two methods for determining the derivatives.

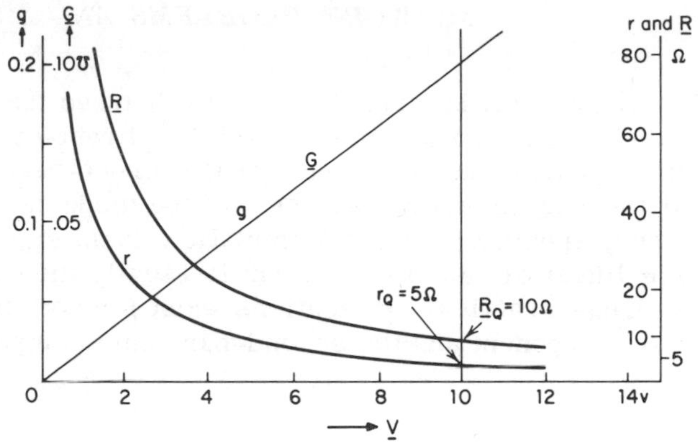

Fig. 1.2

(C,D) The direct-current conductance in any Q-point is $\underline{G} = \underline{i}/\underline{v} = \underline{K}\underline{v}$, which is a straight line as shown in Fig. 1.2. Its inverse value is the direct-current resistance $\underline{R} = 1/\underline{G}$, which is also shown in Fig. 1.2. As a check we note that the triangle $OQ\underline{V}$ in Fig. 1.1 has the coordinates, 10/1 = 10 ohm, which is precisely the value of $\underline{R}_Q$ given by the $\underline{R}$ curve in Fig. 1.2. The variational-current conductance in any Q-point is $g = d\underline{i}/d\underline{v}$, which is also shown in Fig. 1.2. As a check we note that the tangent in the Q-point triangle, $5Q10$, in Fig. 1.1 has the coordinates, 5/1 = 5 ohm, which is precisely the value of r_Q given by the r curve in Fig. 1.2.

(E1) The direct-current meter movement reacts only to a direct current component, and thus shows the second term in Eq. 1.8 plus 1 amp, unless the bias current is suppressed in some way.

(E2) The last term in Eq. 1.8 is utilized.

Conclusions to this solution

We note the two standard methods of determining a nonlinear-diode current: either to insert the bias voltage plus signal in the basic direct-current equation for the characteristic or to deal with the signal voltage only and use the Taylor series with one variable. The first method gives the total current, including the bias current, whereas the second method yields only signal-current output, consisting of direct-current component plus periodic components. In this case, no load resistance was included in the diode circuit, but had a load existed, a dynamic characteristic would have taken the place of the static characteristic.

It follows that the d-c components produced will change the direct-voltage bias on the diode and thus the Q-point location for the periodic components. In parts C and D, we learned that a parabola has straight-line characteristics both for direct-current conductance and signal conductance and that the direct-current resistance R and the variational resistance r of the diode can be determined for every specific problem formulation. In the signal current obtained, the linear or "amplifier" term is usually the one of least interest, whereas practical applications exist for both the signal-produced d-c component and the second-harmonic component.

PROBLEM 2

The sum of two sine waves is applied to the base-emitter junction of a transistor, in which the bias may be so adjusted that either linear or nonlinear operation results.

(A) Conceive of a general form of the collector output current from the transistor when operated linearly with the junction-signal input voltage

$$v = v_1 + v_2 = V_1 \cos \omega_1 t + V_2 \cos \omega_2 t \tag{2.1}$$

(B) Give an example of a nongenuine product term.

(C) The transistor is now operated nonlinearly. Carry out an analysis with immediate reference to the junction current, accounting for all components produced and explaining how they may be utilized in modulation, single-side-band transmission, and frequency conversion.

(D) Show that nonlinear additive mixing and multiplicative mixing are synonymous concepts.

Solution

(A) The transistor is treated by conventional twoport theory. In the case of a CE-connected transistor with h parameters, we write the output-current-to-input-voltage transfer function and find that the output current is proportional to the input voltage v and therefore contains the linear sum given in Eq. 2.1.

(B) With $V_1 = V_2$, we may express any linear sum, such as the one given by Eq. 2.1, as a product by setting $\omega_1 = (x + y)$ and $\omega_2 = (x - y)$, from which $x = (\omega_1 + \omega_2)/2$ and $y = (\omega_1 - \omega_2)/2$. Writing

Eq. 2.1 in terms of x and y and inserting the expressions for x and y, we obtain a formula which can be expressed trigonometrically as the product term

$$V = 2V_1 \cos \frac{\omega_1 + \omega_2}{2} \cos \frac{\omega_1 - \omega_2}{2} \tag{2.2}$$

This is a nongenuine product term, since it fails to generate sum and difference components.

(C) Although a transistor in nonlinear operation is likely to have considerable third- and higher-order components, the assumption of parabolic operation gives a good account of the operation. We can either use Taylor series for one variable (Eq. 2.3) or for two variables (Eq. 2.4), but since a single-port input exists, both series give the same result:

$$i = \sum_{n=1}^{\infty} \frac{1}{n!}\left(\frac{\partial}{\partial v}\, v\right)^n i \tag{2.3}$$

$$i = \sum_{n=1}^{\infty} \frac{1}{n!}\left(\frac{\partial}{\partial v_1} v_1 + \frac{\partial}{\partial v_2} v_2\right)^n i \tag{2.4}$$

Using Eq. 2.3 we write

$$i = \frac{di}{dv} v + \frac{1}{2}\frac{d^2 i}{dv^2} v^2 = Kv + \underline{K}v^2$$

$$= Kv_1 + Kv_2 + \underline{K}v_1^2 + 2\underline{K}v_1 v_2 + \underline{K}v_2^2$$

$$= KV_1 \cos \omega_1 t + KV_2 \cos \omega_2 t + \underline{K}V_1^2 \cos^2 \omega_1 t$$

$$+ 2\underline{K}V_1 V_2 \cos \omega_1 t \cos \omega_2 t + \underline{K}V_2^2 \cos^2 \omega_2 t$$

or

$$i = \underline{K}V_1^2/2 + \underline{K}V_2^2/2 + KV_1 \cos \omega_1 t + KV_2 \cos \omega_2 t$$

$$+ (\underline{K}V_1^2 \cos 2\omega_1 t)/2 + (\underline{K}V_2^2 \cos 2\omega_2 t)/2 + \underline{K}V_1 V_2 \cos(\omega_1 + \omega_2)t$$

$$+ \underline{K}V_1 V_2 \cos(\omega_1 - \omega_2)t \tag{2.5}$$

The first two terms in the expansion are direct-current components, which move the Q-point if external series resistance to the diode is present. The following two terms are linear "amplification" terms not of interest here. The next two terms represent second harmonics also not of interest. The last two terms, representing sum and difference angular velocities, are of interest. In amplitude modulation, the filtered-out transmission includes the third term, the carrier. The three terms together represent double-sideband transmission. For single-sideband transmission, we filter out one of the sideband terms, or one of the sideband terms and the carrier, as the case may be. In frequency conversion we eliminate one of the sideband terms and the carrier, the remaining angular velocity being the so-called "intermediate frequency" angular velocity.

(D) Multiplicative mixing, the name given to mixing in twoport devices, may be handled by Taylor's series for two variables as given in Eq. 2.4, but not by Taylor's series for one variable as given in Eq. 2.3. The result of multiplicative mixing is a product term similar to the product term obtained above, and in principle, therefore, multiplicative mixing and nonlinear additive mixing give the same sum and difference components.

Conclusions to this solution

We note that for the production of sum and difference components a product term is not sufficient; we must have a genuine product term. In determining nonlinearly generated components, we find that Taylor's series for one variable yields a direct answer, except for the bias-current component, which we may add if we so wish. Each component has a specific meaning and usage depending upon what we are trying to accomplish. With reference to multiplicative mixing obtained in double-port "shifting-Q- point" type converters, we note that nonlinear additive mixing obtained in single-port sliding-Q- point converters is just as "multiplicative." It is often a "hardware" consideration that decides whether we use a single-port or a double-port converter.

PROBLEM 3

A semiconductor diode, governed by the Q-point (1 volt, 1 ma), is to a first approximation represented by the characteristic, $\underline{i} = \underline{K}v^2 = 10^{-3}\underline{v}^2$.

(A) Construct the characteristic, and assume tentatively that the square law relationship can be extended throughout the interval

$0 < \underline{V} < 2\underline{V}$, where $\underline{V}$ is the bias voltage. With the aid of Taylor's series in the form,

$$\Delta \underline{I} = \sum_{n=1}^{N} \frac{1}{n!} \left(\frac{\partial}{\partial \underline{v}} \Delta \underline{V} \right)^{n} \underline{i} \tag{3.1}$$

find all coefficients and write a signal equation in a new axis system with its origin in the Q-point.

(B) Using the semiconductor diode as a Van der Bijl modulator, apply the modulating wave, $e_2 = E_2 \cos \Omega t$, and the carrier wave, $e_1 = E_1 \cos \omega t$. Explain the phenomenon of modulation with reference to the static characteristic, using a load resistance, $R_L \ll r_a$, where r_a is the average diode resistance. Derive formulas for the modulated wave produced and for its degree of modulation.

(C) Using the values, $E_1 = 0.1$ volt and $E_2 = 0.5$ volt, pertaining to an audio-frequency modulated rf wave, write a numerical expression for the amplitude-modulation (AM) wave produced.

(D) With the conductance of the semiconductor device expressed by the expansion

$$\tilde{g} = \sum_{p=1}^{P} \hat{g}_p \cos (p\Omega_0 t + \phi_p) \tag{3.2}$$

approach the problem of frequency conversion by treating the semiconductor diode as a parametric device, selecting one suitable product term in the output. Write the equation for this output term, based on the parametric consideration, and then compare it with the term obtained from a "double input" consideration, with the additional input contributed by the local oscillator. Insert numerical values and prove that both approaches give precisely the same result.[1]

Solution

(A) The required construction is shown in Fig. 3.1. Graphically we determine the slope in the Q-point to be 0.002 mho. Reading the

[1]Stockman, H. E., "Linear or Nonlinear," *American Journal of Physics*, Vol. 31, No. 9, September 1963.

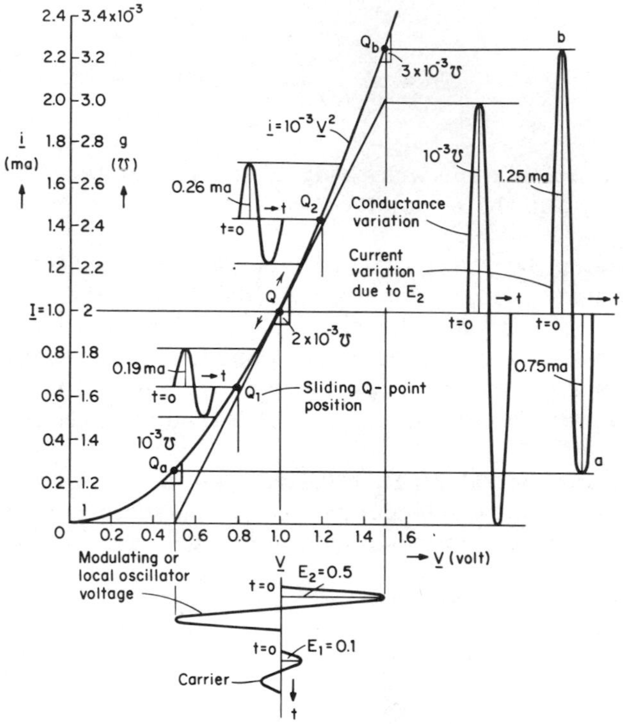

Fig. 3.1

conductance scale against the voltage scale, we find that the slope of the slope is also 0.002 mho/volt. The Taylor series yields

$$\Delta \underline{I} = \frac{1}{1}\frac{d\underline{i}}{d\underline{v}}\,\Delta \underline{V} + \frac{1}{2}\,\frac{d^2\underline{i}}{d\underline{v}^2}\,\Delta \underline{V}^2 \tag{3.3}$$

The coefficients are determined from the equation for the characteristic $\underline{i} = \underline{K}\underline{v}^2$ and are

$$\frac{d\underline{i}}{d\underline{v}} = 2\underline{K}\underline{v} = K \qquad\qquad \frac{d^2\underline{i}}{d\underline{v}^2} = 2\underline{K} \tag{3.4}$$

where $\underline{K}$ is known from the problem formulation to be 10^{-3} mho/volt, and accordingly,

$$K = \frac{di}{d\underline{v}}\bigg|_Q = 2\underline{K} = 2 \times 10^{-3}\text{ mho} \qquad \underline{K} = \frac{1}{2}\frac{d^2\underline{i}}{d\underline{v}^2} = 10^{-3}\text{ mho/volt} \tag{3.5}$$

The required signal equation pertaining to an axes system in the Q-point is

$$\Delta \underline{I} = K\Delta \underline{V} + \underline{K}\Delta \underline{V}^2 = 2 \times 10^{-3}\Delta \underline{V} + 10^{-3}\Delta \underline{V}^2 \tag{3.6}$$

(B) Applying the sum of

$$e_1 = E_1 \cos \omega t \qquad e_2 = E_2 \cos \Omega t \tag{3.7}$$

to the Q-point, we write according to Eq. 3.6, using instantaneous values,

$$\begin{aligned} i &= K(e_1 + e_2) + \underline{K}(e_1 + e_2)^2 \\ &= Ke_1 + Ke_2 + \underline{K}e_1^2 + 2\underline{K}e_1e_2 + \underline{K}e_2^2 \end{aligned} \tag{3.8}$$

The first term here is the carrier "amplifying" term, and the second term is the modulating-wave "amplifying" term. The third and the last terms represent corresponding direct-current contributions and second harmonics. The next to last term, the product term, is the one of interest in modulation. We keep this term and the first term and eliminate the rest, obtaining

$$\begin{aligned} i_{\text{cm}} &= Ke_1 + 2\underline{K}e_1e_2 \\ &= KE_1 \cos \omega t + 2\underline{K}E_1E_2 \cos \omega t \cos \Omega t \end{aligned} \tag{3.9}$$

Subscript "c" here refers to carrier and subscript "m" to modulation. Making use of the trigonometric formula,

$$\cos \omega t \cos \Omega t = \tfrac{1}{2}\cos(\omega + \Omega)t + \tfrac{1}{2}\cos(\omega - \Omega)t \tag{3.10}$$

we write Eq. 3.9, with $KE_1 = I_c$ and $2\underline{K}E_1E_2 = I_m$,

$$i_{\text{cm}} = I_c \cos \omega t + \frac{I_m}{2}\cos(\omega + \Omega)t + \frac{I_m}{2}\cos(\omega - \Omega)t \tag{3.11}$$

Introducing the modulation factor or degree of modulation, m, we write

$$m = \frac{I_m}{I_c} = \frac{2KE_2}{K} \tag{3.12}$$

We may now write Eq. 3.11 in the form

$$i_{\text{cm}} = I_c[\cos \omega t + \frac{m}{2} \cos (\omega + \Omega)t + \frac{m}{2} \cos (\omega - \Omega)t] \tag{3.13}$$

Here the first term represents the carrier, the second term the upper angular velocity, and the third term the lower angular velocity. We may now write Eq. 3.9 in the form

$$i_{\text{cm}} = I_c(1 + m \cos \Omega t) \cos \omega t \tag{3.14}$$

which clearly portrays the wave diagram of the modulated wave produced, the amplitude of the carrier wave expanding and contracting periodically due to the term, $m \cos \Omega t$.

(C) Much of the modulation phenomenon is evident from a study of Fig. 3.1, in which the static and dynamic characteristics coincide due to the relatively small value of the load resistance. As the modulating voltage slides the Q-point along the characteristic, the Q-point encounters a varying slope. Typical positions are Q_1 and Q_2. Swinging down 0.2 volt to Q_1, we obtain a positive current swing of only 0.19 ma, whereas swinging up 0.2 volt to Q_2, we obtain 0.26 ma. A still greater difference occurs if we consider the extreme Q-point positions, Q_a and Q_b. We note with reference to Q-points Q_1 and Q_2 how distorted the current responses are, as described by term number three in Eq. 3.8. The same distortion pertaining to the modulating voltage—the last term in Eq. 3.8—is evident from the current response shown to the right in Fig. 3.1, the positive swing being 1.25 ma whereas the negative swing is 0.75 ma. Although all waves for simplicity have been shown in Fig. 3.1 with the same period, one may easily visualize how the carrier voltage wave is superimposed upon the modulation-voltage wave, and, as far as the current responses go, how the large carrier wave appears at point "b" and the small carrier wave at point "a". Upon filtering out undesired components, we obtain the characteristic "breathing" AM wave.

The "local oscillator" controlled diode constitutes a parametric device, and a solution employing variational conductance will yield the results in Eq. 3.13 and Eq. 3.14. Such a solution will be carried out for the case of frequency conversion in part D.

Inserting numerical values in Eq. 3.12, 3.13, and 3.14, we obtain, with $I_C = KE_1 = 2 \times 10^{-3} \times 0.1 = 2 \times 10^{-4}$,

$$m = 2\underline{K}E_2/K = 2 \times 10^{-3} \times 0.5/2 \times 10^{-3} = 0.5 \quad (3.12a)$$

$$i_{\text{cm}} = 2 \times 10^{-4}[\cos \omega t + 0.25 \cos(\omega + \Omega)t + 0.25 \cos(\omega - \Omega)t] \quad (3.13a)$$

$$i_{\text{cm}} = 2 \times 10^{-4}(1 + 0.5 \cos \Omega t) \cos \omega t \quad (3.14a)$$

(D) In case of frequency conversion, E_2 represents the "local oscillator" voltage and E_1 the carrier of an AM wave, which normally carries voice modulation. The diode now represents the nonlinear mixer in a superheterodyne AM radio receiver, and its output angular velocity is referred to as "intermediate angular velocity." If the diode and local oscillator are considered to form one unit, acted upon by the incoming carrier, we refer to this unit as a frequency converter. Let us assume that the lower angular velocity is chosen as desired output. This output is then, from Eq. 3.13a,

$$i_{\text{lower}} = 5 \times 10^{-5} \cos(\omega - \Omega)t \quad (3.15)$$

We shall now consider a variational-conductance solution, typical for a parametric device. We note in Fig. 3.1 that the conductance variation is a sine wave, swinging between 3×10^{-3} mho and 10^{-3} mho. Its maximum amplitude is therefore 10^{-3} mho. Equation 3.2 yields only a fundamental, since the parabolic characteristic fails to produce a second harmonic, and accordingly,

$$\tilde{g} = g_0 \cos \Omega t \quad (3.16)$$

We shall now apply a different reasoning to determine g_0. In accordance with Eq. 3.4, g_0 is one-half of the difference between the extreme slopes, or

$$g_0 = \frac{1}{2}\left(\frac{d\underline{i}}{d\underline{v}}\bigg|_{\underline{V}=1.5} - \frac{d\underline{i}}{d\underline{v}}\bigg|_{\underline{V}=.5}\right) = \frac{1}{2}(2\underline{K}1.5 - 2\underline{K}0.5) = \underline{K} = 10^{-3} \quad (3.17)$$

This is precisely the result we obtained above by graphical construction. Ohm's law now produces the product term as

$$i_{\text{prod}} = \tilde{g}e_1 = g_0 E_1 \cos \omega t \cos \Omega t \quad (3.18)$$

This formula demonstrates the parametric feature of the device.

That this is the same product term we encountered in Eq. 3.14a, with the coefficient 10^{-4}, follows from the calculation $g_0E_1 = 10^{-3} \times .1 = 10^{-4}$. The difference-angular-velocity term derived from Eq. 3.18 is $0.5g_0E_1 \cos(\omega - \Omega)t$, and the maximum amplitude of the intermediate angular velocity wave is therefore 5×10^{-5}, which is precisely the value we obtained in Eq. 3.15 using the Taylor series.

The straight line in Fig. 3.1, providing the third side of the triangle having a base extending from 0.5 to 1.5 volt, and a height extending from 0 to 2 ma, represents at one and the same time two characteristic features, which we should note. Firstly, it is the tangent in the Q-point and has a slope of 2×10^{-3} mho. Secondly, it represents the slope at every point on the current-voltage characteristic, as we slide the Q-point. The value of the slope is read off on the conductance scale on the vertical axis. Thus for the Q-point we correctly read off the value 2×10^{-3} mho. Apparently, the slope of the slope is a constant of dimension mho/volt.

Conclusions to this solution

The introductory part of this solution is quite similar to that in problem 1. We quickly obtain the signal equation in the Q-point and apply both voltages in series to the only existing port. The case treated is that of double input single-port injection. Later we considered the device parametric, with "built-in" modulating or "local oscillator" voltage, and we were then dealing with the case of single-input, single-port injection, discussing the operation of a frequency converter rather than a nonlinear mixer. The variational-conductance method offers distinct advantages, particularly for converters in Class-B and Class-C operation, in which the diode conducts only part of the time, but to a relatively high degree, and the fundamental conductance component described by Eq. 3.2 and Eq. 3.16 becomes replaced by a Fourier spectrum that may have ten or more significant components. Occasionally, the desired component is a specific one out of $|p\omega \pm q\Omega|$, which can be obtained much faster by a graphical Fourier analysis than in any other way. This is an engineering method, the usefulness of which seems to increase with the intricacy of the problem.

While we have made a point here of using the single-variable Taylor series, it should be noted that the double-variable Taylor series gives the same result. This series should, however, be reserved for double-input double-port injection, employed for example in the case of a transistor-nonlinear mixer. This transistor, with its second port and "local oscillator" lumped inside the "box," constitutes a single-input single-port device.

PROBLEM 4

The sum of two sine waves is applied to the input port of a transistor and the port current observed. The biasing is such as to provide nonlinear operation, requiring third-order terms for proper analysis.

(A) Using the equation $\underline{i} = \underline{K}\underline{v}^3$ for the characteristic, determine the signal current when the signal voltage applied to the Q-point is $v = (v_1 + v_2)$. Define all coefficients in terms of derivatives.

(B) Obtain the answer in (A) using the Taylor series for one variable and also for two variables. Which series would be used in case of double-port injection? Explain.

(C) With the transistor junction operating as a nonlinear mixer, and with disregard of any resistance in series with the junction, use the result in (B) to obtain the difference-frequency current, when v_1 is a carrier $V_1 \cos \omega_1 t$ and v_2 a local oscillator voltage $V_2 \cos \omega_2 t$.

(D) As an alternative method to the one employed in (C), consider the transistor as a parametric device and identify its conductance in terms of a Fourier spectrum.

Solution

(A) Applying the voltage deviation in the Q-point, we obtain

$$\underline{i} = \underline{K}\underline{v}^3$$

$$\underline{I} + \Delta\underline{I} = \underline{K}(\underline{V} + \Delta\underline{V})^3 = \underline{K}\underline{V}^3 + 3\underline{K}\underline{V}^2\Delta\underline{V} + 3\underline{K}\underline{V}\,\overline{\Delta\underline{V}^2} + \underline{K}\,\overline{\Delta\underline{V}^3}$$

or, since $\underline{I} = \underline{K}\underline{V}^3$,

$$\Delta\underline{I} = 3\underline{K}\underline{V}^2\,\Delta\underline{V} + 3\underline{K}\underline{V}\,\overline{\Delta\underline{V}^2} + \underline{K}\,\overline{\Delta\underline{V}^3} \tag{4.1}$$

With the coefficients

$$K_1 = 3\underline{K}\underline{V}^2 \tag{4.2}$$

$$K_2 = 3\underline{K}\underline{V} \tag{4.3}$$

this becomes

$$\Delta\underline{I} = K_1 \Delta\underline{V} + K_2 \overline{\Delta\underline{V}^2} + \underline{K}\,\overline{\Delta\underline{V}^3} \tag{4.4}$$

Equation 4.4 is the signal equation in the Q-point. We define the coefficients by formulating derivatives from the equation for the characteristic

$$\frac{d\underline{i}}{d\underline{v}} = 3\underline{K}\underline{v}^2 = 3\underline{K}\underline{V}^2 \Big|_Q = K_1 \tag{4.5}$$

$$\frac{d^2\underline{i}}{d\underline{v}^2} = 6\underline{K}\underline{v} = 6\underline{K}\underline{V} \Big|_Q = 2K_2 \tag{4.6}$$

$$\frac{d^3\underline{i}}{d\underline{v}^3} = 6\underline{K} \tag{4.7}$$

from which K_1, K_2, and $\underline{K}$ are determined.

For $v = (v_1 + v_2)$ we obtain from Eq. 4.4 in terms of instantaneous values,

$$\begin{aligned} i = {} & K_1 v_1 + K_1 v_2 + K_2 v_1^2 + 2K_2 v_1 v_2 + K_2 v_2^2 \\ & + \underline{K} v_1^3 + 3\underline{K} v_1^2 v_2 + 3\underline{K} v_1 v_2^2 + \underline{K} v_2^3 \end{aligned} \tag{4.8}$$

which is the desired expression.

(B) Using the Taylor series for one variable, we write in terms of instantaneous values,

$$i = \sum_{n=1}^{\infty} \frac{1}{n!}\left(\frac{\partial}{\partial v}\, v\right)^n i$$

$$= \frac{1}{1}\frac{\partial i}{\partial v} v + \frac{1}{2}\frac{\partial^2 i}{\partial v^2} v^2 + \frac{1}{6}\frac{\partial^3 i}{\partial v^3} v^3$$

$$\begin{aligned} = {} & \frac{\partial i}{\partial v} v_1 + \frac{\partial i}{\partial v} v_2 + \frac{1}{2}\frac{\partial^2 i}{\partial v^2} v_1^2 + \frac{\partial^2 i}{\partial v^2} v_1 v_2 + \frac{1}{2}\frac{\partial^2 i}{\partial v^2} v_2^2 + \frac{1}{6}\frac{\partial^3 i}{\partial v^3} v_1^3 \\ & + \frac{1}{2}\frac{\partial^3 i}{\partial v^3} v_1^2 v_2 + \frac{1}{2}\frac{\partial^3 i}{\partial v^3} v_1 v_2^2 + \frac{1}{6}\frac{\partial^3 i}{\partial v^3} v_2^3 \end{aligned} \tag{4.9}$$

There is no distinction here between previously used derivatives and partial derivatives, and with the aid of Eqs. 4.5, 4.6, and 4.7

we find that the result in Eq. 4.9 agrees fully with that in Eq. 4.8. We note that it does not make any difference whether we determine the constants from the direct-current equation for the characteristic, as we did in Eqs. 4.5, 4.6, and 4.7, or from the signal equation 4.4. Using Taylor's series for two variables, we write

$$i = \sum_{n=1}^{\infty} \frac{1}{n!}\left(\frac{\partial}{\partial v_1} v_1 + \frac{\partial}{\partial v_2} v_2\right)^n i$$

$$= \frac{1}{1}\frac{\partial i}{\partial v_1} v_1 + \frac{1}{1}\frac{\partial i}{\partial v_2} v_2 + \frac{1}{2}\frac{\partial^2 i}{\partial v_1^2} v_1^2 + \frac{\partial^2 i}{\partial v_1 \partial v_2} v_1 v_2 + \frac{1}{2}\frac{\partial^2 i}{\partial v_2^2} v_2^2$$

$$+ \frac{1}{6}\frac{\partial^3 i}{\partial v_1^3} v_1^3 + \frac{1}{2}\frac{\partial^3 i}{\partial v_1^2 \partial v_2} v_1^2 v_2 + \frac{1}{2}\frac{\partial^3 i}{\partial v_1 \partial v_2^2} v_1 v_2^2 + \frac{1}{6}\frac{\partial^3 i}{\partial v_2^3} v_2^3 \qquad (4.10)$$

This expansion pertains to a single port, and derivatives with respect to v_1 are therefore identical with derivatives with respect to v_2. Similarly, cross derivatives simplify to just the variable v in the denominator. A term-by-term comparison with Eq. 4.9 then shows that the expansions are identical, and for a single port it does not matter whether we use Taylor's series for one variable or for two variables, although the use of the former is more natural. For a twoport device, however, the following distinctions appear

$$\frac{\partial i}{\partial v_1} \neq \frac{\partial i}{\partial v_2} \qquad \frac{\partial^2 i}{\partial v_1^2} \neq \frac{\partial^2 i}{\partial v_2^2} \neq \frac{\partial^2 i}{\partial v_1 \partial v_2} \quad \text{etc.} \qquad (4.11)$$

(C) Writing Eq. 4.4 in terms of the variables i, v and disregarding certain terms, we obtain, looking for the fundamental difference-frequency term,

$$i' = K_2 v^2 = K_2(v_1 + v_2)^2 = \cdots 2K_2 v_1 v_2$$

$$= \cdots 2K_2 V_1 V_2 \cos \omega_1 t \cos \omega_2 t \qquad (4.12)$$

$$i'' = K_2 V_1 V_2 \cos (\omega_1 - \omega_2)t \qquad (4.13)$$

which is the desired current.

(D) We now let v_2 vary the conductance encountered by v_1, and we are only interested in the fundamental component in the conductance variation. Starting again as in part C, we consider $2K_2 v_2$

the conductance encountered by v_1, In accordance with Ohm's law, we write

$$i''' = \tilde{g}v_1 = g_0 \cos \omega_2 t \; V_1 \cos \omega_1 t = 2K_2 V_1 V_2 \cos \omega_1 t \cos \omega_2 t \qquad (4.14)$$

This is the same expression we obtained in Eq. 4.12. The advantage of the method is that g_0 can be determined graphically from the given characteristic, so that the analysis work becomes reduced. In class-B or class-C operation of nonlinear mixers, a rather complete Fourier spectrum would have to be provided, including perhaps five to ten terms, but all this can be done graphically, and all possible sum and difference components determined just as would be the case in a more elaborate analytical derivation.

Conclusions to this solution

The pattern for higher-order curves has been set, and a fourth-order or fifth-order characteristic is handled in precisely the same manner. The use of Taylor's series for two variables to handle double-port injection has been indicated. The Taylor-series method of treating problems on frequency conversion is explained and the powerful alternative of the variational-conductance treatment is discussed.

SOME FINAL THOUGHTS

In the previous problems, the equation for the diode has either been known or has resembled a second- or third-order curve so closely that we could assume the diode characteristic to be such a curve. All diode characteristics do not actually pass through the origin of the axes system, but the existence of an ordinate in the origin does not markedly complicate the problem. We have learned to use the practical variational-conductance method, which often should be the engineer's first choice. This method requires good familiarity with Fourier's series, and particularly so for devices in Class-B and Class-C operation.

There exists an additional powerful method of treating such nonlinear devices as modulators and frequency converters. In accordance with this method, we enclose the device in a "black box," specifying two ports between which some known linearity exists. In this way we can treat a nonlinear problem by means of linear network theory, employing twoport theory, and if we so wish, we can determine the twoport parameters by means of laboratory measurements. Using the frequency converter in an amplitude-modulation superheterodyne as application example, we note that a linear relationship exists between the amplitude of the incoming radio-frequency wave and the amplitude of the outgoing intermediate-frequency wave, and the method can therefore be used.[1] See Appendix B, part 3.

[1]Stockman, H. E., "A Treatment of Nonlinear Devices Based Upon the Theory of Related Linear Functions," *Journal of Applied Physics*, No. 12, Dec. 1943. Also by the same author: "Use of Frequency Conversion Diagrams," *Proceedings of the IRE*, No. 11, Nov. 1944; "UHF Converter Analysis," *Electronics*, No. 2, Feb. 1945; and "Calculation of the Output from Nonlinear Mixers," *Journal of Applied Physics*, No. 2, Feb. 1946.

8

Mixed Problems

In the following the reader will find some additional problems, included for extra exercise. Some review what we have already learned about single-stage and cascaded amplifiers, cutoff frequencies, use of matrix techniques, and applications of the Laplace Transform. Some of the problems bring up new material, such as the combination of transistors and transmission lines, measurements on transistors, and the use of y parameters for the treatment of parallel amplifiers.

In solving these problems, the reader may like to review the list of rules given at the end of the first chapter and also to review the conclusions and final thoughts given in the other chapters. Through sustained practice, the reader will finally arrive at a point where he more or less automatically selects the right approach for the solution, and having become familiar with the calculation techniques, he will be able to obtain desired answers fast and accurately.

PROBLEM 1

Given is an emitter follower utilizing a transistor, which is known from the matrix,

$$|r|_{CE} = \begin{vmatrix} r_{11}' & r_{12}' \\ r_{21}' & r_{22}' \end{vmatrix}$$

This active device is used for matching purposes, feeding a transmission line of characteristic impedance, R_c. (Note: matching is not necessarily at hand.) Assume input voltage constant.

(A) Make up a TEE equivalent in which the inequality $r_{21}'' \neq r_{12}''$ is represented by a function source in one of the series arms. Calculate $A_V''(\omega)$, R''_{in}, and R''_{out} in terms of the given parameters.

(B) Make up a TEE equivalent in which the inequality $r_{21}'' \neq r_{12}''$ is represented by a function source in the mid-arm. Again determine $A_V''(\omega)$, R''_{in}, and R''_{out}.

<u>Solution</u>

(A) We shall begin by determining the CC-connection parameters. This transformation was carried out in the solution to problem 8 in chapter 3, with the following result:

$$r_{11}'' = r_{11}' + r_{22}' - r_{12}' - r_{21}' = r_b' + r_c' - r_m'$$

$$r_{12}'' = r_{22}' - r_{12}' = r_c'$$

$$r_{21}'' = r_{22}' - r_{21}' = r_c' - r_m' \qquad r_{22}'' = r_{22}' = r_c' + r_u' \tag{1.1}$$

$$\Delta_r'' = \Delta_r' = r_{11}'r_{22}' - r_{12}'r_{21}' \tag{1.2}$$

The conventional active TEE network equivalent in Fig. 1.1a fulfills the stated requirement. The desired formulas are:

$$A_V''(\omega) = \frac{r_{21}''}{r_{11}'' + \Delta_r''G_C} = \frac{r_{22}' - r_{21}'}{r_{11}' + r_{22}' - r_{12}' - r_{21}' + \Delta_r'G_C} \tag{1.3}$$

$$R_{in}'' = \frac{r_{11}'' + \Delta_r''G_C}{1 + r_{22}''G_C} = \frac{r_{11}' + r_{22}' - r_{12}' - r_{21}' + \Delta_r'G_C}{1 + r_{22}'G_C} \tag{1.4}$$

$$R_{out}'' = \frac{\Delta_r''}{r_{11}''} = \frac{\Delta_r'}{r_{11}' + r_{22}' - r_{12}' - r_{21}'} \tag{1.5}$$

(B1) Starting from the "r" CE TEE equivalent and using the Arm Interchange Method, we interchange the output arm and the shunt arm, thus obtaining the equivalent network shown in Fig. 1.1b, in which the function source appears in the shunt arm. Applying standard twoport parameter definitions, we obtain:

$$r_{11}'' = \left.\frac{V_{10}''}{I_1''}\right|_{2\ op} = r_b' + r_c' - r_m' = r_{11}' + r_{22}' - r_{12}' - r_{21}'$$

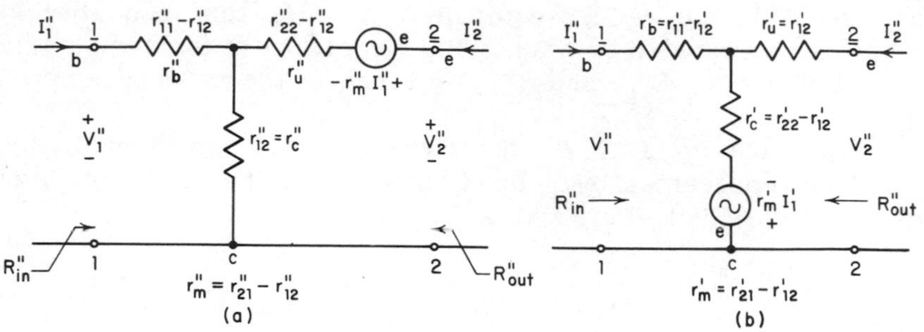

Fig. 1.1

$$r_{12}'' = \left.\frac{V_1''}{I_{20}''}\right|_{1\text{ op}} = r_c' = r_{22}' - r_{12}'$$

$$r_{21}'' = \left.\frac{V_2''}{I_{10}''}\right|_{2\text{ op}} = r_c' - r_m' = r_{22}' - r_{21}'$$

$$r_{22}'' = \left.\frac{V_{20}''}{I_{20}''}\right|_{1\text{ op}} = r_c' + r_u' = r_{22}' \qquad (1.6)$$

These results agree with those in Eq. 1.1, and the expressions for $A_V''(\omega)$, R_{in}'', and R_{out}'' are therefore identical to the ones given in Eqs. 1.3, 1.4, and 1.5.

(B2) As an alternative method of solution, we may start from the already obtained CC-equivalent in Fig. 1.1a. This time we are not shifting the positions of any arms, since the arms already are in their final positions. We merely draw the requested network, here shown in Fig. 1.2, and call it an equivalent of the one in Fig. 1.1a.

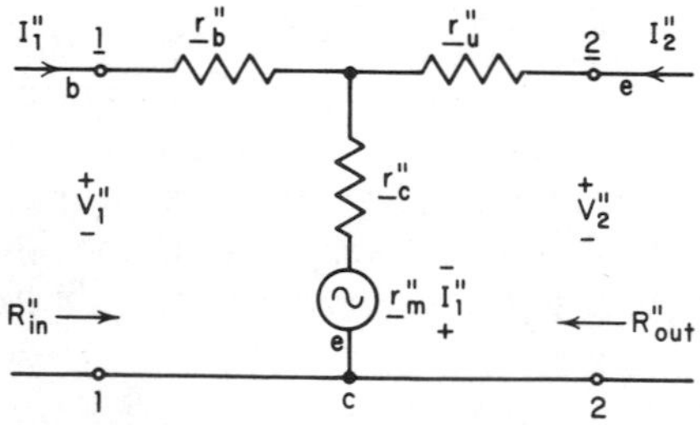

Fig. 1.2

We write the following relationships, using the results in Eq. 1.1:

$$\underline{r}_{11}'' = \left.\frac{V_{10}''}{I_1''}\right|_{2\text{ op}} = \underline{r}_b'' + \underline{r}_c'' - \underline{r}_m'' = r_b' + r_c' - r_m'$$

$$\underline{r}_{12}'' = \left.\frac{V_1''}{I_{20}''}\right|_{1\text{ op}} = \underline{r}_c'' = r_c'$$

$$\underline{r}_{21}'' = \left.\frac{V_2''}{I_{10}''}\right|_{2\text{ op}} = \underline{r}_c'' - \underline{r}_m'' = r_c' - r_m'$$

$$\underline{r}_{22}'' = \left.\frac{V_{20}''}{I_2''}\right|_{1\text{ op}} = \underline{r}_c'' + \underline{r}_u'' = r_c' + r_u' \qquad (1.7)$$

from which,

$$r_b'' = r_b' \qquad r_u'' = r_u' \qquad r_c'' = r_c' \qquad r_m'' = r_m' \qquad (1.8)$$

These are the same values that appear in the TEE in Fig. 1.1 and the values of $A_V''(\omega)$, R''_{in}, and R''_{out} are therefore the ones given by Eqs. 1.3, 1.4, and 1.5.

Conclusions to this solution

With reference to this solution we might recall that there exist at least three fundamental methods of transformation, for example, from a CE-connection to a CC-connection. The most important one is no doubt the "Floating" Matrix Method, which, in the form we have given it, requires that we proceed via a y parameter presentation. Another method frequently used in these solutions is the Equation System Comparison Method, in which we prefer to work with either z or y parameters. A third method is the Arm Interchange Method used above in Eq. 1.6, where we shift arms in a known connection in order to obtain a desired connection. The reader who is fluent in all three methods has a definite advantage when it comes to flexibility and speed.

PROBLEM 2

Given is the two-stage CE-connected low-frequency transistor amplifier shown in Fig. 2.1, employing "model" transistors. The

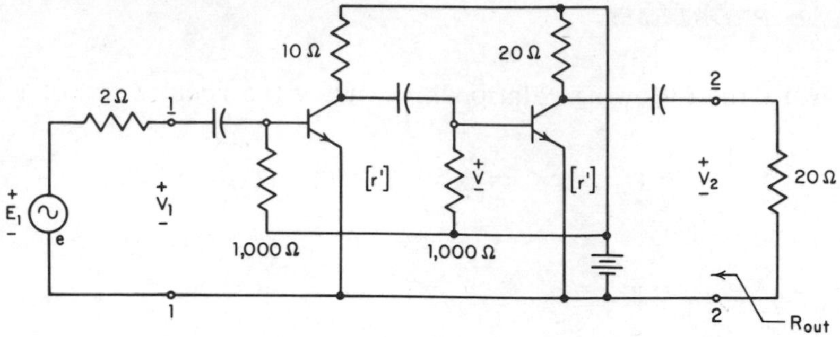

Fig. 2.1

transistors are identical and are described by the matrix

$$|r|_{CE} = \begin{vmatrix} 2 & 1 \\ -20 & 4 \end{vmatrix}$$

The amplifier is operated at mid-frequency. Use sound approximations in your solution.

(A) What are the numerical values of r_b', r_u', r_c', b, β, r_b, r_u, r_c, a, and α?

(B) Using the stage-by-stage-analysis method, determine the voltage amplification of the total amplifier and its output resistance.

(C) Repeat part B, representing the first stage by a series-form generator.

(D) Among methods of determining total voltage amplification, does the often used procedure in (C) imply just a variation in the calculation methods, or does it represent a time-saving method of great importance?

Solution

(A) We obtain from the given matrix:

$$\begin{aligned} r_{11}' &= 2\Omega = r_b' + r_u' &\quad \text{thus} \quad r_b' &= 1\Omega \\ r_{12}' &= 1\Omega = r_u' & r_u' &= 1\Omega \\ r_{21}' &= -20\,\Omega = r_m' + r_u' & r_m' &= -21\Omega \\ r_{22}' &= 4\Omega = r_c' + r_u' & r_c' &= 3\Omega \end{aligned} \qquad (2.1)$$

From the solution to problem 10 in Chapter 3 we obtain:

$$b = -r_m'/r_c' = 21/3 = 7 \qquad \beta = -r_{21}'/r_{22}' = 20/4 = 5 \tag{2.2}$$

$$\begin{aligned} r_{11} &= r_{11}' - 2\Omega = r_b + r_u & \text{Thus,}\quad r_u &= 1\Omega \\ r_{12} &= r_{11}' - r_{12}' = 1\Omega = r_b & r_b &= 1\Omega \\ r_{21} &= r_{11}' - r_{21}' = 22\Omega = r_m + r_b & r_m &= 21\Omega \\ r_{22} &= r_{11}' + r_{22}' - r_{12}' - r_{21}' = 25 = r_b + r_c & r_c &= 24\Omega \end{aligned} \tag{2.3}$$

$$a = r_m/r_c = 21/24 = 0.875 \qquad \alpha = r_{21}/r_{22} = 22/25 = 0.88 \tag{2.4}$$

(B) From the equivalent network, we calculate for the second stage

$$A_{V2}(\omega) = \frac{V_2}{V} = \frac{r_{21}'}{r_{11}' + \Delta_r' G_L} = \frac{-20}{2 + 28/10} \doteq -4.17 \tag{2.5}$$

$$G_{\text{in}\,2} = \frac{1 + r_{22}' G_L}{r_{11}' + \Delta_r' G_L} = \frac{1 + 4/10}{2 + 28/10} \doteq 0.29\,\mho \tag{2.6}$$

The first stage is loaded by 0.29 mho plus 0.1 mho and may be extended to include the generator resistance. Thus we write

$$A_{V1}(\omega) = \frac{V}{E_1} = \frac{-20}{2 + 2 + 36 \times 0.39} = -1.1 \tag{2.7}$$

The total voltage amplification is therefore

$$A_{V\,\text{tot}} = V_2/E_1 = A_{V1}(\omega) A_{V2}(\omega) \doteq (-1.1)(-4.17) \doteq 4.62 \tag{2.8}$$

The fastest method here to determine the output resistance is to apply the Output Immittance Theorem. We could have done that easily by maintaining G_L intact in the denominators of Eqs. 2.5 and 2.7, in which case we would have obtained $4(2 + 28G_L) + 36 \times (1 + 4G_L)$, from which

$$R_{\text{out}} = 4.6 \text{ ohm} \tag{2.9}$$

(C) To represent the extended first stage as a series-form generator, we have only to apply the author's Equivalent Generator Theorem,[1] from which

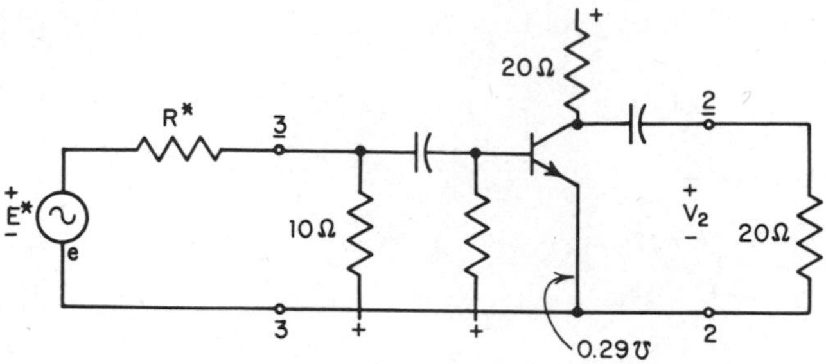

Fig. 2.2

$$E^* = \frac{-20E_1}{4 + 36 \times 0} = -5E_1 \qquad R^* = 36/4 = 9\Omega \qquad (2.10)$$

The amplifier network now takes the form shown in Fig. 2.2. Further extending the series-form generator to include the 10-ohm load resistance, we write

$$E^{**} = \frac{10}{10+9} E^* \doteq -2.63E_1 \qquad R^{**} = R^* /\!\!/ 10 \doteq 4.74\,\Omega \qquad (2.11)$$

We might just as well extend the series-form generator to include all the loading encountered, which is 0.39 mho, or 2.57 ohm, obtaining

$$E^{***} = \frac{2.57}{2.57+9}(-5E_1) = -1.1E_1 \qquad (2.12)$$

This is precisely the result we obtained in Eq. 2.7, as it must be. By multiplying as before with A_{V_2} we obtain the same value for the total voltage amplification as in Eq. 2.8: $A_{V\,\text{tot}} = E^{***}A_{V_2}/E_1$.

(D) The method in part C only represents a variation in the calculation methods. Most definitely, it is not any cure-all method. However, it is important to know many different calculation methods. The most suitable will depend on the case at hand.

Conclusions to this solution

It is a forgone conclusion that we could have changed the given matrices to *a* matrices and obtained the total voltage amplification

[1]Stockman, H. E., "A New Tool for Easier Network Synthesis," *Electronic Design*, vol. 13, pp. 20-21, Feb. 1965, continued in *Electronic Design*, vol. 13, pp. 26-30, April 1965.

by means of matrix multiplication. Depending upon the individual's familiarity with matrix tables, this method may be the quickest one. Due to the simplicity of this problem, the matrix method, the method in part B and the method in part C are just about equally fast. If the problem had been more intricate, one of the methods might easily have proved to be twice as fast as any of the remaining ones.

PROBLEM 3

Two CB-connected "model" transistors are cascaded as shown in Fig. 3.1, not for the purpose of providing an amplifier but for a special purpose. A high quality audio transformer is added in the output with a very high impedance termination (See Fig. 3.1). The components are changed around to provide a different amplifier, and essentially the transformer and the 1-ohm coupling resistor are interchanged, with the proper changes in the biasing arrangement (which is supposed not to interfere with the mid-frequency operation of the transistors). As the transformer is shifted in position, it is turned around so that the small winding now becomes the primary winding. Answer the following questions in terms of the turns ratio, n, and then follow up with numerical answers, using the value, $n = 2$. Use matrix methods.

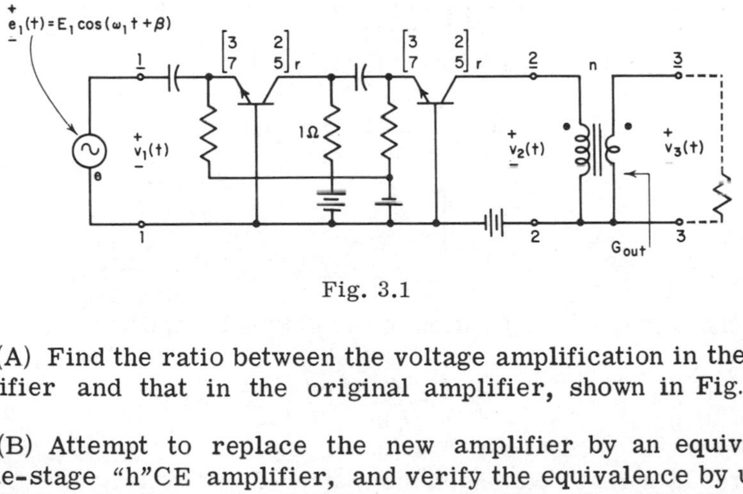

Fig. 3.1

(A) Find the ratio between the voltage amplification in the new amplifier and that in the original amplifier, shown in Fig. 3.1.

(B) Attempt to replace the new amplifier by an equivalent single-stage "h"CE amplifier, and verify the equivalence by using the single stage to calculate the over-all voltage amplification and the output conductance.

(C1) Is this single-stage amplifier realizable or not? (C2) If not, is there any change in the new amplifier that would make realizability possible?

Solution

(A) We begin by analyzing the original amplifier, changing the second stage r matrix to a g matrix, lumping the 1-ohm resistor into the first leg of the PI equivalent, and then changing the resulting g matrix into an a matrix. The first-stage r matrix is directly changed to an a matrix. Accordingly,

$$\begin{vmatrix} 6 & -2 \\ -7 & 3 \end{vmatrix}_{g_2} \rightarrow \begin{vmatrix} 3/7 & 1/7 \\ 4/7 & 6/7 \end{vmatrix}_{a_2} \tag{3.1}$$

$$\begin{vmatrix} 3/7 & 1/7 \\ 1/7 & 5/7 \end{vmatrix}_{a_1} \tag{3.2}$$

By applying the a parameter definitions to the transformer, we obtain its a matrix $|a_3|$, whereupon we proceed with the matrix multiplication as follows:

$$\begin{vmatrix} A_{11} & A_{12} \\ A_{21} & A_{22} \end{vmatrix} = \begin{vmatrix} 3/7 & 1/7 \\ 1/7 & 5/7 \end{vmatrix} \begin{vmatrix} 3/7 & 1/7 \\ 4/7 & 6/7 \end{vmatrix} \begin{vmatrix} n & 0 \\ 0 & 1/n \end{vmatrix}$$

$$= \begin{vmatrix} (9/49 + 4/49)n & (3/49 + 6/49)1/n \\ (3/49 + 20/49)n & (1/49 + 30/49)1/n \end{vmatrix}$$

$$= \begin{vmatrix} 13n/49 & - \\ - & - \end{vmatrix} \tag{3.3}$$

The total voltage amplification of the original amplifier is

$$A_V(\omega)_{\text{orig}} = 1/A_{11} = \frac{49}{13n} = \frac{49}{26}\bigg|_{n=2} \doteq 1.9\bigg|_{n=2} \tag{3.4}$$

This result can be obtained somewhat quicker if we leave the transformer out of the matrix calculation, obtaining 49/13 for the amplifying stages. Reducing the voltage n times in the transformer, we then obtain $49/13n$.

The new amplifier shown in Fig. 3.2 has the same a matrix

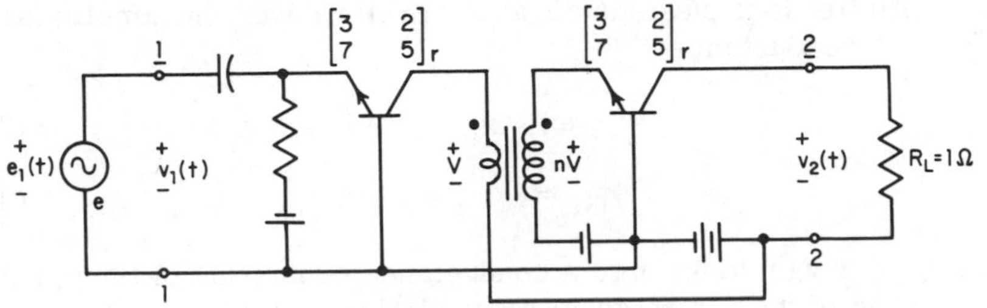

Fig. 3.2

for the first stage, and the same transformer matrix, except that $1/n$ now takes the place of n. The second amplifier has the same matrix as the first one, provided we keep the load resistance outside. The matrix chain now becomes

$$\begin{vmatrix} A_{11} & A_{12} \\ A_{21} & A_{22} \end{vmatrix} = \begin{vmatrix} 3/7 & 1/7 \\ 1/7 & 5/7 \end{vmatrix} \begin{vmatrix} 1/n & 0 \\ 0 & 1/n \end{vmatrix} \begin{vmatrix} 3/7 & 1/7 \\ 1/7 & 5/7 \end{vmatrix}$$

$$= \begin{vmatrix} \dfrac{9+n^2}{49n} & \dfrac{3+5n^2}{49n} \\ \dfrac{3+5n^2}{49n} & \dfrac{1+25n^2}{49n} \end{vmatrix} \tag{3.5}$$

The total voltage amplification of the new amplifier is therefore

$$A_V(\omega)_{\text{new}} = \frac{1}{A_{11} + A_{12}G_L} = \frac{49n}{6(2+n^2)} = \frac{49}{18}\bigg|_{n=2} \doteq 2.72 \bigg|_{n=2} \tag{3.6}$$

The ratio between the two amplifications becomes

$$\frac{A_V(\omega)_{\text{new}}}{A_V(\omega)_{\text{orig}}} = \frac{13n^2}{6(2+n^2)} = \frac{13}{9}\bigg|_{n=2} \doteq 1.44 \bigg|_{n=2} \tag{3.7}$$

Real transistors would give a much different result and would be likely to employ voltage step-down between the two transistors. (Note that dots on transformer windings indicate that currents directed in at the dots produce magnetic fields in the same direction, maintaining the voltage polarity.)

We might like to check the above results with a nonmatrix solution, using $n = 2$ from the beginning. The second stage looks into infinite load resistance and therefore has the amplification and input conductance

$$A_{V2}(\omega) = r_{21}/r_{11} = 7/3 \tag{3.8}$$

$$G_{\text{in}2} = 1/r_{11} = 1/3\,\Omega \tag{3.9}$$

The first stage looks into a conductance consisting of the parallel connection of the 1-mho coupling conductance and $G_{\text{in}2}$. Accordingly

$$A_{V1}(\omega) = r_{21}/(r_{11} + \Delta_r G_L) = 7/(3 + 4/3) = 21/13 \tag{3.10}$$

The total voltage amplification in both stages is thus $A_{V1}(\omega)A_{V2}(\omega) = (7/3)\ (21/13) = 147/39$. With the transformer the value is 147/78, or approximately 1.9, which agrees with the result obtained in Eq. 3.4.

In the new amplifier in Fig. 3.2, the amplification and input conductance of the second stage are

$$A_{V2}(\omega) = r_{21}/(r_{11} + \Delta_r G_L) = 7/4 \tag{3.11}$$

$$G_{\text{in}2} = \frac{1 + r_{22}G_L}{r_{11} + \Delta_r G_L} = \frac{3}{2} \tag{3.12}$$

On the primary side of the transformer, the conductance is increased to $n^2 G_{\text{in}2} = 4(3/2) = 6$ mho. The amplification in the first stage is therefore

$$A_{V1}(\omega) = r_{21}/(r_{11} + \Delta_r G_L) = 7/(3 + 6) = 7/9 \tag{3.13}$$

and the total amplification becomes $A_{V1}(\omega) n A_{V2}(\omega) = 49/18 \doteq 2.72$, which agrees with the result in Eq. 3.6. The value of the ratio is therefore the one given by Eq. 3.7, so that full agreement between the two calculation methods exists.

(B) The desired single-stage amplifier is described by the *a* matrix in Eq. 3.5, and the single-stage voltage amplification is therefore given by Eq. 3.6. The output conductance of the single stage is, in accordance with the Denominator Output Immittance Theorem,

$$G_{\text{out}} = \underline{A}_{11}/\underline{A}_{12} = \frac{9 + n^2}{3 + 5n^2} = \frac{13}{23}\ \mho \Big|_{n=2} \tag{3.14}$$

To carry through the same calculation without matrices, we begin by determining the output resistance of the first stage, which is $R_{\text{out}\,1} = \Delta_r/r_{11} = 1/3$ ohm. On the right side of the transformer, this becomes n^2 times greater, or $(2^2)\,(1/3) = 4/3$ ohm. Adding this to $r_{11} = 3$ ohm, we obtain 13/3 ohm, so that the output conductance of the total amplifier is

$$G_{\text{out}} = \underline{r}_{11}/\underline{\Delta}_r = \frac{13}{23}\mho \doteq .566\,\mho \tag{3.15}$$

which agrees with the result in Eq. 3.14.

(C1) With the transformer reversed to give the polarity indicated in Fig. 3.2, the total amplifier has zero phase shift, and it is logical for us to interpret the single-stage equivalent as having a CB-connected transistor. If we were to attempt to use a CE-connected transistor, it would become fictitious and would not be realizable. This is true whether we use h parameters or not. Nevertheless, it can be done if we postulate that the new single-stage amplifier must have the same amplification, the same input conductance, and the same output conductance as the single-stage amplifier described by the a matrix in Eq. 3.5. The transistor called for will, however, be fictitious.

Rather than look for a CE-connected transistor, let us calculate one employing the more realistic CB-connection that we started out with in the two individual stages. Using h parameters, we obtain from Eq. 3.5

$$\begin{vmatrix} h_{11} & h_{12} \\ h_{21} & h_{22} \end{vmatrix} = \begin{vmatrix} \dfrac{3+5n^2}{1+25n^2} & \dfrac{196n}{49(1+25n^2)} \\ \dfrac{-49n}{1+25n^2} & \dfrac{3+5n^2}{1+25n^2} \end{vmatrix} \doteq \begin{vmatrix} 0.228 & 0.0793 \\ -0.970 & 0.228 \end{vmatrix} \tag{3.16}$$

Inserting these values in the formulas for voltage amplification and output conductance, we obtain

$$A_V(\omega) = \frac{-h_{21}}{\Delta_h + h_{11}G_2} \doteq \frac{0.97}{0.129 + 0.228} \doteq 2.72 \tag{3.17}$$

$$G_{\text{out}} = \frac{\Delta_h}{h_{11}} \doteq \frac{0.129}{0.228} = 0.566 \tag{3.18}$$

Thus full agreement exists with the results that were obtained in Eqs. 3.6, 3.14, and 3.15.

(C2) The realization has already been discussed. If the transformer in Fig. 3.2 has the connections to one winding reversed so as to introduce a 180° phase shift, the total amplification will have a 180° phase shift, and now a CE-connected single-stage equivalent would fit in, whereas a CB-connected equivalent would use a fictitious transistor and thus not be realizable. So far, numerical values have been disregarded and limited to "model" transistors, we can not say whether or not a single transistor can be found that will do the job. First of all, such a transistor would have to give the right sign. With real transistors, an answer may be formulated, and if the two transistors in Fig. 3.2 are of modern type, it is most unlikely that they can be replaced by any single transistor.

Conclusions to this solution

Many of the conclusions have already been given. Again we had an example of the advantage of having at our disposal two entirely different methods of calculation, one serving as a check on the other. Using the matrix method, we noticed how an entirely different amplifier performance was obtained by changing the order of the matrix multiplication. Certain facts were brought out in determining a single transistor equivalent stage. First, the sign of amplification must be right, and second, the numerical values of the parameters must be reasonable. Even if an (rCB) transistor would fit as far as the sign goes, it must not provide improper ratios between the parameter values. We can, of course, give up the requirement on realizability and still come up with a mathematical model of a single transistor equivalent that gives correct answers, even if it is fictitious.

PROBLEM 4

A two-stage cascaded amplifier is known from the block diagram shown in Fig. 4.1.

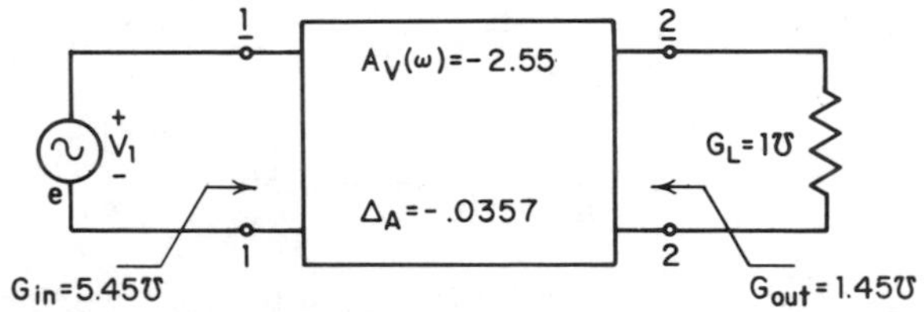

Fig. 4.1

(A) From the given information, determine the a matrix for the total amplifier.

(B) If the second stage is known by the matrix

$$|r|_{CB} = \begin{vmatrix} 3 & 2 \\ 7 & 5 \end{vmatrix}$$

what is the h matrix for the first stage?

Solution

(A) Writing the formulas for the given quantities in terms of A parameters, we obtain

$$G_{in} = \frac{A_{21} + A_{22}G_L}{A_{11} + A_{12}G_L} = 5.45 \tag{4.1}$$

$$G_{out} = \frac{A_{11}}{A_{12}} = 1.45 \tag{4.2}$$

$$A_V(\omega) = \frac{1}{A_{11} + A_{12}G_L} = -2.55 \tag{4.3}$$

From this and Δ_A we obtain the matrix

$$|A| = \begin{vmatrix} -0.232 & -0.160 \\ -1.36 & -0.79 \end{vmatrix} \tag{4.4}$$

(B) Using the tables, we change the given r into an a matrix,

$$\begin{vmatrix} 3 & 2 \\ 7 & 5 \end{vmatrix} \rightarrow \begin{vmatrix} 3/7 & 1/7 \\ 1/7 & 5/7 \end{vmatrix} = \begin{vmatrix} 0.428 & 0.143 \\ 0.143 & 0.715 \end{vmatrix} \tag{4.5}$$

Matrix multiplication now yields

$$\begin{vmatrix} a_{11} & a_{12} \\ a_{21} & a_{22} \end{vmatrix} \begin{vmatrix} 0.428 & 0.143 \\ 0.143 & 0.715 \end{vmatrix} = \begin{vmatrix} -0.232 & -0.160 \\ -1.36 & -0.79 \end{vmatrix} \tag{4.6}$$

from which

$$a_{11} \times 0.428 + a_{12} \times 0.143 = -0.232, \quad a_{11} \times 0.143 + a_{12} \times 0.715 = -0.160$$
$$a_{21} \times 0.428 + a_{22} \times 0.143 = -1.36, \quad a_{21} \times 0.143 + a_{22} \times 0.715 = -0.79 \tag{4.7}$$

Solving for a_{11}, a_{12}, a_{21}, and a_{22}, we obtain

$$|a| = \begin{vmatrix} -0.5 & -0.125 \\ -3 & -0.5 \end{vmatrix} \quad \Delta_a = -0.125 \tag{4.8}$$

The desired h matrix is therefore

$$|h| = \begin{vmatrix} 0.25 & 0.25 \\ 2 & 6 \end{vmatrix} \tag{4.9}$$

Conclusions to this solution

This is a conventional problem on cascading, except that we have reversed the procedure; what is generally appearing in the answer is here given. After having obtained the matrix for the total network, we are requested to find the matrix for the first stage. The initial slide-rule calculations must therefore be rather accurate, or the subsequent matrix manipulations may make the final answers ambiguous. The four equations and four unknowns in Eq. 4.7 are easily handled by determinants if Cramer's Rule is applied.

PROBLEM 5

The transistor audio amplifier shown in Fig. 5.1 utilizes a "model" transistor and feeds the load R_L via an attenuator, consisting of three cascaded units.

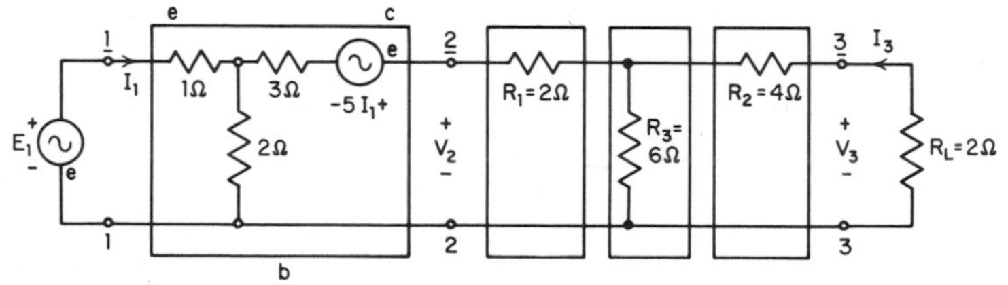

Fig. 5.1

(A) Find the a matrix for each unit in the attenuator, and then determine the TEE equivalent for the entire attenuator by means of matrix multiplication.

(B) Using the matrix-multiplication method, find the voltage- and current-transfer functions for the total network.

(C) Lump R_1 into the transistor amplifier, change the PI $R_3R_2R_L$ into a TEE and lump its input arm into the transistor amplifier. Then derive an expression for the voltage-transfer function of the total amplifier, (1) not using matrix methods, and (2) using matrix methods.

Solution

(A) Obtaining the a matrices for the cascaded units from Table 6, Appendix C, we carry out the following matrix multiplication

$$\begin{vmatrix} a_{11} & a_{12} \\ a_{21} & a_{22} \end{vmatrix} = \begin{vmatrix} 1 & 2 \\ 0 & 1 \end{vmatrix} \begin{vmatrix} 1 & 0 \\ 1/6 & 1 \end{vmatrix} \begin{vmatrix} 1 & 4 \\ 0 & 1 \end{vmatrix} = \begin{vmatrix} 4/3 & 22/3 \\ 1/6 & 5/3 \end{vmatrix} \tag{5.1}$$

To verify the correctness of the result, we switch to an r matrix, from which the correct values for R_1, R_2, and R_3 are obtained:

$$\begin{vmatrix} 4/3 & 22/3 \\ 1/6 & 5/3 \end{vmatrix}_a \rightarrow \begin{vmatrix} 8 & 6 \\ 6 & 10 \end{vmatrix}_r \qquad \begin{aligned} R_1 &= 8 - 6 = 2\Omega \\ R_2 &= 10 - 6 = 4\Omega \\ R_3 &= 6\Omega \end{aligned} \tag{5.2}$$

(B) We read off the r matrix for the amplifier and change it into an a matrix, whereupon we obtain the matrix for the total network by matrix multiplication

$$\begin{vmatrix} 3 & 2 \\ 7 & 5 \end{vmatrix}_r \rightarrow \begin{vmatrix} 3/7 & 1/7 \\ 1/7 & 5/7 \end{vmatrix}_a \tag{5.3}$$

$$\begin{vmatrix} 3/7 & 1/7 \\ 1/7 & 5/7 \end{vmatrix} \begin{vmatrix} 4/3 & 22/3 \\ 1/6 & 5/3 \end{vmatrix} = \begin{vmatrix} 25/42 & 71/21 \\ 13/42 & 47/21 \end{vmatrix} = \begin{vmatrix} A_{11} & A_{12} \\ A_{21} & A_{22} \end{vmatrix} \tag{5.4}$$

The current- and voltage-transfer functions are from conventional formulas.

$$A_I(\omega) = \frac{I_3}{I_1} = \frac{-1}{A_{22} + A_{21}R_L} = \frac{-1}{47/21 + (13/42)2} = -0.35$$

$$A_V(\omega) = \frac{V_3}{E_1} = \frac{1}{A_{11} + A_{12}G_L} = 0.44 \qquad (5.5)$$

(C1) To change the PI into a TEE we use the direct procedure described in Appendix A, Part 9.

$$Z = \frac{Z_{left}\, Z_{right}}{Z_{all}}$$

$$Z_{all} = 6 + 4 + 2 = 12\,\Omega$$

$$Z_{left\ arm} = \frac{6 \times 4}{12} = 2\,\Omega$$

$$Z_{right\ arm} = \frac{4 \times 2}{12} = \frac{2}{3}\,\Omega$$

$$Z_{mid\text{-}arm} = \frac{6 \times 2}{12} = 1\,\Omega \qquad (5.6)$$

First, we lump $R_1 = 2$ ohm into the transistor and then inject 2 ohm, leaving the mid-arm 1 ohm as the only network element outside the transistor (since the right arm of the TEE does not carry any current). Accordingly,

$$A_V(\omega) = r_{21}/(r_{11} + \Delta_r G_L) = 7/(3 + 13 \times 1) = 0.44 \qquad (5.7)$$

which agrees with the result in Eq. 5.5.

(C2) We only need to consider one matrix, that of the transistor. Changing to a parameters would be required only if we produce a second matrix for the 1-ohm resistor left outside the transistor. Although this is a lengthy solution, we shall follow it up, using a table formula identical with that describing the second-unit section in the given problem. Accordingly,

$$\begin{vmatrix} 3 & 2 \\ 7 & 9 \end{vmatrix}_r \rightarrow \begin{vmatrix} 3/7 & 13/7 \\ 1/7 & 9/7 \end{vmatrix}_a$$

$$\begin{vmatrix} 3/7 & 13/7 \\ 1/7 & 9/7 \end{vmatrix} \begin{vmatrix} 1 & 0 \\ 1 & 1 \end{vmatrix} = \begin{vmatrix} 16/7 & - \\ - & - \end{vmatrix}$$

$$A_V(\omega) = \frac{1}{16/7} = 0.438 \qquad (5.8)$$

This result agrees with those in Eq. 5.5 and Eq. 5.7. Note that the load for the two stages now is a zero conductance.

Conclusions to this solution

We are here again encountering the important technique of sectionalizing networks into unit sections of known a matrices. We are not supposed to derive these a matrices each time we need them but rather to pick them from an available table. Each unit section is not necessarily limited to just one network element; in fact, the unit sections can be just as big as the available table allows. Thus, a complete TEE or a complete PI is a very useful unit section. For arithmetical rather than algebraic quantities, this method of determining transfer functions may very well prove to be the fastest one. As is indicated by the solution to part C, even the sectionalizing method may be improved by getting rid of certain network elements, lumping them into existing network elements.

PROBLEM 6

A transistor amplifier is preceded by a coupling network and followed by another coupling network (see Fig. 6.1). The total network has been sectionalized in two different fashions, one alternative using the sections, S_1 to S_5, the other the sections S_a to S_d. In the latter case a cut is taken through the amplifier; the reader decides where.

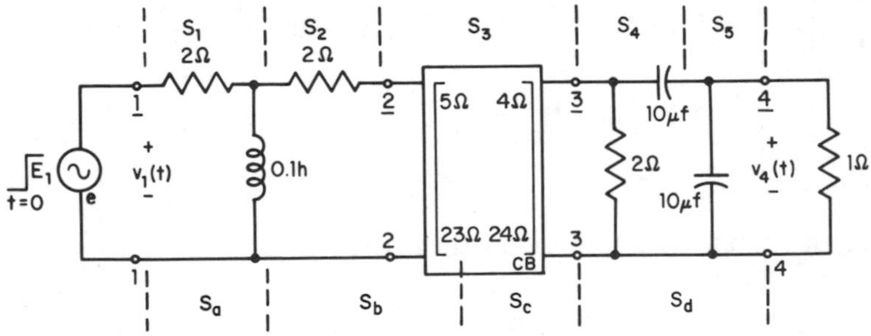

Fig. 6.1

(A) Derive an expression for the transform output voltage $\overline{V}_4$ when the first alternative is used.

(B) Determine $\overline{V}_4$ in accordance with the second alternative and compare results.

(C) Give some sound viewpoints on the procedure of sectionalizing cascaded transistor amplifiers in practical engineering.

Solution

(A) Reading off the section matrices from a table, we obtain

$$\begin{vmatrix} A_{11} & A_{12} \\ A_{21} & A_{22} \end{vmatrix} = \begin{vmatrix} (s+20)/s & 2 \\ 10/s & 1 \end{vmatrix}_1 \begin{vmatrix} 1 & 2 \\ 0 & 1 \end{vmatrix}_2 \begin{vmatrix} 5/23 & 28/23 \\ 1/23 & 24/23 \end{vmatrix}_3$$

$$\times \begin{vmatrix} 1 & 10^5/s \\ 1/2 & (s2+10^5)/s2 \end{vmatrix}_4 \begin{vmatrix} 1 & 0 \\ s10^{-5} & 1 \end{vmatrix}_5$$

$$\doteq \begin{vmatrix} (s+20)/s & 4(s+10)/s \\ 10/s & (s+20)/s \end{vmatrix}_{1,2} \begin{vmatrix} 0.217 & 1.22 \\ 0.044 & 1.04 \end{vmatrix}_3$$

$$\times \begin{vmatrix} 2 & 10^5/s \\ (s10^{-5}+1) & (s2+10^5)/s2 \end{vmatrix}_{4,5}$$

$$\doteq \begin{vmatrix} (0.39+6.1/s) & (5.4+66/s) \\ - & - \end{vmatrix}_{1,2,3} \begin{vmatrix} - & - \\ - & - \end{vmatrix}_{4,5}$$

$$\doteq \begin{vmatrix} s(5.4\times 10^{-5}) & 5.4+\frac{1}{s}(3.1\times 10^5) \\ +6.2+\frac{1}{s}(78.2) & +\frac{1}{s^2}(39\times 10^5) \\ \_\_\_\_ & \_\_\_\_ \end{vmatrix} \tag{6.1}$$

The output transform voltage is therefore

$$\overline{V}_4 = \overline{V}_1 \frac{1}{A_{11} + A_{12}G_L}$$

$$\overline{V}_4 = \overline{V}_1 \frac{s^2}{s^3(5.4 \cdot 10^{-5}) + s^2(11.6) + s(3.1 \cdot 10^5) + 39 \cdot 10^5}$$

$$= E_1 \frac{s(18,500)}{s^3 + s^2(2.15 \cdot 10^{10}) + s(0.57 \cdot 10^{10}) + (7.2 \cdot 10^{10})} \qquad (6.2)$$

Rough slide-rule calculations were used in obtaining this answer.

(B) Since the matrix S_d has already been determined, we only need to obtain the matrix corresponding to the product of the matrices for S_1, S_2, and S_3. Here S_a is the same as S_1. Accordingly, with the arbitrary value of 0.5 ohm taken out of the transistor input arm and added to the 2-ohm resistance in S_2, we obtain,

$$\begin{vmatrix} (s+20)/s & 2 \\ 10/s & 1 \end{vmatrix}_1 \begin{vmatrix} 1 & 2.5 \\ 0 & 1 \end{vmatrix}_b \begin{vmatrix} 4.5/23 & 16/23 \\ 1/23 & 24/23 \end{vmatrix}_c$$

$$\doteq \begin{vmatrix} (s+20)/s & (4.5s+50)/s \\ — & — \end{vmatrix}_{1,b} \begin{vmatrix} 0.196 & 0.696 \\ 0.044 & 1.04 \end{vmatrix}_c$$

$$\doteq \begin{vmatrix} 0.39+6.1/s & 5.38+65.9/s \\ — & — \end{vmatrix}_{1,b,c} \qquad (6.3)$$

It is seen that, within rough slide-rule accuracy, this matrix is the same as the one obtained on the fifth line in Eq. 6.1.

(C) Usually, we presume the existence of a table of a matrices, and we make each section as big as the table allows (see Table 6, Appendix C). Any simple combination of network elements that can be made prior to the sectionalizing should be carried out. Generally, there is no point in placing a cut inside an amplifier, but occasionally there may be special reasons for doing this, for example, to make a certain amplifier identical with another already calculated amplifier or to absorb a negative resistance or conductance.

Conclusions to this solution

It is important that numerical calculation be kept down to a precise, concise form. To save time, one should avoid calculating any matrix elements that are not going to be used in the formulation of the final answer. For cuts inside ampifiers see part C.

PROBLEM 7

Calculate the instantaneous output voltage due to an applied step voltage:

(A) For the transistor amplifier shown in Fig. 7.1a

(B) For the same transistor amplifier rearranged to form two twoports in parallel, using matrix techniques (see Fig. 7.1b)

(C) For the same transistor amplifier rearranged to form three cascaded twoports, using matrix techniques (see Fig. 7.1C)

Solution

(A) Since we are dealing with transform quantities only, we shall omit the bars and thus write for example, y_{11} instead of $\overline{y}_{11}$ and V_1 instead of $\overline{V}_1$. The twoport long-hand equation system and the network matrix are

$$\left.\begin{aligned} I_1 &= y_{11}V_1 + y_{12}V_2 \qquad (7.1)\\ I_2 &= y_{21}V_1 + y_{22}V_2 \qquad (7.2)\end{aligned}\right\}$$

$$|y| = \begin{vmatrix} y_{11} & y_{12} \\ y_{21} & y_{22} \end{vmatrix} \qquad (7.3)$$

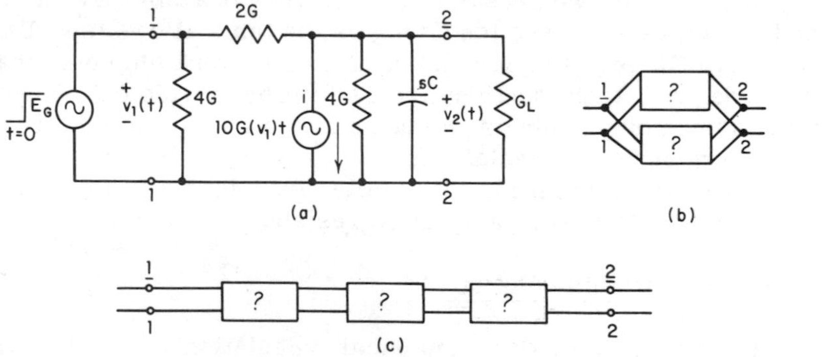

Fig. 7.1

The y parameters are defined from the relationships

$$
\begin{aligned}
4G &= y_{11} + y_{12} & y_{11} &= 6G \\
2G &= -y_{12} & y_{12} &= -2G \\
10G &= y_m = y_{21} - y_{12} & y_{21} &= 8G \\
sC + 4G &= y_{22} + y_{12} & y_{22} &= sC + 6G
\end{aligned}
\tag{7.4}
$$

The twoport voltage amplification (from Table 1, Appendix B) is

$$A = \frac{V_2}{V_1} = \frac{-y_{21}}{y_{22} + G_L} = \frac{-8G}{sC + 6G + G_L} = \frac{-8G}{C} \times \frac{1}{s + (6G + G_L)/C} \tag{7.5}$$

The output voltage transform is therefore, with $V_1 = E_G/s$,

$$V_2 = \frac{-8G}{C} \times \frac{1}{s[s + (6G + G_L)/C]} \tag{7.6}$$

for which the conventional transform-pair table gives

$$v_2(t) = \frac{8G}{6G + G_L}\left(e^{-\frac{6G+G_L}{C}\, t} - 1\right) \tag{7.7}$$

This is the desired expression for the instantaneous output voltage. It is seen that this will change exponentially to approach a final negative value of $8G/(6G + G_L)$.

(B) We can split up the transistor network any way we wish. Arbitrarily, we shall choose to split it up as is shown in Fig. 7.2. Formulating the respective matrices by applying the conventional definitions of y parameters, we obtain

$$\begin{vmatrix} 2G & -2G \\ 8G & 2G \end{vmatrix}_{\text{Top}} + \begin{vmatrix} 4G & 0 \\ 0 & (sC+4G) \end{vmatrix}_{\text{Bottom}} = \begin{vmatrix} 6G & -2G \\ 8G & (sC+6G) \end{vmatrix}_{\text{Total}} \tag{7.8}$$

Here we have written the matrices so as to form a sum, and we have carried out the implied addition. We find that the matrix elements in the sum matrix are the same as those in Eq. 7.4.

(C) We split up the transistor network arbitrarily as is shown in Fig. 7.3. Here we readily obtain the first and the second a matrix

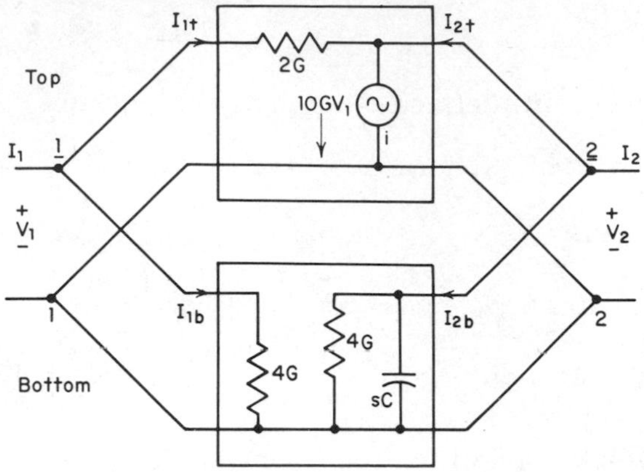

Fig. 7.2

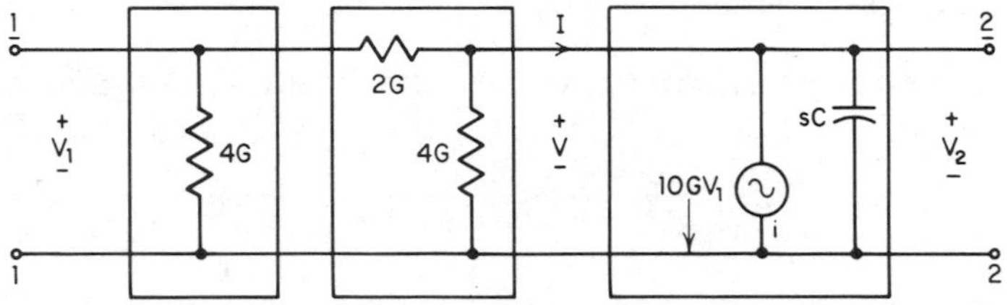

Fig. 7.3

from Table 6 in Appendix C, writing the multiplication:

$$\begin{vmatrix} 1 & 0 \\ 4G & 1 \end{vmatrix} \begin{vmatrix} 3 & 1/28 \\ 4G & 1 \end{vmatrix} = \begin{vmatrix} 3 & 1/28 \\ 16G & 3 \end{vmatrix} \tag{7.9}$$

To obtain the matrix for the third section, we write the following:

$$a_{11} = \frac{V}{V_2}\bigg|_{I_2=0} = 1 \qquad a_{12} = \frac{V}{-I_2}\bigg|_{V_2=0} = 0$$

$$a_{21} = \frac{I}{V_2}\bigg|_{I_2=0} = -\frac{sC}{4} - \frac{15G}{2} \qquad a_{22} = \frac{I}{-I_2}\bigg|_{V_2=0} = -\frac{1}{4} \tag{7.10}$$

Here we made use of the ratio V_2/V_1 derived in Eq. 7.5. Carrying out the final matrix multiplication, we obtain

$$\begin{vmatrix} 3 & 1/28 \\ 16G & 3 \end{vmatrix} \begin{vmatrix} 1 & 0 \\ -(sC/4) - (15G/2) & -\frac{1}{4} \end{vmatrix}$$

$$= \begin{vmatrix} -\frac{sC}{8G} - \frac{3}{4} & -\frac{1}{8G} \\ -\frac{sC3}{4} - \frac{13G}{2} & -\frac{3}{4} \end{vmatrix}_a = |A| \qquad (7.11)$$

The only thing remaining now is to convert from a to y parameters by means of the matrix table, and accordingly we obtain, for $\Delta_A = -1/4$,

$$\begin{vmatrix} \frac{A_{22}}{A_{12}} & \frac{-\Delta_A}{A_{12}} \\ \frac{-1}{A_{12}} & \frac{A_{11}}{A_{12}} \end{vmatrix}_a \rightarrow \begin{vmatrix} 6G & -2G \\ 8G & (sC+6G) \end{vmatrix}_y \qquad (7.12)$$

A comparison with the matrix elements in Eq. 7.8 shows that full agreement exists.

Conclusions to this solution

Both in network analysis and synthesis, the sectionalizing of an amplifier and rearrangement in blocks provides a most useful technique. The blocks may be cascaded or paralleled, or some blocks may be cascaded and other blocks paralleled. More intricate port connections may appear, for example a "paralleled" amplifier with series connection on the input side and shunt connection on the output side. As this solution tends to show, there are an infinite number of ways in which an existing amplifier may be broken up without any change in the system characteristics. The technique has many useful applications. As an example, the bottom twoport in an arrangement such as the one shown in Fig. 7.2 may represent the feedback path, provided for the top twoport. As another example, the bottom twoport may contribute the neutralization network which guarantees that the amplifier represented by the top network remains stable.

In providing arbitrary cascading, we often find that a function source has become far separated from its controlling variable. This solution shows how the difficulty may be handled by the introduction of the proper transfer function to eliminate the controlling variable, and accordingly, we obtain an algebraic expression and a matrix which is free from variables. Thus one can freely sectionalize in spite of the presence of function sources. We can go still further and split a function source between two sections, putting x per cent of it in one section and the missing $(100-x)$ per cent in an adjacent section, or with some caution, in any section for that matter. This technique makes it possible for us to manipulate a certain network, so that, within reason, it looks like another, specified network. The universal tool that makes all this possible is the tool of matrix algebra.

PROBLEM 8

Given is the CE-connected transistor audio amplifier shown in Fig. 8.1 in which the biasing arrangement is considered not to affect the transistor parameters. These are: $r_b' = 1{,}000$ ohm, $r_u' = 25$ ohm, $r_c' = 40{,}000$ ohm, and $\beta = 24$. Further, $G_G = 500$ ohm, $R_L = 10{,}000$ ohm, and $1/\omega C \doteq 0$. Using rough approximations, find:

(A) The current amplification

(B) The voltage amplification

(C) The input resistance

(D) The output resistance

(E) The value R_{Gm} for matching

(F) The value R_{Lm} for matching

(G) The values R_{Gmm} and R_{Lmm} for simultaneous matching with a discussion of the possibilities and usefulness of such matching.

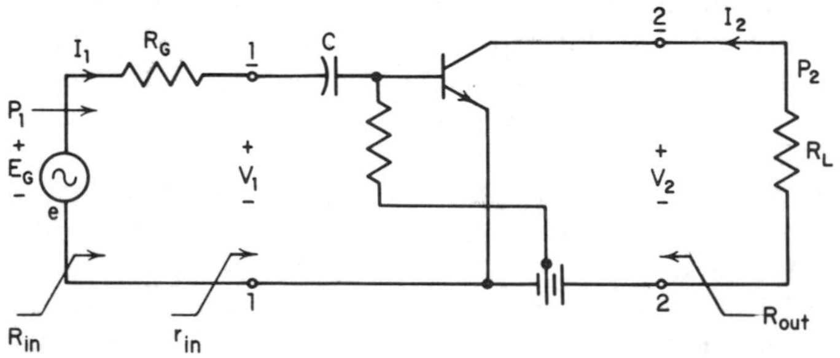

Fig. 8.1

(H) The output power

(I) The gain

Solution

(A) The current amplification is, with $r_{21}' \doteq r_m' = -\beta r_c' = -24 \times 40{,}000 = -96 \times 10^4$.

$$A_I(\omega) = \frac{I_2}{I_1} = \frac{-r_{21}'}{r_{22}' + R_L} \doteq \frac{-(-96 \times 10^4)}{4 \times 10^4 + 10^4} = 19.2 \qquad (8.1)$$

(B) We obtain

$$\Delta_r' = r_{11}'r_{22}' - r_{12}'r_{21}' \doteq r_b'r_c' - r_u'(-\beta r_c')$$

$$= 10^3 \times 4 \times 10^4 + 25 \times 96 \times 10^4 \doteq 6.4 \times 10^7 \qquad (8.2)$$

$$\Delta_{r1}' = (r_{11}' + R_G)r_{22}' - r_{12}'r_{21}' = \Delta_r' + R_G r_{22}'$$
$$= 6.4 \times 10^7 + 500 \times 40{,}000 = 8.4 \times 10^7 \qquad (8.3)$$

Thus

$$A_V(\omega) = \frac{V_2}{V_1} = \frac{r_{21}'}{r_{11}' + \Delta_r' G_L} \doteq \frac{-96 \times 10^4}{10^3 + 6.4 \times 10^7 \times 10^{-4}} = -130 \qquad (8.4)$$

$$A_E(\omega) = \frac{V_2}{E_G} = \frac{r_{21}'}{(r_{11}' + R_G) + \Delta_{r1}' G_L}$$

$$\doteq \frac{-96 \times 10^4}{(10^3 + 500) + 8.4 \times 10^7 \times 10^{-4}} = -97 \qquad (8.5)$$

(C) The input resistances are

$$r_{in} = \frac{r_{11}' + \Delta_r' G_L}{1 + r_{22}' G_L} \doteq \frac{10^3 + 6.4 \times 10^7 \times 10^{-4}}{1 + 4 \times 10^4 \times 10^{-4}} \doteq 1{,}480\,\Omega \qquad (8.6)$$

$$R_{in} = \frac{(r_{11}' + R_G) + \Delta_{r1}' G_L}{1 + r_{22}' G_L} \doteq \frac{1.5 \times 10^3 + 8.4 \times 10^7 \times 10^{-4}}{1 + 4 \times 10^4 \times 10^{-4}} = 1{,}980\,\Omega \qquad (8.7)$$

$$R_{in} = r_{in} + R_G = 1{,}480 + 500 = 1{,}980\,\Omega \qquad (8.8)$$

(D) Using the Output Immittance Theorem, we obtain directly from Eq. 8.4:

$$r_{\text{out}} = 6.4 \times 10^7/10^3 = 64{,}000\,\Omega \tag{8.9}$$

and from Eq. 8.5:

$$R_{\text{out}} = 8.4 \times 10^7/1.5 \times 10^3 = 56{,}000\,\Omega \tag{8.10}$$

(E) For matching, $R_{Gm} = r_{\text{in}} = 1{,}480$ ohm (8.11)

(F) For matching, $R_{Lm} = R_{\text{out}} = 56{,}000$ ohm (8.12)

(G) The following conditions must be fulfilled

$$R_{Gmm} = \frac{r_{11}' + \Delta_r' G_{Lmm}}{1 + r_{22}' G_{Lmm}} \qquad R_{Lmm} = \frac{\Delta_{r1}''}{r_{11}' + R_{Gmm}} \tag{8.13}$$

or

$$R_{Gmm} = \frac{10^3(1 + 6.4 \times 10^4 \times G_{Lmm})}{1 + 4 \times 10^4 G_{Lmm}} \quad R_{Lmm} = \frac{10^4(6400 + 4R_{Gmm})}{10^3 + R_{Gmm}} \tag{8.14}$$

from which

$$R_{Gmm} \doteq 1{,}300\,\Omega \qquad R_{Lmm} \doteq 50{,}000\,\Omega \tag{8.15}$$

(H) The output power is, with given values of R_G and R_L,

$$P_2 = \frac{V_{2\,\text{rms}}^2}{R_L} = \frac{A_E^2(\omega) E_{G\,\text{rms}}^2}{R_L} = \frac{|-97|^2 E_{G\,\text{rms}}^2}{10^4} = 0.94 E_{G\,\text{rms}}^2 \text{watt} \tag{8.16}$$

As an extension of part H, we may like to determine $P_{2\,\max}$ for the generator resistance R_{Gmm}, or rather the value of R_L, which we call $R_{L\,\text{opt}}$, that produces $P_{2\,\max}$. We write

$$P_2 = \frac{E_{G\,\text{rms}}^2}{R_L} A_E^2(\omega)$$

$$= \text{const.} \times \frac{G_L}{[(r_{11}' + R_{Gmm}) + \Delta_{r1}'' G_L]^2} = \text{const.} \times \frac{G_L}{(a + bG_L)^2}$$

$$u = \frac{a}{\sqrt{G_L}} + b\sqrt{G_L} \rightarrow \text{min.} \tag{8.17}$$

$$\frac{du}{dG_L} = \left(-\frac{1}{2}\right) a G_{L\,\text{opt}}^{-3/2} + \left(\frac{1}{2}\right) b\, G_{L\,\text{opt}}^{-\frac{1}{2}} = 0$$

$$R_{L\,\text{opt}} = \frac{b}{a} = \frac{\Delta_{r1}''}{r_{11}' + R_{Gmm}} = \frac{11.6 \times 10^7}{10^3 + 1,300} \doteq 50,400\Omega \tag{8.18}$$

Within slide-rule accuracy this result agrees quite well with that obtained in Eq. 8.15. For a discussion of simultaneous matching, see the following conclusions.

(I) The gain is

$$G = \frac{P_2}{P_1} = \frac{V_{2\,\text{rms}}^{\;2}}{R_L} \times \frac{R_{\text{in}}}{E_{G\,\text{rms}}^{\;2}} = \frac{R_{\text{in}}}{R_L} A_E^{\,2}(\omega) = \frac{1980}{10^4} \times |-97|^2 = 1,860 \tag{8.19}$$

Conclusions to this solution

We must note the significance of the matching conditions in this problem. When the immittance connected to one port is given, the input immittance at the other port has a fixed value. As one immittance varies, the other one will also vary. For any fixed value of R_G, such as 500 ohm, maximum output power is obtained for a specific value R_{Lm} of R_L. We could plot a curve, showing how the power reaches a maximum value, as R_G is varied, and the pair of values we finally settle for are R_{Gmm} and R_{Lmm}. To verify that we actually extract maximum power from the generator, we may calculate r_{in} for the load resistance R_{Lmm}, and we then obtain r_{in} = 1,300 ohm $= R_{Gmm}$. Simultaneous matching is not often secured in practical engineering.

PROBLEM 9

A CE-connected video transistor amplifier, known by its r parameters, is shown in Fig. 9.1 where the dotted-in capacitances

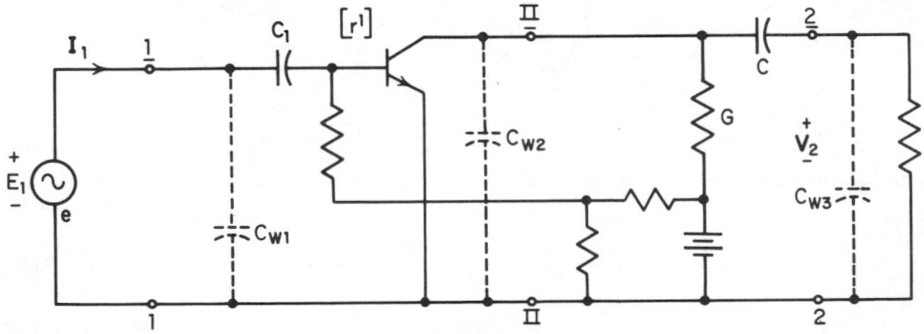

Fig. 9.1

represent wiring capacitance. Under the assumption that β remains the same throughout the frequency range, carry out the following assignments (C_1 is very large and may be disregarded):

(A) Draw a network equivalent that holds for all frequencies. (Note that the transistor has internal capacitances. At least we should acknowledge a collector capacitance C_c, shunting r_c' in the shunt-form generator representation of the output arm in the equivalent TEE.)

(B) Draw a simplified network equivalent for mid-frequency and calculate $A_{Vm}(\omega)$.

(C) Draw a simplified network equivalent for low frequency, and calculate $A_{V1}(\omega)$. Also determine the lower cutoff frequency, $\omega_1/2\pi$.

(D) Draw a network equivalent for high frequency, and calculate $A_{V2}(\omega)$. Also determine the upper cutoff frequency, $\omega_2/2\pi$.

Solution

(A) Since the amplifier is driven by a constant-voltage source, we disregard the capacitance C_{w1}. The desired equivalent network is shown in Fig. 9.2a.

(B) At mid-frequency all capacitances are neglected, so that the network equivalent becomes the one shown in Fig. 9.2b. The voltage amplification is

$$A_{Vm}(\omega) = \frac{V_2}{E_1} = \frac{r_{21}'}{r_{11}' + \Delta_r' G_2} \tag{9.1}$$

where

$$\Delta_r' = r_{11}'r_{22}' - r_{12}'r_{21}' \tag{9.2}$$

(C) The low-frequency network equivalent is shown in Fig. 9.2c. The load admittance at port II, $\underline{\text{II}}$ is, with $s = j\omega$,

$$\mathbf{Y} = \frac{GG_L + sC(G + G_L)}{G_L + sC} \tag{9.3}$$

The voltage amplification is

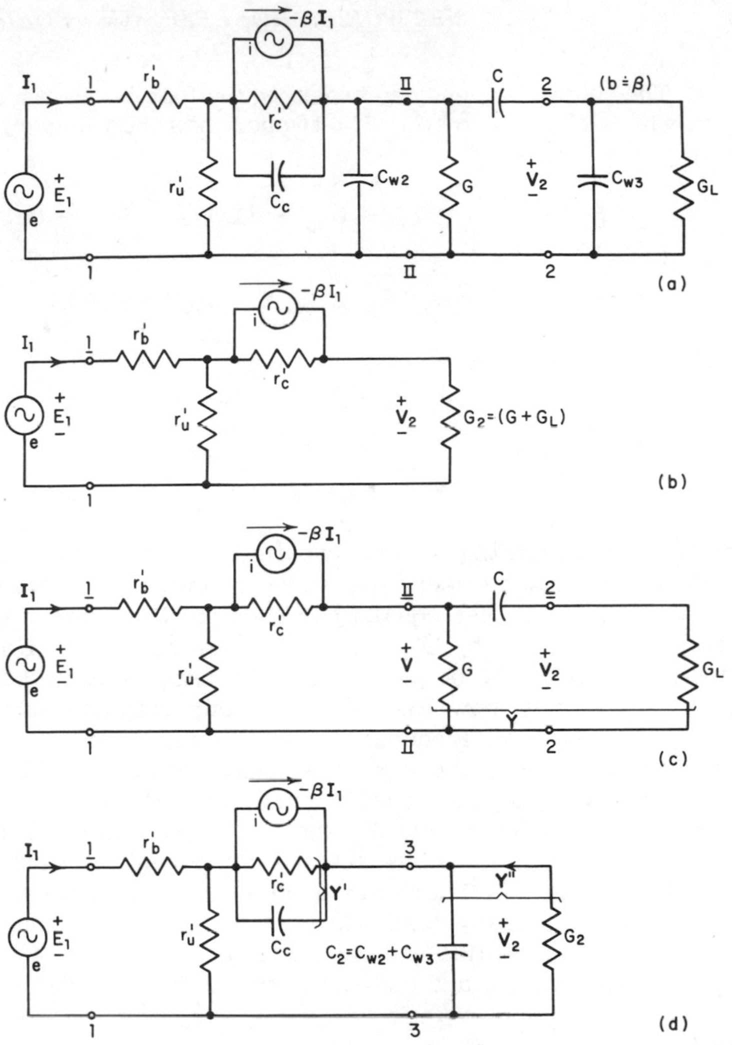

Fig. 9.2

$$\mathbf{A}_{V1}(\omega) = \frac{\mathbf{V}_2}{E_1} = \frac{r_{21}'}{r_{11}' + \Delta_r'\mathbf{Y}} \times \frac{sC}{G_L + sC} \tag{9.4}$$

which we write

$$\mathbf{A}_{V1}(\omega) = \omega C r_{21}' / \{ \omega C[r_{11}' + \Delta_r'(G + G_L)] - j(r_{11}' + \Delta_r' G)G_L \} \tag{9.5}$$

The lower cutoff angular velocity is obtained for equal real and j-parts, so that

$$\omega_1 = 2\pi f_1 = (r_{11}' + \Delta_r' G)G_L / C[r_{11}' + \Delta_r'(G + G_L)] \tag{9.6}$$

(D) The high-frequency network equivalent is shown in Fig. 9.2d, in which $\mathbf{Y}' = (g_c' + sC_c)$. The twoport has the following parameters

$$R_{11}' = r_{11}' \qquad R_{12}' = r_{12}' \qquad \mathbf{Z}_{21}' = (r_{12}' - \beta \mathbf{Z}') \qquad \mathbf{Z}_{22}' = (r_{12}' + \mathbf{Z}') \tag{9.7}$$

$$\mathbf{\Delta}_R' = r_{11}'r_{12}' - (r_{12}')^2 + \mathbf{Z}'(r_{11}' + \beta r_{12}') = A + jB \tag{9.8}$$

The voltage amplification is

$$\mathbf{A}_{V2}(\omega) = \mathbf{V}_2/E_1 = \mathbf{Z}_{21}'/(R_{11}' + \mathbf{\Delta}_R'\mathbf{Y}'') \tag{9.9}$$

for

$$\mathbf{Y}'' = (G_2 + sC_2) \tag{9.10}$$

Inserting proper quantities here, we find that the amplification is expressed as a ratio between two complex quantities. The magnitude of this expression is set equal to $1/\sqrt{2}$ times the amplification at mid-frequency, given by Eq. 9.1. A higher-order equation in ω now results which may be plotted for a better insight in the cutoff conditions. We may now like to modify our definition of what is meant by upper cutoff frequency. For one thing, in an amplifier with violent wiggles in the curve, we may not accept a 3-db upswing in the curve as constituting cutoff while we would consider a 3-db downswing as cutoff. Further, we may consider a 2-db downswing as cutoff, if we suspect that component tolerances may cause a 1-db variation. There are a number of viewpoints on this subject, treated in many textbooks. As an exercise, the reader may work out the resulting equation, assume a few sets of reasonable parameter values, and plot the curves for comparison.

Conclusions to this solution

In this solution, we have employed the procedure of drawing several different network equivalents, one for each significant frequency interval. This is done quite often and adds clarity to the calculations. We may extend the procedure by deriving the formulas for low-frequency amplification and high-frequency amplification in terms of the mid-frequency amplification. Cutoff frequencies are generally easy to calculate in simple networks with monotonous roll-off, but the calculations can become very involved in case of networks with several storage elements in different places. The computation labor can be greatly reduced if valid approximations are introduced by logical reasoning.

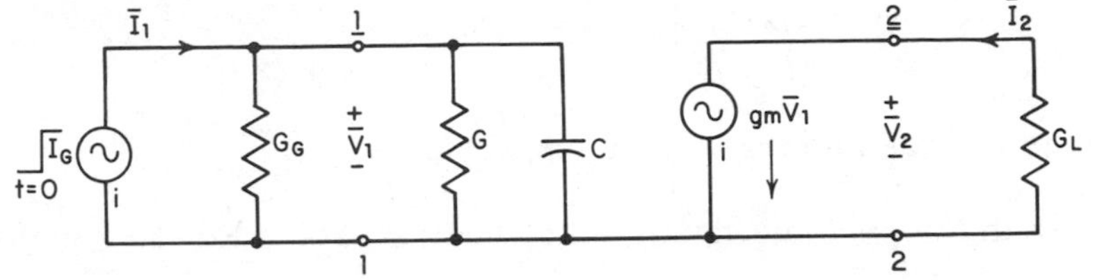

Fig. 10.1

PROBLEM 10

A transistor pulse amplifier employs a CE-connected rf transistor and is expected to have a 3-db cutoff in the hundreds of kilocycles-per-second region. The low-frequency response of the amplifier is considered to be of minor importance, and the equivalent network takes the simplified form shown in Fig. 10.1. The amplifier load is a transmission line with an input impedance of $(600 + j0)$ ohm. Electronic and other capacitances appearing at port 2,2 are therefore disregarded. For simplicity, we may consider all transistor parameters to be frequency-independent.

(A) Derive a transform expression for the output voltage when the input is driven by a step-current source.

(B) Determine the periodic-steady-state time-domain output voltage when the step-current source is replaced by a source, $i(t) = I_G \cos(\omega t + \alpha)$.

(C) Determine the upper cutoff frequency and the amplification-bandwidth product. Also formulate a figure of merit.

(D) Obtain numerical values for the above quantities when $g_m = 0.04$ mho, $R = 1/G = 3{,}000$ ohm, $R_G = 1/G_G = 5{,}000$ ohm, $R_L = 1/G_L = 600$ ohm, and $C = 300$ $\mu\mu$f.

Solution

(A) We obtain, with $(G_G + G) = G_1$,

$$\overline{V}_1 = \overline{I}_1/(sC + G_1) \quad (10.1)$$

$$\overline{V}_2 = -g_m R_L \overline{V}_1 \quad (10.2)$$

Accordingly,

$$\bar{V}_2 = \frac{-g_m R_L \bar{I}_1}{sC + G_1} = \frac{-g_m R_L I_G}{C} \times \frac{1}{s(s + G_1/C)} \tag{10.3}$$

which is the desired transform expression.

(B) In the periodic steady state, the first part of Eq. 10.3 yields, with $\bar{I}_1 = \mathbf{I}_G = I_G \underline{|\alpha}$,

$$\begin{aligned}\mathbf{V}_2 &= -g_m R_L I_G \underline{|\alpha}/(G_1 + j\omega C)\\ &= g_m R_L I_G \underline{|\alpha + \pi}/\sqrt{G_1^2 + \omega^2 C^2}\ \underline{|tan^{-1}\omega C/G_1}\end{aligned} \tag{10.4}$$

from which

$$\mathbf{V}_{2t} = \mathbf{V}_2 e^{j\omega t} = g_m R_L I_G \underline{|\omega t + \alpha + \pi - tan^{-1}\omega C/G_1}/\sqrt{G_1^2 + \omega^2 C^2} \tag{10.5}$$

Accordingly,

$$v_2(t) = g_m R_L I_G \cos(\omega t + \alpha + 180° - tan^{-1}\omega C/G_1)\sqrt{G_1^2 + \omega^2 C^2} \tag{10.6}$$

(C) The upper cutoff frequency is obtained by setting the real part in the denominator of Eq. 10.4 equal to the j-part, thus

$$f_c = G_1/2\pi C \tag{10.7}$$

The current amplification at mid or low frequency is from Eq. 10.4: $A_I'(\omega) = g_m/G_1$. The amplification-bandwidth product is therefore

$$\text{ABP} = A_I'(\omega) \times f_c = g_m/2\pi C \tag{10.8}$$

If C is split up here into electronic and other capacitances peculiar to the transistor, on the one hand, and external capacitance, on the other hand, the transistor capacitance, C_{tr}, may be used in a figure of merit, F_t.

$$\text{ABP}\bigg|_{C=C_{tr}} = F_t = \frac{g_m}{2\pi C_{tr}} \tag{10.9}$$

With C_{tr} designating the capacitance in the transistor itself, F_t becomes a figure of merit for the transistor as used in this amplifier.

(D) We obtain $g_m R_L = 0.04 \times 600 = 24$, $G_1 = 1/5{,}000 + 1/3{,}000 = 53 \times 10^{-5}$, $G_1/C = 1.8 \times 10^6$. Accordingly,

$$g_m R_L/C = 8 \times 10^{10} \qquad g_m/C = 133 \times 10^6$$

$$\overline{V}_2 \doteq -8 \times 10^{10} I_G \frac{1}{s(s + 1.8 \times 10^6)} \tag{10.3a}$$

$$f_c \doteq 0.29 \text{ Mcps} \tag{10.7a}$$

$$\text{ABP} \doteq 21.3 \text{ Mcps} \tag{10.8a}$$

Conclusions to this solution

This is a routine problem. We note the usefulness of the transform method with regard to both the transient and the periodic steady-state solutions. If we had started with the latter, it would have been useful for a transient solution only if it had been worked in the complex variables as a guarantee against loss of j:s. The meanings of amplification-bandwidth product and figure of merit have been clarified.

PROBLEM 11

A video transistor amplifier, requiring a good compromise between high input resistance, large bandwidth, and large voltage amplification, is to be designed. CE connection with degeneration was chosen with an extra series resistance in the input arm (see Fig. 11.1). The bias arrangement has been omitted. The transistor proper is known by its h' matrix, and pending measurements, it must initially be assumed that all its parameters are complex. The observed transient response was peculiar, and an investigation revealed that the load employed had poor video characteristics, since in reality it consisted of an inductance L in series with a resistance R, the latter being shunted by a capacitance, C, as in Fig. 11.1.

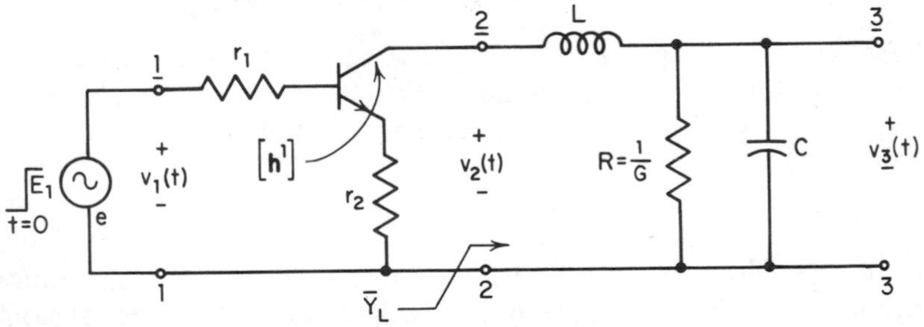

Fig. 11.1

(A) Using the Laplace Transform Method, but not classical feedback theory, derive an expression for the output voltage, $v_3(t)$, from the time $t = 0$. For simplicity, disregard energized conditions. It is sufficient if the nature of the complete solution is indicated, so long as a solution is given in terms of real h parameters.

(B) What is the general form of the transient output voltage $v_3(t)$, and to what extent can the general form of the output transient be modified by changes in the transistor parameters?

Solution

(A) We begin by transforming from h parameters to r' parameters as follows, noting that all parameters are complex quantities, representative of the periodic steady state

$$\begin{vmatrix} \mathbf{h}_{11}' & \mathbf{h}_{12}' \\ \mathbf{h}_{21}' & \mathbf{h}_{22}' \end{vmatrix} \rightarrow \begin{vmatrix} \Delta_h'/\mathbf{h}_{22}' & \mathbf{h}_{12}'/\mathbf{h}_{22}' \\ -\mathbf{h}_{21}'/\mathbf{h}_{22}' & 1/\mathbf{h}_{22}' \end{vmatrix} = \begin{vmatrix} \mathbf{z}_{11}' & \mathbf{z}_{12}' \\ \mathbf{z}_{21}' & \mathbf{z}_{22}' \end{vmatrix} \qquad (11.1)$$

Extending to a complex z matrix which encompasses the entire network, we obtain

$$\begin{vmatrix} \mathbf{z}_{11}' & \mathbf{z}_{12}' \\ \mathbf{z}_{21}' & \mathbf{z}_{22}' \end{vmatrix}_{\text{tot}} = \begin{vmatrix} \left(\dfrac{\Delta h'}{\mathbf{h}_{22}'} + r_1 + r_2\right) & \left(\dfrac{\mathbf{h}_{12}'}{\mathbf{h}_{22}'} + r_2\right) \\ \left(\dfrac{-\mathbf{h}_{21}'}{\mathbf{h}_{22}'} + r_2\right) & \left(\dfrac{1}{\mathbf{h}_{22}'} + r_2\right) \end{vmatrix}_{\text{tot}} \qquad (11.2)$$

Anyone of the matrix elements in Eq. 11.2 is here of the general form

$$\mathbf{z}_{ij}' = r_{ij}' + j\omega l'_{ij} + 1/j\omega c'_{ij} \qquad (11.3)$$

where as an example $i = j = 1$, and where $\omega/2\pi = \omega_G/2\pi$ is the frequency of the driving generator. With the restriction that $s = s_G$ means $j\omega_G$, we may write Eq. 11.3 in the form

$$z_{ij}'(s) = \bar{z}_{ij}' = r_{ij}' + sl_{ij}' + 1/sc'_{ij} \qquad (11.4)$$

We cannot extend this formula to the general s-domain, since we may have lost j:s in squaring, or otherwise. The general nontime domain formula must therefore be written as the polynomial

$$\bar{z}_{ij}' = \frac{s_0N + sN_1 + s^2N_2 + \ldots}{s_0D + sD_1 + s^2D_2 + \ldots} = \frac{N(s)}{D(s)} \tag{11.5}$$

Writing all matrix elements in this form, we shall proceed to formulate the desired transfer function. It is

$$\frac{\bar{V}_2}{\bar{V}_1} = \frac{\bar{z}_{21}'}{\bar{z}_{11}' + \bar{\Delta}_z'\bar{Y}_L} \tag{11.6}$$

$$\bar{Y}_L = \frac{sC + G}{s^2CL + sGL + 1} = \frac{n(s)}{d(s)} \tag{11.7}$$

$$\frac{\bar{V}_3}{\bar{V}_2} = \frac{1}{s^2CL + sGL + 1} = \frac{1}{d(s)} \tag{11.8}$$

$$\frac{\bar{V}_2}{\bar{V}_1} \times \frac{\bar{V}_3}{\bar{V}_2} = \frac{\bar{V}_3}{\bar{V}_1} \tag{11.9}$$

Here, Eq. 11.8 was obtained by a direct application of the Voltage Proportioning Method. Following Eq. 11.9, we write

$$\frac{\bar{V}_3}{\bar{V}_1} = \frac{\bar{z}_{21}'}{\bar{z}_{11}' + \bar{\Delta}_z'[n(s)/d(s)]} \times \frac{1}{d(s)} = \frac{\bar{z}_{21}'}{\bar{z}_{11}'d(s) + \bar{\Delta}_z'n(s)} = \frac{\mathcal{N}(s)}{\mathcal{D}(s)} \tag{11.10}$$

This is the s-combine that we must treat for a complete solution, when the matrix has complex elements. The s-combine probably would have to be broken up into smaller ones, of which each part must be found in a transform-pair table, giving the proper transformations to the time domain. With some labor we shall finally be able to write out a time response representing $v_3(t)$.

Proceeding to the simplified case where the matrix elements are real, we write from Eq. 11.10

$$\frac{\bar{V}_3}{\bar{V}_1} = \frac{r_{21}'}{r_{11}'d(s) + \Delta_r'n(s)} = \frac{r_{21}'}{CLr_{11}'} \times \frac{1}{s^2 + s2a + b^2} \tag{11.11}$$

where

$$a = \frac{r_{11}'GL + \Delta_r'C}{2CLr_{11}'} \qquad b^2 = \frac{r_{11}' + \Delta_r'G}{CLr_{11}'} \tag{11.12}$$

Inserting in Eq. 11.11, $\bar{V}_1 = E_1/s$, we obtain

$$\overline{V}_3 = \frac{r_{21}'E_1}{CLr_{11}'} \times \frac{1}{s(s^2 + s2a + b^2)} \tag{11.13}$$

We use the transform-pair formula

$$\frac{1}{s[(s+a)^2 + \Omega^2]} \rightarrow \frac{1}{b^2} - \frac{e^{-at}}{b\Omega} sin\left(\Omega t + tan^{-1}\frac{\Omega}{a}\right) \tag{11.14}$$
$$\Omega^2 = b^2 - a^2$$

Accordingly,

$$v_3(t) = \frac{r_{21}'E_1}{CLr_{11}'}\left[\frac{1}{b^2} - \frac{e^{-at}}{b\Omega} sin\left(\Omega t + tan^{-1}\frac{\Omega}{a}\right)\right] \tag{11.15}$$

which is the answer, in which we may insert previously given quantities.

(B) The general form of the transient output is a damped sinusoid or cosinusoid, originating at a coordinate determined partly by the driving function. Without inserting values and making detailed calculations, one may state from inspection of Eq. 11.15 that the transistor parameters have a great influence on the transient output, since they appear not only in the magnitude but also in the electric angle of the wave. Thus the decay of the wave is strongly influenced by the transistor parameters.

Conclusions to this solution

Probably, the most important thing that we learned from this solution is to be careful in interpreting complex quantities in general s-form. To make sure that no j:s are lost, we may work steady-state problems in the s-variable from the beginning, whenever there is a possibility that we later might extend the limited meaning of $s = j\omega_G$ to a more general meaning, making possible transient calculations. In accordance with one school of thought, a network should be presented either in the time domain or in the non-time domain, but we can see from Fig. 11.1 that it is entirely practical to mix instantaneous values with complex parameters and transform symbols.

PROBLEM 12

The complex amplification of a CE-connected transistor amplifier is measured in the audio frequency range by means of the indi-

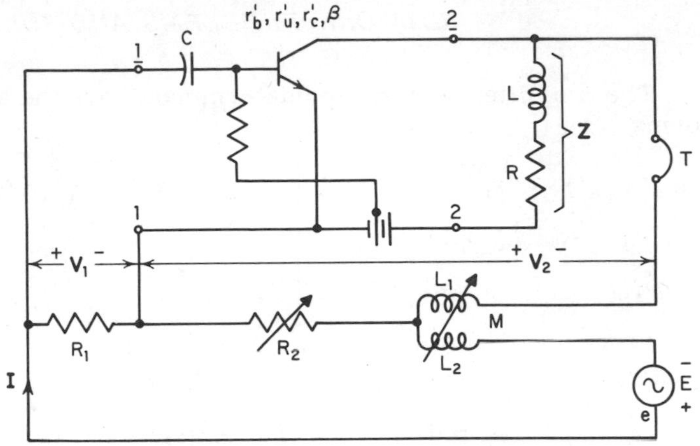

Fig. 12.1

cated balancing network (see Fig. 12.1). The source E gives a sine wave of frequency 1,000 cps, at which frequency the impedance of the capacitor C may be disregarded. The tester is going to be used for production-run measurements on amplifiers that are permitted to vary only ±10 per cent in magnitude and phase angle. Since an accurately calibrated mutual inductor must be employed, it is desirable that a preliminary calculation be carried out to find the value of M and its sign.

(A) Discuss the basic principle of the measurement device.

(B) Considering the amplifier known, R_1 preset to a relatively small value, and R_2 available in any value from zero to 10 megohm, calculate the value of M and its sign for zero signal in the phone T.

Solution

(A) For a resistive load ($L = 0$), no mutual inductance M is required, and a value of R_2 will be found for which the signal in the phone becomes zero. When the amplifier load has a phase angle other than zero, the mutual inductance M is required to shift the phase of the applied voltage until full compensation is secured, so that the signal in the phone again becomes zero.

(B) For a fully known amplifier, the twoport equation system yields the formula

$$\mathbf{A}_V(\omega) = \mathbf{V}_2/\mathbf{V}_1 = -r_{21}'\mathbf{Z}/(r_{11}'\mathbf{Z} + \Delta_r') \tag{12.1}$$

With zero phone current, $\mathbf{Z}$ actually represents the total load impedance. The amplifier matrix and determinant have the approximate forms

$$\begin{vmatrix} r_{11}' = (r_b' + r_u') & r_{12}' = r_u' \\ r_{21}' = (r_u' + r_m') & r_{22}' = (r_u' + r_c') \\ \doteq -\beta r_c' & \doteq r_c' \end{vmatrix} \qquad \Delta_r' \doteq r_c'(r_b' + \beta r_u') \tag{12.2}$$

Accordingly,

$$\mathbf{A}_V(\omega) \doteq \beta r_c' \mathbf{Z}/[(r_b' + r_u')\mathbf{Z} + r_c'(r_b' + \beta r_u')] \tag{12.3}$$

or, where $X = \omega L = 2\pi 1{,}000L$,

$$\begin{aligned} \mathbf{A}_V(\omega) &\doteq \beta r_c'(R + jX)/[(r_b' + r_u')R + r_c'(r_b' + \beta r_u') + j(r_b' + r_u')X] \\ &= \beta r_c'(R + jX)/(A + jB) \end{aligned} \tag{12.4}$$

Thus

$$\mathbf{A}_V(\omega) = \beta r_c' \sqrt{\frac{R^2 + X^2}{A^2 + B^2}} \underline{\left| tan^{-1} \frac{X}{R} - tan^{-1} \frac{B}{A} \right.} \tag{12.5}$$

As a practical example, we may consider a case where L represents the inductance of an essentially resistive load, in which case we may write the following approximation

$$\mathbf{A}_V(\omega) \doteq A_V(\omega) \underline{|\phi(\omega)} \doteq \frac{\beta r_c' \sqrt{R^2 + \omega^2 L^2} \, \underline{|tan^{-1}(\omega L/R)}}{(r_b' + r_u')R + r_c'(r_b' + \beta r_u')} \tag{12.6}$$

We assume R_1 to be very much smaller than the input resistance of the transistor. Thus we may write

$$\mathbf{V}_1 = R_1 \mathbf{I} \qquad \mathbf{V}_2 = (R_2 + j\omega M)\mathbf{I} \tag{12.7}$$

$$\frac{\mathbf{V}_2}{\mathbf{V}_1} = \frac{R_2 + j\omega M}{R_1} = \frac{\sqrt{R_2^{\,2} + \omega^2 M^2}}{R_1} \underline{\left| tan^{-1} \frac{\omega M}{R_2} \right.} = A_V(\omega) \underline{|\phi(\omega)} \tag{12.8}$$

which implies one equality between magnitudes and one between phase angles. Accordingly,

$$A_V(\omega) = \frac{\sqrt{R_2^{\,2} + \omega^2 M^2}}{R_1} \qquad \phi(\omega) = tan^{-1} \frac{\omega M}{R_2} \tag{12.9}$$

Since $\omega = 2\pi\ 1{,}000$, $A_V(\omega)$ and $\phi(\omega)$ may be calculated if the values of R_1, R_2, and M are known from calibrations. We may designate the phase angle produced by the comparator as positive. Alternatively, M and its sign can be determined if the other quantities are known.

Conclusions to this solution

In this problem, the transistor merely plays the role of the measurement object, but to obtain a complete picture of the situation, we must derive the magnitude and phase angle of the complex amplification. Note that a CB-connected transistor would require that the leads to the resistor R_1 be reversed, meaning that $(R_2 + j\omega M)$ in Eq. 1.7 would be extended to $(R_1 + R_2 + j\omega M)$. This type of measurement device is very useful in the laboratory, particularly since it also allows open-loop measurements on transistor feedback amplifiers. (Note that in this case the proper terminations at the ends of the open loop must be restored as accurately as possible before any open-loop measurements are undertaken.)

PROBLEM 13

Given is a long transmission line of characteristic admittance, $\mathbf{Y}_C$, driven by an emitter follower shown without bias supplies (see Fig. 13.1). The matrix for the emitter follower and the characteristics of the line are as follows:

$$|g|_{cc} = \begin{vmatrix} 0.62\,\mho & -0.62 \\ -15.38 & 15.39 \end{vmatrix} \times 10^{-3} \qquad \begin{aligned} r &= 85\,\Omega/\text{km} \\ g &= 10^{-6}\,\mho/\text{km} \\ l &= 0.65\ \text{mh/km} \\ c &= 0.035\,\mu\text{f/km} \end{aligned}$$

The design requires that the emitter follower feed into a conductive load, at the same time as the line looks back into a conductance of

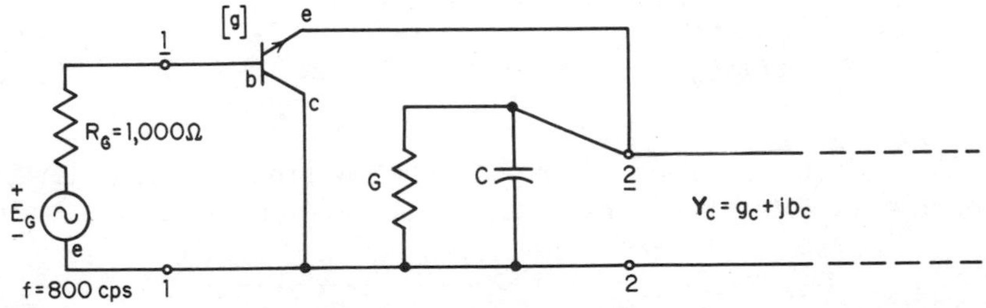

Fig. 13.1

the same value as its characteristic conductance. To meet these termination requirements, lumped dissipative and storage elements are available. To begin with, a shunt conductance G and a capacitance C are inserted (not necessarily the final arrangement).

(A) Determine the line characteristic admittance $\mathbf{Y}_C$ and its real and j-parts.

(B) Determine the storage element required for a solution of the problem, and show its connection.

(C) Determine the dissipative element required for a solution of the problem, and show its connection.

(D) To what extent will the problem become further complicated if it is found that the transistor has one or more complex matrix elements?

Solution

(A) The input admittance of the transmission line is

$$\mathbf{Y}_C = g_c + jb_c = \sqrt{g_c{}^2 + b_c{}^2}\,\underline{\Big| tan^{-1} \frac{b_c}{g_c}} = \sqrt{\frac{g + j\omega c}{r + j\omega l}}$$

$$= \sqrt{\frac{10^{-6} + j2\pi\,800 \times 0.035 \times 10^{-6}}{85 + j2\pi\,800 \times 0.65 \times 10^{-3}}} = 1.01 \times 10^{-3} + j10^{-3}$$

$$= 0.00143\,\underline{|44.75^\circ}$$
                                                                        (13.1)

(B) The line, as a load, has a capacitance

$$C_L = b_c/\omega = 10^{-3}/2\pi\,800 \doteq 0.2 \times 10^{-6}\text{f} = 0.2\mu\text{f}   \qquad (13.2)$$

To cancel this we need a shunt inductance, L, rather than a shunt capacitance, C. The required inductance is

$$L = 1/\omega^2 C_L = 1/(2\pi\,800)^2 \times 0.2 \times 10^{-6} \doteq 0.2\text{h}   \qquad (13.3)$$

(C) To determine the output conductance of the emitter follower, we derive the following formula from the two-port equation system

$$G_{out} = \frac{g_{22} + \Delta g R_G}{1 + g_{11} R_G} = \frac{g_{22} + (g_{11}g_{22} - g_{12}g_{21})R_G}{1 + g_{11} R_G}$$

$$= 10^{-3}\frac{15.39 + (0.62 \times 15.39 - 0.62 \times 15.38)10^{-3} \times 10^{3}}{1 + 0.62 \times 10^{-3} \times 10^{3}}$$

$$= 9.5 \times 10^{-3}\,\mho \qquad (13.4)$$

This output conductance appears as a shunt to the conductance, G. The requirement on the looking-in conductance is, therefore,

$$G_{\text{out}} + G = g_C$$

$$G = g_C - G_{\text{out}} = 1.01 \times 10^{-3} - 9.5 \times 10^{-3} \doteq -8.5 \times 10^{-3}\,\mho \qquad (13.5)$$

Thus, no positive value of G exists that satisfies the requested condition. We must, therefore, insert a series resistance, R_S, in the emitter lead, the value of R_S determined from the following consideration,

$$R_{\text{out}} + R_S = r_C$$

$$R_S = r_C - R_{\text{out}} = \frac{10^3}{1.01} - \frac{10^3}{9.5} \doteq 885\,\Omega \qquad (13.6)$$

(D) If the transistor has one or more complex elements, the output conductance will turn into an output admittance. This admittance has a certain conductance, and we can still find a value and a correct position for the dissipative element. An additional susceptance now appears at the port 2,2̲, and we must consult the new problem formulation to find out whether we may disregard this susceptance, since it might be relatively small, or what we are supposed to do with it.

Conclusions to this solution

Combinations between transistors and transmission lines are quite common today. Often the storage elements are disregarded, particularly in audio-frequency applications. At higher frequency, we cannot neglect the storage elements in the transistor network, and we must acknowledge a phase angle both in the transistor parameters and in the line immittance. When a line is not sufficiently long at the prevailing frequency to provide its characteristic immittance as input immittance, the termination at the far end must be taken into consideration. This termination may have the form of an antenna, and the transducer between the antenna and the transistor may consist of a combination of distributed- and lumped-parameter devices. In all cases of linear operation, the total system can be analyzed, although considerable labor may be involved. In other words, the transistor does not offer any calculation obstacles beyond those encountered in conventional system analysis pertaining to linear systems.

PROBLEM 14

An exponential-line coupler is used as a matching device between the two known impedances, $\mathbf{Z}_0$ and $\mathbf{Z}_S$ which may be considered to have negligible phase angles (see Fig. 14.1). A monitor is provided in the form of a CB-connected transistor, known by its h matrix, which at the frequency encountered is all complex. (The transistor is indicated in Fig. 14.1 without its supplies.) The monitoring transistor operates an oscilloscope, which is assumed to have the input impedance, $R + j0$. The coupler has an unknown flaring coefficient, k. The coupler inductance and capacitance vary along the x coordinate in accordance with the formulas

$$L_x = L_0 e^{kx} \qquad C_x = C_0 e^{-kx}$$

where L_0 and C_0 pertain to the input end. It is assumed that the amplifier connection does not interfere with the operation of the coupler, and it is further assumed that the tap-off point at $x = x_1$ gives a proportional part of the total phase delay, t_{ds}.

(A) Find the phase delay at point x_1.

(B) If the phase delay in the amplifier can equal that in the tapped-off part of the coupler, but not exceed it, and the output

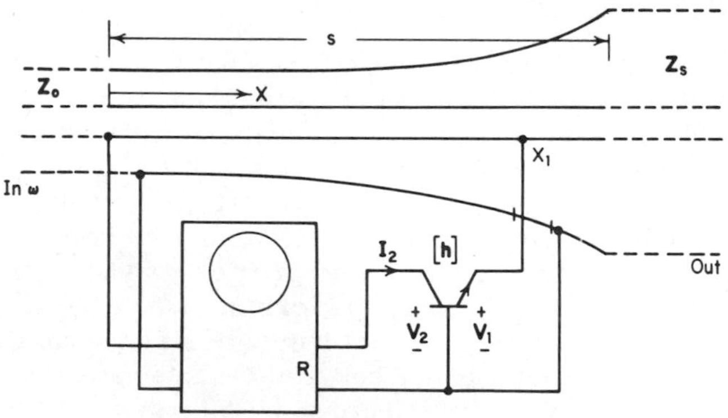

Fig. 14.1

voltage $\mathbf{V}_2$ is utilized as monitoring signal, what is the maximum value of the phase angle of $\mathbf{h}_{21}$, if for simplicity we assume that $\boldsymbol{\Delta}_h = \Delta_h$, and that $\mathbf{h}_{11}$ has fixed magnitude and phase angle?

Solution

(A) The phase delay is $x\sqrt{L_x C_x} = x\sqrt{L_0 C_0}$ for any arbitrary coordinate x; thus, for the coordinate x_1

$$t_{dx1} = x_1 \sqrt{L_0 C_0} \tag{14.1}$$

(B) We shall first determine the phase delay in the amplifier, writing the formula for the current-voltage transfer function from the two-port equation system:

$$\mathbf{A}(\omega) = \frac{\mathbf{I}_2}{\mathbf{V}_1} = \frac{\mathbf{h}_{21}}{\boldsymbol{\Delta}_h R + \mathbf{h}_{11}} = \frac{h_{21} \underline{|\theta}}{\Delta_h R + h_{11P} + jh_{11Q}}$$

$$= \frac{h_{21}}{\sqrt{(\Delta_h R + h_{11P})^2 + h^2_{11Q}}} \underline{|\theta - \phi} \tag{14.2}$$

where θ is the phase angle of $\mathbf{h}_{21}$ and ϕ the phase angle of the denominator. The phase delay now becomes

$$t_d' = \frac{\theta - \phi}{\omega} = \frac{1}{\omega}\left(\theta - tan^{-1}\frac{h_{11Q}}{\Delta_h R + h_{11P}}\right) \tag{14.3}$$

As a minimum condition, $t_d' = t_{dx_1}$, so that

$$\frac{1}{\omega}\left(\theta - tan^{-1}\frac{h_{11Q}}{\Delta_h R + h_{11P}}\right) = x_1\sqrt{L_0 C_0} \tag{14.4}$$

and

$$\theta = \omega x_1 \sqrt{L_0 C_0} + tan^{-1}\frac{h_{11Q}}{\Delta_h R + h_{11P}} \tag{14.5}$$

which is the desired answer. In inserting numerical values for $\mathbf{h}_{21}$, it should be noted that a minus sign will appear, implying a 180° phase shift in the answer. As an alternative, therefore, we may introduce the 180° phase shift in Eq. 14.2, setting $\mathbf{h}_{21} = -\underline{\mathbf{h}}_{21}$.

Conclusions to this solution

This is a problem from the domains of ultra-high frequency

and microwaves. We must remember that basically all transistor parameters are complex quantities. Quantities such as α and β are also complex. Almost prohibitive approximations have been made here to make possible a simple solution. The phase delay, together with the differential phase delay, are important quantities in the calculation of transistor amplifiers at very high frequencies.

PROBLEM 15

A semiconductor light-sensitive device is exposed to periodic light and used as a nonlinear device in a modulation system. When light-irradiated, the semiconductor shows one resistance part, r_0, which is independent of the light intensity, and one resistance part, $r(t)$, which varies at the frequency $\omega/2\pi$, following to a first approximation the law, $r(t) = R/(1 + K \cos \omega t)$, where R and K are constants. (See Fig. 15.1.)

(A) Write a series expansion of the current $i(t)$, including at least second-order terms.

(B) Discuss the meaning (1) of the linear and nonlinear parts of the series expansion and indicate how the device may be used (2) as an a-m modulator and (3) as a frequency converter.

(C) Attempt to find an equivalent network for the semiconductor device, in which the total semiconductor resistance is considered time invariant, this total semiconductor resistance appearing together with a periodic voltage source of frequency, $\omega/2\pi$.

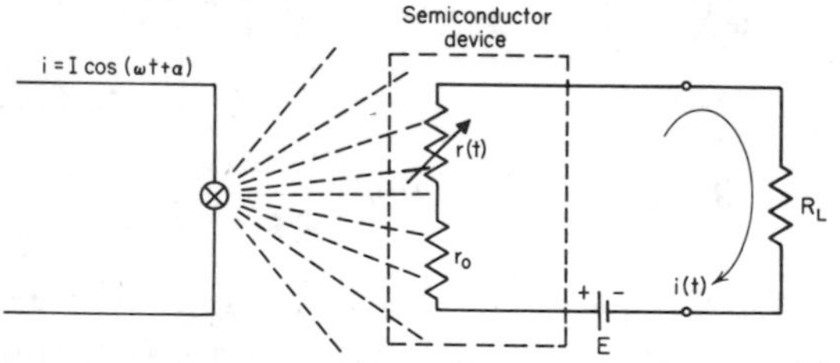

Fig. 15.1

Solution

(A) In accordance with Ohm's Law, the variational current takes the form

$$i(t) = \frac{E}{r_0 + R_L + \dfrac{R}{1 + K\cos\omega t}} = E\frac{1 + K\cos\omega t}{r_0 + R_L + R + K(r_0 + R_L)\cos\omega t}$$

$$= \frac{aE}{R} \times \frac{1 + K\cos\omega t}{1 + b\cos\omega t} \tag{15.1}$$

where

$$a = \frac{R}{r_0 + R_L + R} \tag{15.2}$$

$$b = K\frac{r_0 + R_L}{r_0 + R_L + R} \tag{15.3}$$

Dividing the denominator into the numerator, we obtain, noting that $(K - b) = aK$,

$$\begin{array}{r|l} & 1 + aK\cos\omega t - abK\cos^2\omega t + \dots \\ \hline 1 + b\cos\omega t & 1 + K\cos\omega t \\ & -(1 + b\cos\omega t) \\ & (K - b)\cos\omega t \\ & \quad -(aK\cos\omega t + abK\cos^2\omega t) \\ & \quad -abK\cos^2\omega t \end{array} \tag{15.4}$$

Accordingly,

$$i(t) = \frac{aE}{R}(1 + aK\cos\omega t - abK\cos^2\omega t + \dots) \tag{15.5}$$

or

$$i(t) = \frac{E}{r_0 + R_L + R}\left(1 + \frac{KR}{r_0 + R_L + R}\cos\omega t - \frac{K^2R(r_0 + R_L)}{(r_0 + R_L + R)^2}\cos^2\omega t + \dots\right) \tag{15.6}$$

which is the desired expression.

As an alternative, we may use the following series (derived from the binomial series)

$$\frac{1}{1 + x} = (1 - x + x^2 - x^3 + x^4 \dots) \tag{15.7}$$

From this, we obtain, with $x = b \cos \omega t$,

$$\frac{1}{1 + b \cos \omega t} = (1 - b \cos \omega t + b^2 \cos^2 \omega t \ldots) \qquad (15.8)$$

and thus

$$i(t) = \frac{aE}{R} \times \frac{1 + K \cos \omega t}{1 + b \cos \omega t}$$

$$= \frac{aE}{R}(1 - b \cos \omega t + b^2 \cos^2 \omega t + K \cos \omega t - bK \cos^2 \omega t + b^2 K \cos^3 \omega t \ldots)$$

$$= \frac{aE}{R}[1 + (K - b) \cos \omega t - b(K - b) \cos^2 \omega t + b^2 K \cos^3 \omega t \ldots]$$

$$= \frac{aE}{R}[1 + aK \cos \omega t - abK \cos^2 \omega t + \ldots] \qquad (15.9)$$

which agrees with Eq. 15.5. Note the use of the equality, $(K - b) = aK$.

(B1) If all terms are disregarded in Eqs. 15.6 and 15.9 except the first two terms, the linear current output is obtained. This output takes the form

$$i(t) = \frac{E}{r_0 + R_L + R} + \frac{KRE}{(r_0 + R_L + R)^2} \cos \omega t \qquad (15.10)$$

The periodic contribution of the third term represents a second-harmonic current.

(B2) If E contains a periodic voltage of angular velocity ω_1, a sequence of product terms are generated, since the variational resistance is periodic and of angular velocity, ω. If $\omega_1 \neq \omega$, a spectrum $|p\omega_1 \pm q\omega|$ is generated. For $\omega_1 \gg \omega$, the three components typical for an amplitude modulated wave may be extracted from the network.

(B3) In a frequency-conversion scheme, we may select the wave of angular velocity $(\omega_1 - \omega)$ as "intermediate angular velocity," in which case ω_1 may be of the same order of magnitude as ω. The combination of the light source and the semiconductor device then represents a parametric device, to which we apply the wave of angular velocity, ω_1. On the other hand, if the applied wave would cause a resistance variation in the network—which is likely to happen if the voltage amplitude is made large enough—then additional product terms are generated, and the possibility of utilizing the scheme as an optical-signal superheterodyne exists.

(C) To find a suitable network equivalent that yields the periodic current of Eq. 15.10, we only have to write the desired part of Eq. 15.10 in the form

$$i_1(t) = \frac{E \cos \omega t}{(r_0 + R_L + R)^2/KR} = \frac{e_1(t)}{R_1} \tag{15.11}$$

where

$$R_1 = \frac{(r_0 + R_L + R)^2}{KR} \tag{15.12}$$

This network equivalent, shown in Fig. 15.2a, has the disadvantage that the resistance, R_1, is a function of the load, but R_1 is not the same thing as the load resistance, R_L. Nevertheless, we have fulfilled the requirement stated, since R_1 is time-invariant. For the special case of $R = R_L$, we can produce a network equivalent which can be drawn in such a manner that R_L appears in an output port precisely as in the given network in Fig. 15.1. While this is a rather academic procedure, the resulting network is shown in Fig. 15.2b, merely to demonstrate that this kind of reasoning yields a network from which the correct current value may be obtained.

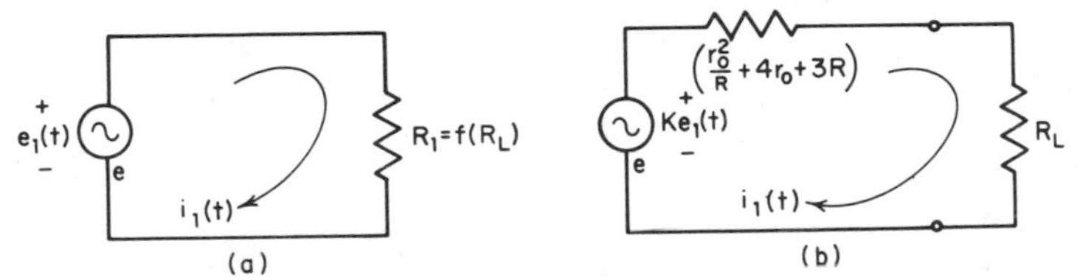

Fig. 15.2

Conclusions to this solution

This problem is somewhat off the beaten track, confronting us with parametric action caused by other than network means, in this case by light irradiation. Two somewhat different methods for analyzing a network with variational immittance are presented, and the terms in the resulting current series indicate both linear and nonlinear applications. In a light-sensitive device, we usually play down the nonlinearities and design a device which yields a sine wave output. In an intentionally nonlinear design, we may visualize a large number of possible applications, dependent upon parametric action. The equivalent networks derived in the solution indicate perhaps that a network equivalent may be produced for every specified function, and that for every network equivalent produced, the source, the internal immittance, and the external immittance may be changed around considerably without any change in the resulting variable, in our case a mesh current.

SOME FINAL THOUGHTS

In this and previous chapters, we have only used a few specific matrix techniques, the last one making possible the treatment of paralleled amplifiers with the help of y parameters. Many additional and highly useful matrix techniques exist, which space will not permit us to discuss. An immediate extension would be the treatment of oscillators by means of the paralleled networks scheme. Further, the matrix and determinant theories are constantly expanded, and new methods for network analysis appear every year. The reader who is already familiar with matrix calculations is in a good position to avail himself of new techniques, as they come along.

Some of the problems in this chapter touch upon radio frequency and microwave applications, and here we encounter a new field of semiconductor developments, filled with new discoveries. Calculations with complex parameters are often unavoidable, and the dependence of the engineer upon laboratory measurements is much greater than for low-frequency devices. The problem of parametric operation has been discussed in some of our solutions, but it has been limited to periodic "pumping" of dissipative parameters. In the microwave field, "pumping" of storage elements in semiconductor devices is of great importance—for example, the periodic variation of the capacitance of special diodes for the purpose of producing amplification. Problem solutions relating to periodic "pumping" of dissipative parameters may serve as an introduction to the more advanced phases of this fascinating branch of semiconductor science.

Appendix A
Common Network Rules And Theorems

1. Ohm's Law

$$v = Ri \qquad v = L\,di/dt \qquad v = S\int i\,dt = Sq$$

$$i = Gv \qquad i = C\,dv/dt \qquad i = \Gamma \int v\,dt = \Gamma\phi \qquad \text{(A1)}$$

q = electric charge; i = current; $R = 1/G$ = resistance; $G = 1/R$ = conductance; $L = 1/\Gamma$ = inductance; $\Gamma = 1/L$ = reciprocal inductance; $C = 1/S$ = capacitance; $S = 1/C$ = elastance; ϕ = magnetic field; v = voltage.

2. Kirchhoff's Generalized Law[1]

$$\sum_{\nu=1}^{n} u_\nu = \sum \text{uncommon variable} = 0 \qquad \text{(A2)}$$

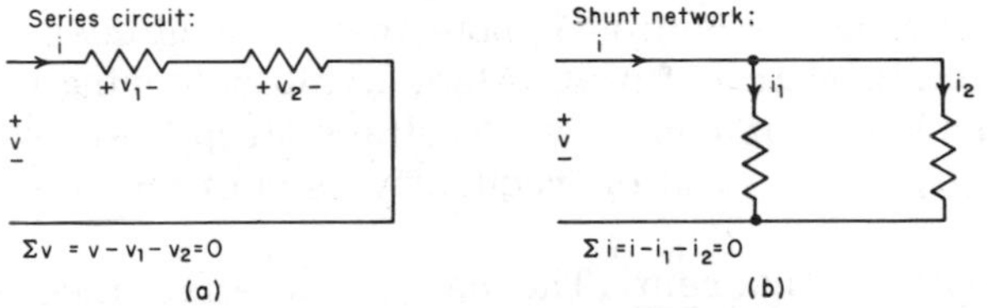

Fig. A1

Common variable:	(a) $c = i$ = current	(b) $c = v$ = voltage
Uncommon variable:	(a) $u = v$ = voltage	(b) $u = i$ = current

With reference to the common network elements, the variables are related as follows:

$$\text{Uncommon variable} = \text{constant} \times \begin{cases} (d/dt)\ \text{common variable} \\ \text{common variable} \\ \int (\text{common variable})\,dt \end{cases} \qquad \text{(A3)}$$

[1] Stockman, H. E., "Circuit Theory in a Unified Curriculum," *IRE Transactions on Education*, No. 1, p. 43, March 1961.

Note: Ohm's and Kirchhoff's laws in Sections 1 and 2 are written for instantaneous values of current and voltage. In the periodic steady state, the current and voltage

$$i = I \cos(\omega t + \alpha) \tag{A4}$$

$$v = V \cos(\omega t + \beta) \tag{A5}$$

are represented by the sinors, $\mathbf{I} = Ie^{j\alpha}$ and $\mathbf{V} = Ve^{j\beta}$ and Ohm's and Kirchhoff's laws are applied in the time-free domain in accordance with the Symbolic Method, originated by Steinmetz and Kennelly (in 1893).[1] For both periodic steady-state and transient occurrences, current and voltage are represented by the Laplace Transform symbols:

$$\bar{I} = i(s) = \mathscr{L}[i(t)] \tag{A6}$$

$$\bar{V} = v(s) = \mathscr{L}[v(t)] \tag{A7}$$

After a relatively long time

$\bar{I}$ goes to $\mathbf{I}$ or I_0 $\qquad$ $\bar{V}$ goes to $\mathbf{V}$ or V_0

where subscript zero indicates a direct quantity, which may be zero.

With reference to Section 1, note that current does not "flow," whereas electric charge flows. Also, avoid referring to a voltage across a network component as "voltage drop," since this term has never been defined and is frequently used erroneously.

3. Superposition Theorem (The cause and effect theorem, cause and effect being proportional)

Arbitrarily located current and voltage sources in a linear network produce currents and voltages in any part of the network, which are the sums of the component currents and voltages, originated by the individual sources, acting one at a time.

Note 1: The Superposition Theorem can also be applied to function sources, but caution is necessary.

Note 2: This and other theorems listed here hold for the sym-

[1]For a brief history, see Stockman, H. E., *The jω or Symbolic Method,* SINE-SER Co., 1956.

bolic and the transform methods, although Laplace Transform Superposition Theorem solutions often are longer than other solutions.

4. Reciprocity Theorem

If, in a linear network, a voltage source at point A produces a current, I, *at point B, then the same voltage source when transferred to point B will produce the same current,* I, *at point A.*

or

If a linear network inserted between a voltage source and a zero-impedance load provides a certain current in this load, the network may be flipped around between its terminations without any change in the steady-state value of the current.

5. Compensation Theorems

Theorem 1: Any impedance in a network may be replaced by a voltage source equal to and of the same sign as the voltage across the impedance.

Theorem 2a (for mesh network): The effect of an impedance change, $\Delta\bar{Z}$, *in a network branch is equivalent to that of a voltage source,* $\bar{I}\Delta\bar{Z}$, *inserted in series with the changed branch, where* $\bar{I}$ *is the current in the unchanged branch and the polarity of* $\bar{I}\Delta\bar{Z}$ *is such as to produce a current opposing the original current* $\bar{I}$.

Theorem 2b (for node network): The effect of an admittance change, $\Delta\bar{Y}$, *in a network branch is equivalent to that of a current source,* $\bar{V}\Delta\bar{Y}$, *inserted in parallel with the changed branch, where* $\bar{V}$ *is the voltage across the unchanged branch and the direction of the current such as to produce a voltage across the branch of opposite polarity to the original voltage,* $\bar{V}$.

Note: In the above formulations, quantities with a superior bar signify transform quantities in the application of the Laplace Transform Method. For Symbolic Method applications in the periodic steady state, the superior bar is eliminated and bold-face type used. The theorems are formulated for positive immittance changes $\Delta\bar{Z}$ and $\Delta\bar{Y}$. Note that these quantities can be negative.

6. Thévenin-Norton Theorem[1]

For any linear network with independent sources and an accessible port, there exists an equivalent generator consisting of the impedance of the passivated network, having either the open-port voltage in series or the closed-port current in parallel.

Note 1: Of these two classical theorems, here combined by the author, the Thévenin theorem is the oldest, and many references to it appear in the literature. The origin of the Norton Theorem is less well known, and some facts about its history may be in order.[2] The theorem was conceived by E. L. Norton, presently head of the High Speed Data Terminals Department, Bell Telephone Laboratories, Holmdel, N.J. The first published statement appeared in the first edition of Professor W. L. Everitt's book on network theory, published in the late 1920's or early 1930's. Dr. Norton's earliest recorded date of his new theorem pertains to a patent communication dated November 3, 1926, dealing with mechanical networks. While the Thévenin theorem is very much older than the Norton theorem, the two theorems are of equal importance from a scientific point of view, and since both theorems describe the same basic principle, it is pointless to keep them apart any longer, particularly as the common formulation can be given a brief and concise form.

Note 2: The original or classical Thévenin theorem suffers from the limitation that it does not hold for dependent sources. The same is true for the original or classical Norton theorem. It is important that this is realized in the classification of equivalent generators. Such generators are of two basic kinds: series-form generators and shunt-form generators. A series-form generator has a voltage source in series with an impedance; a shunt-form generator has a current source in parallel with an admittance. We define a Thévenin generator as a series-form generator with an independent voltage source and an impedance with positive real part. Similarly, we define a Norton generator as a shunt-form generator with an independent current source and an admittance with positive real part. In general, a linear network with driving

[1] Stockman, H. E., "Three Output Immitance Theorems," *Electronic Industries*, Jan. 1958. Also see *Time-Saving Network Calculations* by the same author, SINE-SER Co., 1956, App. 1, p. 3.

[2] Based on information in a personal letter from Dr. Norton, dated April 24, 1963.

generator constitutes a system which has four basic equivalent generators: the Thévenin and Norton generators mentioned above and the series- and shunt-form generators with dependent sources, which have as generator immittance the system immittance seen from the output port when all sources are eliminated from the system. Since this latter generator-pair represents a special case, it is easy to realize that every linear system in general has an infinite number of equivalent generators. (The term "in general" used above implies that the system contains both dependent and independent sources.)

Various formulations of Thévenin's and Norton's theorems have appeared in the literature, some of modified form, allowing applications to systems with dependent sources. The rule is then that only independent sources are manipulated. A further discussion of this subject matter is included in the note in Paragraph 11.

7. Generator-Transformation Theorem (Corollary to Thévenin-Norton Theorem)

A series-form generator, $\bar{E}^*$, $\bar{Z}^*$, *and a shunt-form generator,* $\bar{I}^*$, $\bar{Z}^*$, *are interchangeable via Ohm's Law,* $\bar{E}^* = \bar{Z}^*\bar{I}^*$.

8. Maximum Power-Transfer Theorem

Maximum power transfer through a port common to two networks is obtained when the immittance of the driven network is the conjugate of the immittance of the driving network.

9. TEE-PI Transformations Without Handbook Formulas[1]

A passive linear TEE transforms to a PI, and vice versa, via the formula

$$\bar{7} = \frac{\bar{7}_{\text{left}}\,\bar{7}_{\text{right}}}{\bar{7}_{\text{all}}}$$

where $\bar{7}$ *designates either impedance or admittance.*

Note: Figure A2 shows that for a TEE, $\bar{7}_{\text{all}}$ is an admittance,

[1] Stockman, H. E., "TEE to PI Transformations Simplified," *Electronics*, No. 10, October 1942. Also see *Time-Saving Network Calculations*, Appendix 1, p. 14.

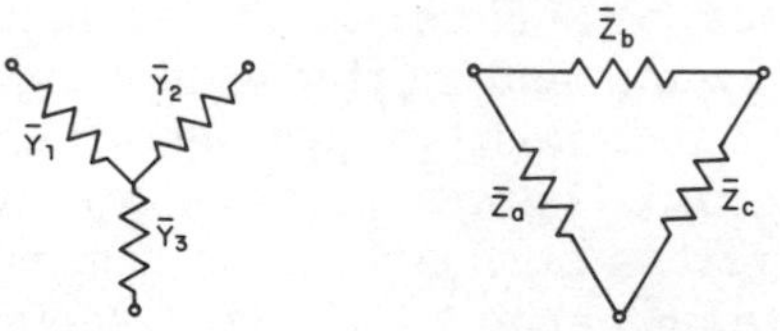

Fig. A2

since we encounter the beginning of a parallel connection. For a PI, 7_{all} is an impedance, since series connection is employed. For $\bar{Z}_a$, 7_{left} is $\bar{Y}_1$ and 7_{right} is $\bar{Y}_3$, or vice versa. For the meaning of the bar symbol here and elsewhere, see the note relating to the Compensation Theorem.

$$\bar{Y}_{\text{all}} = \bar{Y}_1 + \bar{Y}_2 + \bar{Y}_3 \qquad \bar{Z}_{\text{all}} = \bar{Z}_a + \bar{Z}_b + \bar{Z}_c$$

10. Output Immittance Theorem[1]

The output immittance of a twoport is the denominator of its proper transfer function with vanished load immittance term.

Note: This theorem provides the fastest known method for calculating the output immittance of a network, provided its proper transfer function is known, which is generally the case. The "proper" transfer function is simply the one which comprises the total network; for example, we cannot very well include a series-form generator impedance if we use a current-transfer-function formula. The theorem holds equally well for impedance and admittance. Factors multiplying the denominator are considered to belong to the numerator. The load immittance term consists of one quantity only—the load immittance. It should be noted that the theorem works also in cases where the physical form of the network is unknown, such as may be encountered in network synthesis.

11. Equivalent Generator Theorem[2]

A linear network with any arrangement of dependent and independent sources may with regard to a specified port be

[1]The author originated this theorem in 1955. It was subsequently described in the publications listed in the footnote for Section 6.

[2]This theorem is an extension of the Output Immittance Theorem. On the other hand, we may say that the Output Immittance Theorem is contained

represented by an equivalent generator with an immittance equal to the denominator of the vanished load immittance term in the proper transfer function, either with the open-port voltage in series or the closed-port current in parallel.

Note: Thévenin's Theorem is not valid for networks with dependent sources. Similarly, the original Norton's Theorem is not valid for networks with dependent sources. Combining these two theorems in the manner of the Generator-Transformation Theorem, one can use the Thévenin theorem and the Norton Theorem together in calculations pertaining to dependent sources. As an alternative, dependent sources may be removed by means of the Compensation Theorem, or by other means. In contrast to this, the new Equivalent Generator Theorem is a single theorem that is valid for all linear networks, with or without dependent sources. It therefore replaces the Thévenin theorem, the Norton Theorem, and the Thévenin-Norton theorem. In cases where the proper transfer function is known, the theorem yields a very fast solution. In cases where the proper transfer function must be derived, the labor is about the same as that required by the original theorems, if the original theorems apply. The new theorem gives directly both the Thévenin generator and the Norton generator of any network, and once these networks are obtained, an infinite number of fictitious generators may be produced by means of the Compensation Theorem. A fictitious generator is here defined as a generator employing a dependent source, and it therefore possesses a generator immittance unequal to the output immittance.

in the Equivalent Generator Theorem, so that only the latter is required. The Equivalent Generator Theorem was first published in "Transistor and Diode Experiments," 1953, p. A2-5. Also see Stockman, H. E., "Thévenin and Norton," *Wireless World*, vol. 70, no. 6, pp. 295-296 (correspondence), and "A New Tool for Easier Network Synthesis," *Electronic Design*, vol. 13, pp. 20-21, Feb. 1965, continued in *Electronic Design*, vol. 13, pp. 26-30, April 1965.

Appendix B
Elements of Twoport Theory

1. GENERAL. One requirement of the networks to be discussed is that they must be linear, that is, they must be composed of linear network elements. A linear network element is here defined as a network element that is independent of the magnitude of the applied current or voltage. We discriminate between active and passive networks. In accordance with one definition, the network is active when its output depends upon sources of power apart from those driving the network but controlled by one or more of the driving sources. We call these internal sources dependent sources or function sources. They represent a current or voltage which is a specified function of some given current or voltage in the network. In accordance with the definition adopted in this text, a network is active if it contains one or more sources or function sources.

The passive network may be considered to be a degenerated form of the active network, obtained by the process of passivating the active network, which is done by removing all its sources. By the same token we can activate a passive network by inserting sources in it. One way of doing this is to inject stimulance in the network. A somewhat different terminology results if the terms active and passive are replaced by terms spelled out by the current-voltage relations at specified terminals. The network is then externally observed, and we talk about amplificative and dissipative networks, depending upon whether the network yields more or less power in its load than it receives as input power. The borderline case then depicts the lossless network.[1]

We distinguish between bilateral networks, for which the Reciprocity Theorem holds, and nonbilateral networks, for which this theorem does not hold. (Networks of the first kind are also called reciprocal networks, but this term is here avoided, since it is used in mathematics in the meaning "inverse.") The diagram in Fig. B1 has at the top one extreme, the bilateral network. The other extreme at the bottom is represented by the unilateral network, in

[1]See Zadeh, L. A., "On Passive and Active Networks and Generalized Norton's and Thévenin's Theorems," *Proceedings of the IRE*, vol. 44, No. 3, p. 378, March 1956 (correspondence).

which signal transfer takes place in one direction only.[1] Networks which are neither bilateral nor unilateral are here called quasi-bilateral. Note that we are all the time discussing linear networks. As an example, we may consider a simple single-tube audio amplifier operating at low audio frequency. A signal voltage, such as a 100-cps audio voltage, will cause an appreciable audio signal current in the plate circuit, but the same audio voltage properly applied to the plate may not cause a measurable signal current in the grid circuit. The tube is therefore unilateral and may be very linear in its operation. If the same tube were operated in the microwave region, it is quite possible that signal transfer would take place in both directions, and perhaps to the same extent. The tube is then bilateral, and it may be quite linear in its operation. Finally, if we operate the same tube at some in-between frequency, such as 100,000 cps, it may yield some amplification from grid to plate, and some attenuation from plate to grid. We have here an example of the tube operating as a quasibilateral network, possibly one that is quite linear. Whether the tube is quite linear or not is not of primary importance; in Fig. B1 we are concerned only with the linear part of the operation. If we were to increase the applied voltage appreciably, however, the nonlinearity would become of such proportions that Fig. B1 would lose its significance.

	BILATERAL →	Transmission in both directions. Reciprocity Theorem holds.
NONBILATERAL	QUASIBILATERAL →	Transmission in both directions. Reciprocity Theorem does not hold.
	UNILATERAL →	Transmission in one direction only. Reciprocity Theorem does not hold.

Fig. B1 Signal transfer relationships

The above discussion of signal transfer does not specify the nature of the network inputs and outputs. A large class of networks have the terminals so arranged that they can be paired together,

[1]The definitions in Fig. B1 are not in full agreement with conventional standards, as far as they go. Thus the term "bilateral" is often used for all extents of signal transfer in both directions, except for zero signal transfer in one direction, in which case the term "unilateral" is employed. Many different terms and definitions exist.

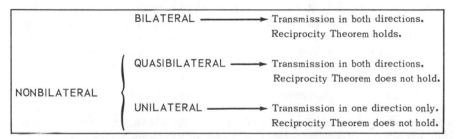

two and two. If the device has only two terminals, we call it a oneport. An example of a passive oneport is the resistor R in Fig. B2a, and an example of an active oneport, the voltage source e in Fig. B2b. Here the small e next to the source symbol signifies "voltage source." Note that the voltage designation e to the right of the source symbol must be provided with direction indication; here it is furnished by a plus and a minus sign. When three terminals are at hand, we call the device a three-terminal network, and an example of such a network is shown in Fig. B2c. This network does not possess any specified input or output, but it has what we call a "1-end," provided by the terminal pair $\underline{1}$,0 and a "2-end," provided by the terminal pair $\underline{2}$,0. Either the 1-end or the 2-end, or both ends, may be driven ends. This terminology of a 1-end and a 2-end will prove useful in the following, since we occasionally drive networks in the reverse direction, and since it is illogical to say that the input end now is the output end. When four terminals are grouped in two pairs, we refer to the network as a four-terminal network. Very often such a network is also a twoport, but not necessarily so. In the past, four-terminal networks have also been referred to as four-poles, or fourpole networks, in which case the oneport is referred to as a twopole.[1] If the driving generator is externally connected to the load by some overlooked current path, the network is not a twoport. Another demand on a twoport is that the current appearing at one terminal of a port must be the same as the current appearing at the other terminal of the port, except for direction.[2] The twoport concept applies to the majority of tube and transistor networks, and it offers a powerful and concise

[1]The "fourpole" designation was introduced in Germany under the name "Vierpol" (Breisig, F., *Electrotechnische Zeitschrift*, vol. 42, 1921, p. 933; also, *Elektrische Nachrichten-Technik*, vol. 3, 1926, p. 161). This designation spread to other countries, and, as an example, in Sweden became "fyrpol." In the USA, fourpoles are mostly referred to as two-terminal-pair devices, twoport nets, and twoports. As will be brought out in the text, all four-terminal networks are not necessarily twoports. The beginning of the twoport theory dates much further back than 1921, however, since it was used introductorily by K. W. Wagner in 1915 (see *Archiv für Electrotechnik*, vol. 3, p. 315) in his formulation of basic filter theory. The basic concepts of the twoport theory were no doubt inherent in the work done by some great nineteenth century masters (see reference to work by J. Wallot in footnote 4).

[2]Rather than to say that the current "passes" or "flows," we say that it is "applied to." Current does not flow; only electrons and holes flow. The current direction in this text is opposite to the direction of electron flow and thus away from the positive terminal of a battery.

method of treatment, implying the use of matrix calculations.[1 to 9] Twoport theory provides one of the cornerstones in modern network theory, streamlining the network analysis whether the driving signal is electrical, mechanical, acoustical, or other.

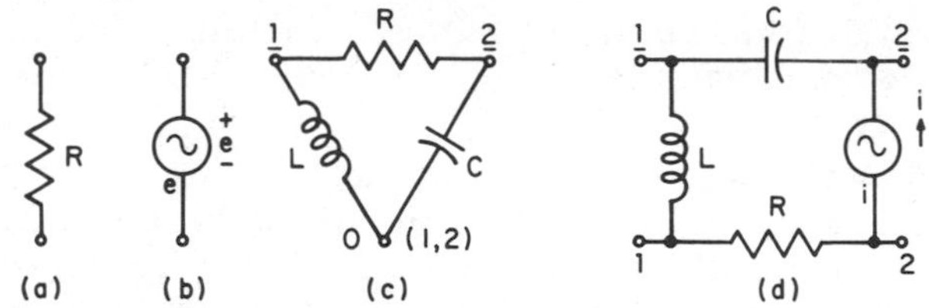

Fig. B2. Simple examples of oneports (a) and (b), a three-terminal network (c), and a typical twoport (d). Note that true or assumed directions of the sources must be indicated.

Figure B2d gives an example of a twoport with three passive network elements, *C, L,* and *R,* and one active network element, the current source, *i.* If resistance *R* is made equal to zero, we note that the four-terminal device becomes a three-terminal device, but it is still a twoport with the ports 1,1 and 2,2. There is now a common connection between terminals 1 and 2. Most tube and transistor networks can be depicted with such a common connection.

We shall next discuss the implications of a ground. Anyone of the terminals in a network may be connected to ground, for example,

[1] Fraenckel, A., *Theorie der Wechselströme*, Springer, Berlin, 1st ed. 1914, 3rd ed. 1930.

[2] Strecker, F., and Feldtkeller, R.,"Grundlagen der Theorie des allgemeinen Vierpols," *ENT* 6, 1929, p. 93. (This is the famous paper that marks the beginning of the practical application of matrix algebra to networks, defining the twoport in concise mathematical form.)

[3] Küpfmüller, K., *Einführing in die theoretische Elektrotechnik*, Springer, Berlin, 1932, p. 215.

[4] Wallot, J., *Theorie der Schwachstromtechnik*, Springer, Berlin, 1932, p. 102.

[5] Guillemin, E. A., *Communications Networks*, Wiley, 1930 and 1953, vol. II, p. 132.

[6] Feldtkeller, R., *Einführing in die Vierpoltheorie der elektrischen Nachrichtentechnik*, Hirzel, Leipzig, 1937.

[7] Oberdorfer, G., *Lehrbuch der Elektrotechnik*, Oldenbourg, Munich and Berlin, 1940, vol. II, p. 282.

[8] Le Corbeiller, "Matrix Analysis of Electric Networks," *Harvard Monograph in Applied Science No.* 1, Wiley, 1950.

[9] LePage, W. R., and Seely, S., *General Network Analysis*, McGraw Hill, 1952, p. 139.

to a water pipe. This often implies that this terminal becomes the reference node or datum node in nodal analysis. Also, it may be a common connection point for supply sources. On the other hand, the network may not have any ground connection, and one should as a rule not provide networks with a ground unless there is a definite need to do so. If, for example, a certain reference terminal is marked "ground" and later on a ground-wire is connected somewhere else, confusion results.

The conventional triode transistor has three electrodes: the emitter, the base, and the collector. If the base is connected to a terminal common to the input and output ports, we call the connection Common-Base or CB-connection. From both a historic and academic point of view, this may be considered the basic connection and is so considered in this text. If the emitter is connected to a terminal common to the input and output ports, we use the term Common-Emitter or CE-connection. Since this is the most important of the three connections, it is often considered the basic one. If the collector is connected to a terminal common to the input and output ports, we call the connection Common-Collector or CC-connection. (Since the common terminal is not always the one that is grounded, we must avoid referring to the three connections as "grounded base," "grounded emitter," and "grounded collector" connections.) Twoport theory is general and describes any one of the three connections with the same ease. The moment we identify a twoport as portraying a transistor of specified connection, we have one of three special cases at hand for which the basic twoport formulas lead to specializations and approximations.

Figure B3 shows a twoport in general. We note that both port currents point inward towards the "box" in accordance with IEEE standards.[1,2] The input immittance is $\mathbf{7}_{in} = \mathbf{V}_1/\mathbf{I}_1$, or its inverse. This quantity has meaning only if the conditions at the 2-end are known, as they are in Fig. B3, with the load impedance $\mathbf{Z}_L$ attached. In accordance with one method of determining the output immittance $\mathbf{7}_{out}$, using the Applied Source Method, the 2-end becomes during this measurement the driven end. The output immittance is then $\mathbf{7}_{out} = \mathbf{V}_{2o}/\mathbf{I}_{2o}$, or its inverse.

We have added the subscript o to indicate that $\mathbf{V}_{2o}$ or $\mathbf{I}_{2o}$ is a

[1]Shea, R. F., *Transistor Circuit Engineering*, Wiley, 1957.

[2]A number of highly useful standards for semiconductor devices have been issued throughout the years by IEEE (IRE). Most of these standards are available for 50 cents to a dollar, but the bulk of them up to 1961 have been collected and issued in book form. Called the *IRE Dictionary*, it is available to both members and nonmembers.

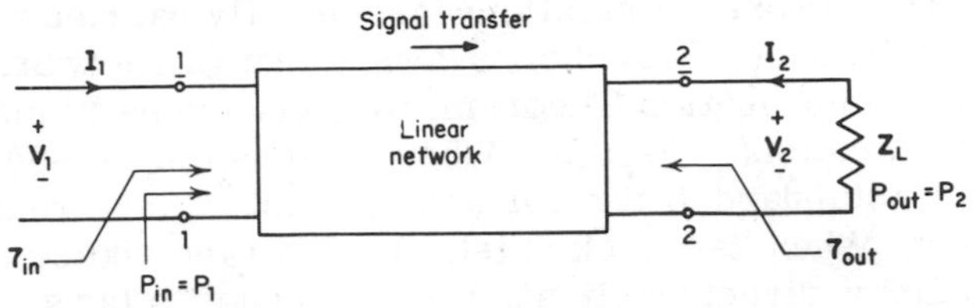

Fig. B3. Currents and voltages for basic twoport, driven from its 1-end. Network inside "box" may be passive or active (in a transistor, active). Load impedance is $-V\ /I\ = \mathbf{Z}_L$.

driving quantity. The immittance, $\mathbf{7}_{\text{out}}$ has meaning only if the conditions at the 1-end are known. In accordance with Fig. B3, there are three possible cases: $\mathbf{V}_1$ represents a constant voltage source, $\mathbf{I}_1$ represents a constant current source, or both $\mathbf{V}_1$ and $\mathbf{I}_1$ may be dependent variables, implying that the twoport is driven by a generator not shown in the figure. $\mathbf{7}_{\text{out}}$ will be different in the three cases, since in the first case we consider the 1-port closed, in the second case the 1-port open, and in the third case we insert the immittance of the driving generator. The procedure is in principle the same in calculations as in measurements in the laboratory, except that in the laboratory we may not bother to remove the driving source from the 1-end, as we carry out the measurements from the 2-end. It is understood that the system can be considered to behave in a linear fashion, and that we can measure at a frequency somewhat different from the driving frequency without risk of error. Strictly speaking, this is only possible if the system is frequency independent. In the measurements of output immittance indicated above, we have, however, made the assumption that the driving source is clearly defined and separated from the twoport proper, so that we can eliminate it. Occasionally, this condition may not be fulfilled, and we may actually carry out measurements with the driving source at the 1-end alive. If, then, the applied source at the 2-end is synchronized with the driving source at the 1-end, a fourth kind of output immittance is obtained which may differ very much from the ones previously obtained. In practical measurements on transistors, when the measurement frequency is purposely made a little higher or a little lower than the driving frequency, the resulting output immittance occasionally fails to verify the value existing with an eliminated driving source. The reason for this may be that the measurement signal locks the driving source to its own frequency (the phenomenon of pulling), so that in reality the measurement result is that discussed as the fourth case above. Thus, care must be exercised in all such measurements.

Twoport network calculations are usually carried out by conventional application of Kirchoff's laws, although a network theorem, such as the Compensation Theorem, may occasionally make worthwhile simplifications possible.[1] When image-immittance operation is at hand, standard filter formulas simplify the treatment to a great extent. When feedback exists, we have the choice of treating the problem by direct application of Kirchhoff's laws, or we may use the much more powerful classical feedback theory. The Current-Voltage Proportioning Method is used extensively for quick solutions, and determinants are employed whenever feasible, particularly when matrices are used initially. Most transistor problems deal only with the periodic steady state, but a considerable number involve transients. Almost all transistor problems originate directly or indirectly in the time domain, where they are portrayed by means of instantaneous values. If such problems belong in the periodic steady state, they are almost always treated with greater brevity and clarity by the Symbolic Method rather than the Laplace Transform Method. In the Steinmetz-Kenelly Symbolic Method of 1893, generally credited to Steinmetz, the spinning sinors in the time domain are frozen, so that the problem can be solved in the time-free domain, which in the Laplace Transform Method is the well-known s-domain. Once the usually simple solution is obtained, the sinors are allowed to begin spinning again, so that the answer may be given in the time domain. The method is direct and entirely independent of tables, and should therefore almost always be used in preference to the Laplace Transform Method. The latter, on the other hand, has the tremendous advantage of being general, giving both the steady-state and the transient solutions. Accordingly, it often provides too heavy a tool to be used for the periodic steady-state only, as it requires transform tables. It should be noted that if, in a Symbolic Method solution, we avoid the loss of j:s by squaring or otherwise, a final non-time domain formula results that can

[1]In the use of Kirchhoff's laws, we avoid the term "voltage drop" as being misleading and inadequate. This term implies direction, since one cannot very well have a "drop" without going from some higher level to a lower level. But our signs have already been taken care of by the sign rules that go with Kirchhoff's laws, and the use of the term "drop" therefore often injects superfluous and contradictory information, beclouding the issue. In most cases when a person uses the term "voltage drop," he does not have direction in mind, but nevertheless he injects the concept of direction. The best thing that can be said about the term "voltage drop" is that it contains a hint that it should be dropped from the English language. For a discussion of signs, see the author's textbook, *The jω- or Symbolic Method*, 1956.

be utilized in the obtaining of a later transient solution, if such a solution is required. (See reference at end of previous footnote).

We shall next discuss how to analyze a network in general, and, if it is a twoport, how to treat it by means of simple twoport theory. From an educational point of view, we begin by discussing the "long-hand" equations for the network, in this manner arriving at the more concise matrix treatment. The discussion is by necessity brief, but the reader who is interested in going deeper into the subject will find ample material in the footnotes listed on these pages.

2. Equation Systems. The network under consideration may contain any number of meshes and nodes. For a given type of network, the number of meshes and nodes are interrelated. If we are asked to produce an analysis of a given network, we may write a set of mesh equations, employing Maxwell's mesh currents, and accordingly obtain an equation system of impedance, or z-type, the driving voltage equaling a summation of **zI** terms in each equation. By solving for the current, **I**, however, we may transform this equation system into an admittance-type or y-type equation system, the driving current equaling a summation of **yV** terms in each equation. As an alternative, we could have started out with node analysis, using Maxwell's node voltages. We would then have obtained the admittance-type equation system directly. Solving for the voltages, we could then transform back to the impedance-type equation system we started out with.

Evidently we can start out any way we wish and end up with the type of equation system we want. One procedure, however, is bound to be faster than the others. We draw the conclusion that mesh analysis does not necessarily go with z-type equation systems and that node analysis does not necessarily go with y-type equation systems. Whichever way we do it, we end up with equations in which the coefficients **z** and **y** represent the parameters of the network, which may be electrical, mechanical, acoustical, or other. We may move the variables around in the equations, and in this way we obtain new equations in which the coefficients are made up of combinations of **z**:*s* and **y**:*s*. These new coefficients again represent the parameters of the original network, but they are determined by variable ratios different from those describing **z** and **y** parameters. As will be shown in the following, we only obtain a limited number of new equations this way; as we keep on trying to create new equations, we shall find that we repeat ourselves.

Starting out with mesh analysis of a given network with n meshes, including the ones at the ports, and with n currents, we

are dealing with a network that we ultimately wish to represent by the twoport in Fig. B3. The voltages $\mathbf{V}_1$ and $\mathbf{V}_2$ only become involved in two of the equations. We may write with the aid of Kirchhoff's Voltage-Sum Law, for $k = 1, 2, \ldots. n$, without specifying the impedances,

$$\left.\begin{array}{r} \mathbf{V}_1 = \sum_{k=1}^{n} \mathbf{zI}_k \\ \text{================} \\ \mathbf{V}_{\text{mesh } n} = \mathbf{V}_2 = \sum_{k=1}^{n} \mathbf{zI}_k \end{array}\right\} \quad \text{(B1)}$$

Eliminating all internal mesh currents, we can reduce this equation system to only two equations, embodying the four basic variables, $\mathbf{V}_1$, $\mathbf{V}_2$, $\mathbf{I}_1$, $\mathbf{I}_2$. These four variables are related via the four coefficients which constitute the four system or network parameters. In the two resulting equations, three of the four variables, such as $\mathbf{V}_1$, $\mathbf{V}_2$, and $\mathbf{I}_2$, may be dependent variables, whereas $\mathbf{I}_1$ may be the given or independent variable. This does not necessarily mean that $\mathbf{I}_1$ is the reference variable of zero phase angle. Conditions vary greatly. As an example, all currents and voltages may be known, and one or more parameters unknown. Whereas four parameters are required to describe the general twoport, which may be an active twoport, only three parameters are required to describe the passive twoport. If it is symmetrical, only two parameters are required. The equation system for the general twoport is written

$$\mathbf{V}_1 = \mathbf{z}_{11}\mathbf{I}_1 + \mathbf{z}_{12}\mathbf{I}_2 \quad \text{(B2)}$$

$$\mathbf{V}_2 = \mathbf{z}_{21}\mathbf{I}_1 + \mathbf{z}_{22}\mathbf{I}_2 \quad \text{(B3)}$$

The double subscripts of the z symbols have the following meaning. If we write the symbol in general as $\mathbf{z}_{ij}$, where i takes on values 1, 2, 3,.... and independently j takes on values 1, 2, 3,...., then the subscripts serve to identify the parameter in the long-hand equation system, or, as we shall see later, to identify the element in the matrix. The symbols $\mathbf{z}_{ij}$ fall into two groups: one in which the two subscripts are the same, $\mathbf{z}_{ii}$ and $\mathbf{z}_{jj}$, and the other in which the two subscripts are different. The first group contains the self-impedances, $\mathbf{z}_{11}, \mathbf{z}_{22}, \mathbf{z}_{33}, \ldots.$, described by a voltage-current ratio with the voltage and current pertaining to one and the same mesh. The second group contains the coupling or transfer impedances, $\mathbf{z}_{12}$, $\mathbf{z}_{13}, \ldots., \mathbf{z}_{21}, \mathbf{z}_{23}, \ldots.$, described by a voltage-current ratio with

the voltage and current pertaining to different meshes. In the established twoport, only the two equations, B2 and B3, are required. Accordingly, only two self-impedances, $\mathbf{z}_{11}$ and $\mathbf{z}_{22}$ exist, and only two coupling or transfer impedances, $\mathbf{z}_{12}$ and $\mathbf{z}_{21}$. For a further definition of the meaning of the subscripts, we shall consider the mathematical definition, in accordance with which the first subscript is the number of the equation in the array of equations, whereas the second subscript is the number of the term. To define any one parameter, $\mathbf{z}_{ij}$, we must eliminate all terms except the term containing $\mathbf{z}_{ij}$. Thus, if we wish to define $\mathbf{z}_{11}$ in Eq. B2, we must eliminate the second term, $\mathbf{z}_{12}\mathbf{I}_2$. Since $\mathbf{z}_{12}$ cannot be zero in the general case, $\mathbf{I}_2$ must be zero, meaning that the opposite end, or 2-end, is open. Accordingly, the z parameters are known as "open-circuit parameters."

If we solve equation-system (B2) (B3) for $\mathbf{I}_1$ and $\mathbf{I}_2$, we obtain the following y-type equation system:

$$\left.\begin{aligned} \mathbf{I}_1 &= \mathbf{y}_{11}\mathbf{V}_1 + \mathbf{y}_{12}\mathbf{V}_2 \qquad \text{(B4)} \\ \mathbf{I}_2 &= \mathbf{y}_{21}\mathbf{V}_1 + \mathbf{y}_{22}\mathbf{V}_2 \qquad \text{(B5)} \end{aligned}\right\}$$

The y parameters are, in terms of the z parameters,

$$\mathbf{y}_{11} = \mathbf{z}_{22}/\Delta_z \qquad \text{(B6)}$$

$$\mathbf{y}_{12} = -\mathbf{z}_{12}/\Delta_z \qquad \text{(B7)}$$

$$\mathbf{y}_{21} = -\mathbf{z}_{21}/\Delta_z \qquad \text{(B8)}$$

$$\mathbf{y}_{22} = \mathbf{z}_{11}/\Delta_z \qquad \text{(B9)}$$

where Δ_z is the determinant,

$$\Delta_z = \mathbf{z}_{11}\mathbf{z}_{22} - \mathbf{z}_{12}\mathbf{z}_{21} \qquad \text{(B10)}$$

To determine a y parameter, we must make the opposite term vanish. Thus if we wish to define $\mathbf{y}_{11}$ in Eq. B4, we must eliminate the second term $\mathbf{y}_{12}\mathbf{V}_2$. Since $\mathbf{y}_{12}$ cannot be zero in the general case, $\mathbf{V}_2$ must be zero, meaning that the opposite end, or 2-end, is closed. Accordingly, the y parameters are known as "short-circuit parameters." In the following, we shall derive mixed equations with term summations containing both currents and voltages. In accordance with the "vanishing-term" criterion, we should then expect the twoport to have one open end and one closed end.

Calculations such as the ones leading to Eqs. B6 - B10 can be avoided if the proper tables are used. If we turn to Table 1 in Appendix C, we find that the first column and second row produces the parameters directly. If as an alternative equation system (B4) (B5) had provided the start for our discussion, we would have proceeded in the opposite direction, using node analysis rather than mesh analysis, and obtained the z-equation system with the parameters:

$$\mathbf{z}_{11} = \mathbf{y}_{22}/\Delta_y \tag{B11}$$

$$\mathbf{z}_{12} = -\mathbf{y}_{12}/\Delta_y \tag{B12}$$

$$\mathbf{z}_{21} = -\mathbf{y}_{21}/\Delta_y \tag{B13}$$

$$\mathbf{z}_{22} = \mathbf{y}_{11}/\Delta_y \tag{B14}$$

with the determinant

$$\Delta_y = \mathbf{y}_{11}\mathbf{y}_{22} - \mathbf{y}_{12}\mathbf{y}_{21} \tag{B15}$$

This result could have been obtained directly from Table 1, Appendix C, second column, first row. Inserting z parameters in Eq. B15, we obtain

$$\Delta_y = (\mathbf{z}_{22}/\Delta_z)(\mathbf{z}_{11}/\Delta_z) - (-\mathbf{z}_{12}/\Delta_z)(-\mathbf{z}_{21}/\Delta_z) = 1/\Delta_z \tag{B16}$$

which result is given in the first column and second row of Table 2, Appendix C. Actually, the combination of Tables 1 and 2 in Appendix C provides us with a fast method of treating all the twoport parameters and their internal relationships. The z and y equations are repeated in Table 3. By mixing the variables in all ways possible, we obtain four additional equation systems, but not more than four. We refer to the z and y equations as immittance parameter equations, the h and k equations as the hybrid parameter equations, and the a and b equations as the transmission parameter equations. We may now realize that the minus signs in Table 3 are the result of our writing all the parameters in the equations in Table 2 with a plus sign preceding the term. The transmission parameters are the oldest ones, so far as engineering usage goes, and depict a chain network with all the currents going in the same direction. Since the twoport symbol at the top of Table 3 applies generally, the currents must be introduced with minus signs in the transmission parameter equations.

The double-subscript symbols used above are widely adopted and have many advantages. It should be noted that since $\mathbf{z}_{11} \neq 1/\mathbf{y}_{11}$, and so on, additional notation is required to make the system foolproof. Also, CB, CE, and CC connections may be indicated by means of a third subscript, b, u, and c, making the symbols quite elaborate. A short-hand set of symbols using only one subscript has therefore been introduced. Referred to as the "irfo" system, it takes the form

$$\begin{matrix} \mathbf{z}_{11} = \mathbf{z}_i & \mathbf{z}_{12} = \mathbf{z}_r & \mathbf{y}_{11} = \mathbf{y}_i & \mathbf{y}_{12} = \mathbf{y}_r \\ \mathbf{z}_{21} = \mathbf{z}_f & \mathbf{z}_{22} = \mathbf{z}_o & \mathbf{y}_{21} = \mathbf{y}_f & \mathbf{y}_{22} = \mathbf{y}_o \end{matrix} \tag{B17}$$

Extending the above discussion of the "vanishing term" criterion, defining each and every one of all the parameters, we can derive a proper name for each parameter (see Table 5, Appendix C). While transfer functions and port functions exist, which depend upon generator and load immittances, the parameter definitions may be considered to represent limit values of those functions. As an example, we may formulate a special form of the input impedance by writing

$$\mathbf{Z}_{\text{in}}\Big|_{\text{output open}} = (\mathbf{V}_1/\mathbf{I}_1)\Big|_{\text{output open}} = \mathbf{z}_{11} = \mathbf{z}_i \tag{B18}$$

Transfer immittances may be formulated in a similar manner.

3. Small-signal Theory. The validity of the definitions introduced above stems from the fact that we may write the ratios between variational quantities as ratios between differentials. In this way we are able to link the sign of a variational quantity to the direction of change of a bias quantity. Let us consider for the moment the input port of a special semiconductor device, represented by the current-voltage graph in Fig. B4. Generally, the characteristic is curved rather than being a straight line. We note that the Q-point, Q_4, is located on the negative-slope branch of the characteristic, $i = f(v)$. Thus the conductance, g_4, is a negative number, representing a stimulance. Still the network may be entirely stable, namely if the driving generator places a smaller resistance across the input port than $1/g_4$. With the network stable, we can treat negative resistance and conductance just as positive resistance and conductance, provided we observe the proper sign.

We may introduce the following definitions, pertaining to direct and variational conductance:

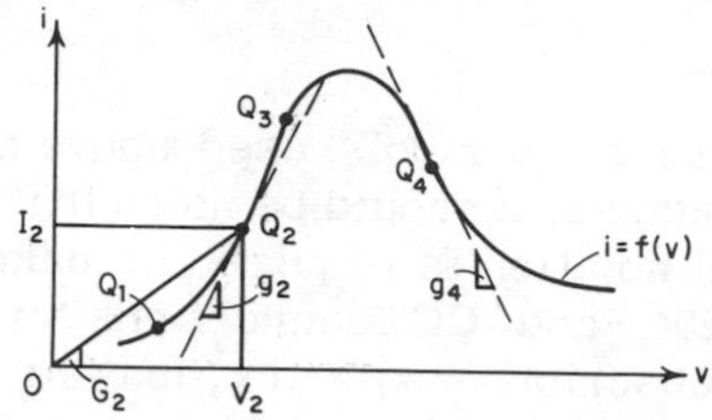

Fig. B4. Input conductance characteristic of special semiconductor device, showing difference between direct conductance, G_2, and variational conductance, g_2. Three Q-points are located in positive conductance range, and one conditional point, Q_4, in negative conductance range (stimulance region).

$$g = \frac{i}{v} \tag{B19}$$

$$G_2 = \frac{I_2}{V_2} \tag{B20}$$

$$g_2 = \frac{\Delta i}{\Delta v}\bigg|_2 \tag{B21}$$

$$g_2 = \frac{di}{dv}\bigg|_2 \tag{B22}$$

Here, Eq. B19 is the general formula for conductance. Equation B20 gives the direct conductance in the Q-point, Q_2. This may be quite different from the variational conductance given by Eq. B21, which is here expressed by finite quantities, representative of small-signal measurements in the laboratory. The mathematically rigid definition is given as the limit in Eq. B22. This is not to be taken as a quotient of two differentials, but as a derivative, indicating the slope of the curve in the point Q_2. Generally, the derivative is our starting point in theoretical considerations, and going from Eq. B22 to Eq. B21, we proceed from infinitesimal to finite quantities, in which Δv may be enlarged to represent the maximum amplitude of a cosine wave. The frequency of the applied wave, $\Delta v \cos \omega t$, could be anything we decide upon, for example, $\omega/2\pi = 400$ cps. The applied voltage and the ensuing current may then be written

$$V + \Delta v = V + \hat{V} \cos \omega t \tag{B23}$$

$$I + \Delta i = I + \hat{I} \cos \omega t \tag{B24}$$

assuming that the port under investigation is free from storage effects. The corresponding expression for the variational conductance is now

$$g_2 = (\widehat{I}/\widehat{V})\,|_2 \tag{B25}$$

In practical measurements, $\widehat{V}$ should be made sufficiently small, or as small as conditions permit (the limit may be set by noise). The change from a derivative to a practical quotient is further elaborated upon in the following, where the g parameter, g_{11}, is used, relating to a transistor operated in a suitable Q-point:

$$g_{11} = (di/dv)\,|_{dv_2=0} \rightarrow (\Delta I/\Delta V)\,|_{\Delta V_2=0} \rightarrow (\widehat{I}/\widehat{V})\,|_{\widehat{V}_2=0} \tag{B26}$$

During the practical measurements in the laboratory, we may fail to keep the signal amplitudes small enough. Due to curvature of the characteristic, a direct-current component is then generated, which due to existing resistance changes the bias voltage in the circuit, moving the Q-point.

To go one step further in defining conductances, we may consider the case of nonlinear mixing, where the output wave differs in frequency from the input wave. In the communications field, the output wave is then referred to as the intermediate-frequency wave. If the input and output waves are of the form

$$v_1 = \widehat{V}_1 \cos \omega_1 t \qquad i_2 = \widehat{I}_2 \cos (\omega_2 t + \alpha) \tag{B27}$$

the conversion conductance or transconductance becomes

$$g_{\text{conv}} = \widehat{I}_2/\widehat{V}_1\,|_{\widehat{V}_{lo}=\text{ const}} \tag{B28}$$

which is a ratio of peak values, and where $\widehat{V}_{lo}$ is the peak value of the local oscillator wave. Note, however, that V_{lo} often is insufficient to describe conditions, unless the impedance seen by the local oscillator is also mentioned. This means a power consideration rather than a voltage consideration. We may go one step further and ask how a change, $\Delta\widehat{V}_1$ in $\widehat{V}_1$, would affect $\widehat{I}_2$. This would represent the case of an amplitude-modulated (AM) wave, applied to a non-linear mixer with local oscillator, that is, a converter. The corresponding variational conductance or transconductance in the Q-point is

$$\widetilde{g}_{\text{conv}} = (\widehat{\Delta\widehat{I}_2/\Delta\widehat{V}_1})\,|_{\widehat{V}_{lo}=\text{const}} \tag{B29}$$

If this quantity is maintained constant within a certain range of operation, then the converter is in this respect a linear device, whereas the mixing diode it contains is highly nonlinear. Thus we can make a linear model of a diode or transistor frequency con-

verter and use conventional twoport formulas to describe its operation, just as if it were linear all the way through. This is a powerful technique that should be kept well in mind (see "Some Final Thoughts," Chapter 7).

If storage effects are present in the semiconductor device, the real term discussed above is supplemented by an s-term representing a particular storage element. Thus, g_{11} in Eq. B26 will have a second term, sc_{11}, in case a capacitance c_{11} shunts g_{11}. This second term, containing the operator s, more rigidly written $\mathbf{s}$, evolves through the same reasoning that was applied to the real part. Being concerned with measurements and definitions, we operate in the periodic steady state, where s takes the form, $s = j\omega_G$, and where $\omega_G/2\pi$ is the frequency of the driving generator or source. We refer to $j\omega_G c_{11} = jb_{11}$ as the j-term or quadrature term, and $\omega_G c_{11} = b_{11}$ as the j-part or quadrature part. (Always avoid the use of the misleading and superfluous term, "imaginary.") The combination of the real term and the j-term is a complex quantity, described by a ratio of two frozen sinors; in this case, a current sinor divided by a voltage sinor. The complete presentation of the immittance parameters now takes the form

$$\mathbf{z}_{ij} = r_{ij} + jx_{ij} = z_{ij} \underline{|\theta_{ij}} \qquad z_{ij} = \sqrt{r_{ij}^2 + x_{ij}^2}$$
$$\phi_{ij} = tan^{-1} x_{ij}/r_{ij} \qquad \text{(B30)}$$

$$\mathbf{y}_{ij} = g_{ij} + jb_{ij} = y_{ij} \underline{|\phi_{ij}} \qquad y_{ij} = \sqrt{g_{ij}^2 + b_{ij}^2}$$
$$\phi_{ij} = tan^{-1} b_{ij}/g_{ij} \qquad \text{(B31)}$$

Most textbooks use these symbols, with exception for the phase angles. Due to the lack of national standards, many different symbols are employed for the hybrid and transmission parameters, and there are no conventional symbols for the real and j-parts that differ from the complex, total symbol. One practical way out of this difficulty is based on the rather common use of P for real and Q for quadrature. Taking the k parameter as an example, we may therefore write

$$\mathbf{k}_{ij} = k_{ijP} + jk_{ijQ} = k_{ij} \underline{|\gamma_{ij}} = \sqrt{k_{ijP}^2 + k_{ijQ}^2}$$
$$\gamma_{ij} = tan^{-1} k_{ijQ}/k_{ijP} \qquad \text{(B32)}$$

Loose usage of symbols must be avoided in calculation work, since it often leads to erroneous results. Thus, whatever our symbols are, we must make sure that they are clearly defined.

4. Use Of Matrix Algebra. The importance of the matrix algebra tool has already been indicated at several points in the previous discussion. Using z parameters, we shall first clarify the relationships between matrix equations B33 and B34, the "long-hand" equation system B35, the network matrices B36 and B37, the symbol for the determinant B38, and the determinant B39. (In this text the same type of bar has been used for both matrices and determinants; text references indicate the interpretation of the bars intended.)

$$|\mathbf{V}| = |\mathbf{z}| \; |\mathbf{I}| \tag{B33}$$

$$\begin{vmatrix} \mathbf{V}_1 \\ \mathbf{V}_2 \end{vmatrix} = \begin{vmatrix} \mathbf{z}_{11} & \mathbf{z}_{12} \\ \mathbf{z}_{21} & \mathbf{z}_{22} \end{vmatrix} \begin{vmatrix} \mathbf{I}_1 \\ \mathbf{I}_2 \end{vmatrix} \tag{B34}$$

$$\left.\begin{aligned} \mathbf{V}_1 &= \mathbf{z}_{11}\mathbf{I}_1 + \mathbf{z}_{12}\mathbf{I}_2 \\ \mathbf{V}_2 &= \mathbf{z}_{21}\mathbf{I}_1 + \mathbf{z}_{22}\mathbf{I}_2 \end{aligned}\right\} \tag{B35}$$

$$|\mathbf{z}| \tag{B36}$$

$$\begin{vmatrix} \mathbf{z}_{11} & \mathbf{z}_{12} \\ \mathbf{z}_{21} & \mathbf{z}_{22} \end{vmatrix} \tag{B37}$$

$$\begin{vmatrix} \mathbf{z}_{11} & \mathbf{z}_{12} \\ \mathbf{z}_{21} & \mathbf{z}_{22} \end{vmatrix} \tag{B38}$$

$$\mathbf{z}_{11}\mathbf{z}_{22} - \mathbf{z}_{12}\mathbf{z}_{21} = \Delta_z \tag{B39}$$

To obtain equation system B35 from B34, we merely go through a mechanical process of "unwinding," following an established matrix-algebra rule. We begin by multiplying the first row in the network matrix by the subsequent column matrix. We do this by first multiplying $\mathbf{z}_{11}$ and $\mathbf{I}_1$ and then adding to this the product of $\mathbf{z}_{12}$ and $\mathbf{I}_2$ with the first equation in B35 as result. We then multiply the second row in the network matrix by the subsequent column matrix, in this fashion obtaining the second equation in B35. In principle, the application of the matrix-multiplication rule is the same for the additional **y**, **h**, **k**, **a**, and **b** parameters. The matrix in B37 and the determinant symbol in B38 might have precisely the same appearance; both may contain algebraical expressions or only numerical

expressions. Whether an element is written in algebraic or numerical form is not necessarily a clue that helps us to determine whether we are dealing with a matrix or with a determinant symbol. We go from a matrix to its determinant when we use the matrix elements for computation purposes, formulating a determinant such as the one given by Eq. B39.

We note that the equation system B1 contains as many equations as terms on the right-hand side, and this characteristic provides us with the typical "square" matrix used in network calculations, a matrix having as many rows as it has columns. The matrix in B37 is said to be of the second order. This is the most common-size matrix used in transistor calculations, but we also use the third-order matrix to a great extent (for example, in the "floating" matrix technique). The most used matrix table is Table 1 in Appendix C, where we recognize the first matrix (with the vertical bars left out) as the z matrix. The corresponding "long-hand" equation systems are shown in Table 3. Apparently, one way of constructing Table 1 is to keep on changing the variables around in the original z long-hand equation system. The determinants in Table 2 are obtained in accordance with the principle shown by Eq. B39. Inside each parameter group, one matrix may be obtained from the other by inversion. The method is here demonstrated for immittance parameters. The z to y parameter transformation is carried out as follows:

$$\text{Divide by } \boldsymbol{\Delta}_z, \text{ change signs} \quad \begin{vmatrix} \dfrac{\mathbf{z}_{11}}{\boldsymbol{\Delta}_z} & \dfrac{\mathbf{z}_{12}}{\boldsymbol{\Delta}_z} \\ \dfrac{\mathbf{z}_{21}}{\boldsymbol{\Delta}_z} & \dfrac{\mathbf{z}_{22}}{\boldsymbol{\Delta}_z} \end{vmatrix} \quad \text{shift elements and obtain} \quad \begin{vmatrix} \dfrac{\mathbf{z}_{22}}{\boldsymbol{\Delta}_z} & \dfrac{-\mathbf{z}_{12}}{\boldsymbol{\Delta}_z} \\ \dfrac{-\mathbf{z}_{21}}{\boldsymbol{\Delta}_z} & \dfrac{\mathbf{z}_{11}}{\boldsymbol{\Delta}_z} \end{vmatrix} = |\mathbf{y}| \tag{B40}$$

We note that the result is the same as we obtained by long-hand calculations in Eqs. B6 to B9. In a similar manner we can obtain the k matrix from the h matrix, and the b matrix from the a matrix, and vice versa. In any one of these transformations, it is very important to realize that we are dealing with one particular device that does not change, for example, a twoport representing a CB-connected transistor. This transistor, driven by a certain generator and feeding a certain load immittance, has a specific voltage amplification, a specific current amplification, a specific input immittance, and a specific output immittance. It does not matter whether we represent the transistor by an equivalent TEE or an equivalent

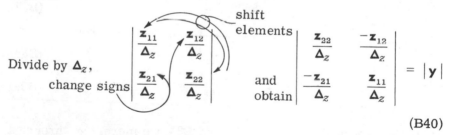

PI, or by z parameters, or h parameters, or any other parameters. The four characteristics listed above do not change as long as we retain the transistor in CB-connection. If we switch to CE- or CC-connection, however, some of the characteristics are bound to change.

Studying the matrix for a transistor, we find that the existence or nonexistence of diagonal symmetry in the matrix reveals important characteristics of the transistor network (see Fig. B5). Here the difference between main-diagonal symmetry and opposite-diagonal symmetry has been demonstrated by examples. Both networks shown obey the Reciprocity Theorem, but the network to the right has the added feature of displaying symmetry with reference to a cut through the mid-branch. We find that main diagonal symmetry, representing the bilateral case, reduces the z and y parameters from four to three. The same symmetry further reduces the hybrid parameters from four to three, except that minus signs enter in, as is evident from Table 1. In case of the transmission parameters, however, no similar parameter simplification obtains. Instead, we find that $\Delta_a = 1/\Delta_b = 1$ (see, for example, Table 6, Appendix C).

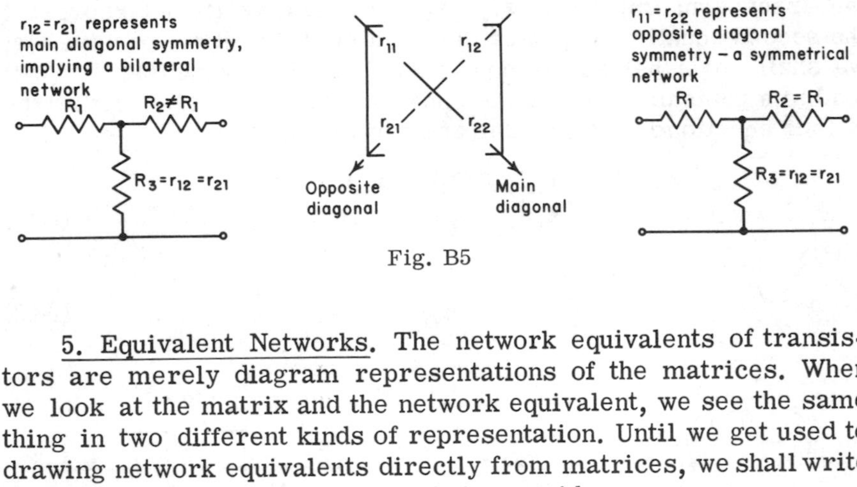

Fig. B5

5. Equivalent Networks. The network equivalents of transistors are merely diagram representations of the matrices. When we look at the matrix and the network equivalent, we see the same thing in two different kinds of representation. Until we get used to drawing network equivalents directly from matrices, we shall write the long-hand equations as an in-between aid.

The network equivalents shown in Fig. B6 are read off directly from equation system B35. They are referred to as double-source equivalents. More precisely, we read off the first equivalent from B35 and then obtain the second one by changing the series-form generators into shunt-form generators. As an alternative, we can change one of the generators but not the other. Accordingly, there

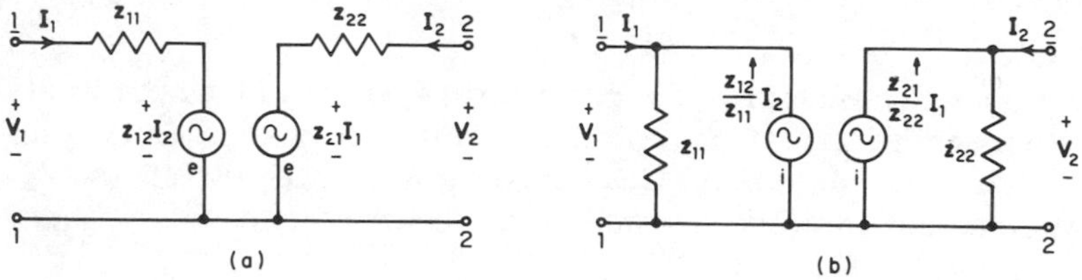

Fig. B6. (a) Double-source equivalent, read off directly from z equations; (b) same equivalent with shunt-form generators replacing series-form generators.

are four network equivalents of this kind for the z parameters, and similarly there are four for the y parameters. Since we can express both the z and the y parameters in h, k, a, or b parameters, it follows that each parameter has four equivalents of this kind. Totally, there are 24 equivalents of the types described.

Of somewhat greater interest are the single-source equivalents, and we shall next derive the single-source equivalent for the z parameters. We may note that the first equation in B35 describes a passive tee just as much as an active tee, and using this equation, we can therefore draw the transistor equivalent up to the cut xx_1, as in Fig. B7a. It is seen that full agreement exists if we label the input arm impedance $\mathbf{z}_{11} - \mathbf{z}_{12}$. Although we cannot represent the second equation in B35 by the remaining part of the passive tee, we shall nevertheless attempt to do so, well knowing that this will lead to a punishing term in the equation. We proceed by writing the second equation in B35, adding and subtracting $\mathbf{z}_{12}\mathbf{I}_1$,

$$\begin{aligned}\mathbf{V}_2 &= \mathbf{z}_{12}\mathbf{I}_1 + \mathbf{z}_{22}\mathbf{I}_2 + \mathbf{z}_{21}\mathbf{I}_1 - \mathbf{z}_{12}\mathbf{I}_1 \\ &= \mathbf{z}_{12}\mathbf{I}_1 + \mathbf{z}_{22}\mathbf{I}_2 + \mathbf{z}_m\mathbf{I}_1 \qquad \text{(B41)}\end{aligned}$$

where

$$\mathbf{z}_m = \mathbf{z}_{21} - \mathbf{z}_{12} \qquad \text{(B42)}$$

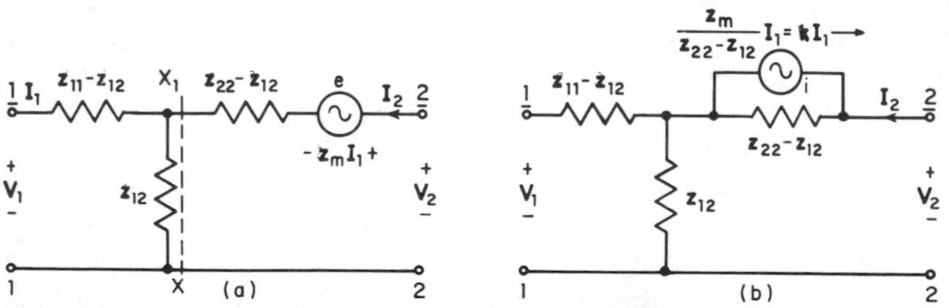

Fig. B7. Active TEE with (a) series-form generator output arm; (b) shunt-form generator output arm.

Here $\mathbf{z}_m$ is a mutual impedance, linking the two meshes together. For $\mathbf{z}_m = 0$, B41 truly describes a passive tee, as is expected, since $\mathbf{z}_m = 0$ means $\mathbf{z}_{12} = \mathbf{z}_{21}$. The term $\mathbf{z}_m \mathbf{I}_1$ is the expected punishment term and represents a voltage source in series with $\mathbf{V}_2$ and bucking $\mathbf{V}_2$. Accordingly, the network to the right of the cut xx_1 takes the form shown in Fig. B7a. A still more important tee equivalent is shown in Fig. B7b. It is obtained by changing the series-form generator in the output arm to a shunt-form generator, which will be discussed later.

The evolution of the y parameter network equivalents follows the same pattern (see Fig. B8). From the matrix and equation system

$$|\mathbf{y}| = \begin{vmatrix} \mathbf{y}_{11} & \mathbf{y}_{12} \\ \mathbf{y}_{21} & \mathbf{y}_{22} \end{vmatrix} \tag{B43}$$

$$\left.\begin{aligned} \mathbf{I}_1 &= \mathbf{y}_{11}\mathbf{V}_1 + \mathbf{y}_{12}\mathbf{V}_2 \qquad \text{(B44)} \\ \mathbf{I}_2 &= \mathbf{y}_{21}\mathbf{V}_1 + \mathbf{y}_{22}\mathbf{V}_2 \qquad \text{(B45)} \end{aligned}\right\}$$

we read off the network equivalent in Fig. B8a, from which we obtain the one in B8b by changing the shunt-form generators to series-form generators. For the single-source equivalent in Fig. B8c, we proceed as in Eqs. B41 and B42, writing

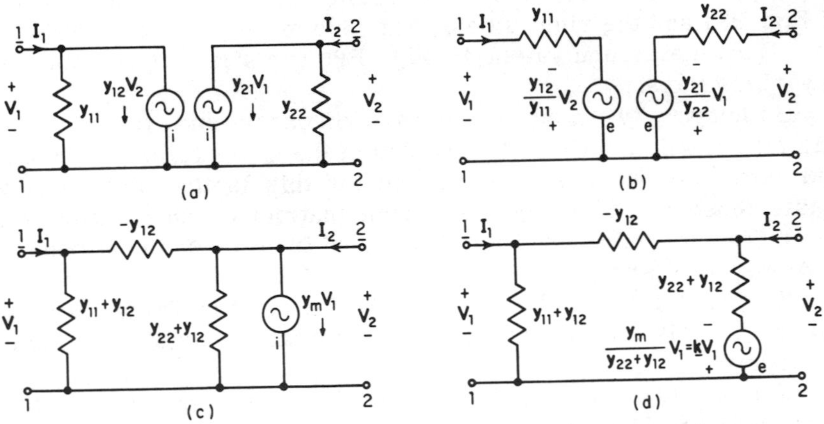

Fig. B8. (a) Double-source equivalent with y parameters; (b) same equivalent with the shunt-form generators replaced by series-form generators; (c) active PI with shunt-form generator output leg; (d) active PI with series-form generator output leg.

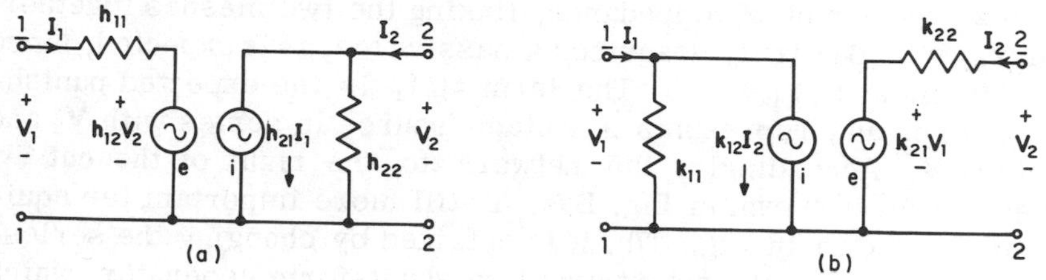

Fig. B9. (a) Double-source equivalent with h parameters; (b) double-source equivalent with k parameters.

$$\begin{aligned}\mathbf{I}_2 &= \mathbf{y}_{12}\mathbf{V}_1 + \mathbf{y}_{22}\mathbf{V}_2 + \mathbf{y}_{21}\mathbf{V}_1 - \mathbf{y}_{12}\mathbf{V}_1 \\ &= \mathbf{y}_{12}\mathbf{V}_1 + \mathbf{y}_{22}\mathbf{V}_2 + \mathbf{y}_m\mathbf{V}_1 \end{aligned} \qquad \text{(B46)}$$

where

$$\mathbf{y}_m = \mathbf{y}_{21} - \mathbf{y}_{12} \qquad \text{(B47)}$$

Here y_m is the mutual admittance. The active PI obtained in Fig. B8c is the important one; the derived form in Fig. B8d is seldom used.

As examples of network equivalents employing parameters other than the z and y parameters, double-source equivalents for h and k parameters are shown in Fig. B9. We read off the network equivalent in Fig. B9a from the h parameter equation system in Table 3, but as an alternative, we could obtain it from the left side of Fig. B8a and the right side of Fig. B6b merely by using Table 1. The parameter equivalent in Fig. B9b can similarly be obtained in various ways.

Although network equivalents are necessary and often very useful, they should as a rule be avoided in the computation of transfer and port immittances. The reason for this is that ordinarily we obtain these quantities quicker from matrices and equation systems. The formulas in Table 1, derived from the twoport equation systems, are very useful.

The output immittances given to the right in Table 1 are obtained directly by means of the Denominator Output Immittance Theorem.

The quantities $\mathbf{k}$ and $\underline{\mathbf{k}}$ introduced in the network equivalents in Figs. B7b and B8d need further explanation. At least the first one warrants a discussion here; $\mathbf{k}$ has been given a specific designation for each one of the three connections, as is seen from Table 2.

Since all parameters and ratios in Table 2 are complex quantities, care must be exercised so that mix-ups between the complex

TABLE 1

Immittance parameters

$\mathbf{A}_I(\omega)_z = \frac{\mathbf{I}_2}{\mathbf{I}_1} = \frac{-\mathbf{z}_{21}}{\mathbf{z}_{22} + \mathbf{Z}_L}$	$\mathbf{Z}_{\text{out}} = \mathbf{z}_{22}$
$\mathbf{A}_I(\omega)_y = \frac{\mathbf{I}_2}{\mathbf{I}_1} = \frac{\mathbf{y}_{21}}{\mathbf{y}_{11} + \mathbf{\Delta}_y \mathbf{Z}_L}$	$\mathbf{Y}_{\text{out}} = \mathbf{\Delta}_y/\mathbf{y}_{11}$
$\mathbf{A}_V(\omega)_z = \frac{\mathbf{V}_2}{\mathbf{V}_1} = \frac{\mathbf{z}_{21}}{\mathbf{z}_{11} + \mathbf{\Delta}_z \mathbf{Y}_L}$	$\mathbf{Z}_{\text{out}} = \mathbf{\Delta}_z/\mathbf{z}_{11}$
$\mathbf{A}_V(\omega)_y = \frac{\mathbf{V}_2}{\mathbf{V}_1} = \frac{-\mathbf{y}_{21}}{\mathbf{y}_{22} + \mathbf{Y}_L}$	$\mathbf{Y}_{\text{out}} = \mathbf{y}_{22}$
$\mathbf{Z}_{\text{in}} = \frac{\mathbf{\Delta}_z + \mathbf{z}_{11}\mathbf{Z}_L}{\mathbf{z}_{22} + \mathbf{Z}_L} = \frac{\mathbf{\Delta}_{z2}}{\mathbf{z}_{222}}$	$\mathbf{Y}_{\text{in}} = \frac{\mathbf{\Delta}_y + \mathbf{y}_{11}\mathbf{Y}_L}{\mathbf{y}_{22} + \mathbf{Y}_L} = \frac{\mathbf{\Delta}_{y2}}{\mathbf{y}_{222}}$

Hybrid parameters

$\mathbf{A}_I(\omega)_h = \frac{\mathbf{I}_2}{\mathbf{I}_1} = \frac{\mathbf{h}_{21}}{1 + \mathbf{h}_{22}\mathbf{Z}_L}$	$\mathbf{Y}_{\text{out}} = \mathbf{h}_{22}$
$\mathbf{A}_I(\omega)_k = \frac{\mathbf{I}_2}{\mathbf{I}_1} = \frac{-\mathbf{k}_{21}}{\mathbf{\Delta}_k + \mathbf{k}_{11}\mathbf{Z}_L}$	$\mathbf{Z}_{\text{out}} = \mathbf{\Delta}_k/\mathbf{k}_{11}$
$\mathbf{A}_V(\omega)_h = \frac{\mathbf{V}_2}{\mathbf{V}_1} = \frac{-\mathbf{h}_{21}}{\mathbf{\Delta}_h + \mathbf{h}_{11}\mathbf{Y}_L}$	$\mathbf{Y}_{\text{out}} = \mathbf{\Delta}_h/\mathbf{h}_{11}$
$\mathbf{A}_V(\omega)_k = \frac{\mathbf{V}_2}{\mathbf{V}_1} = \frac{\mathbf{k}_{21}}{1 + \mathbf{k}_{22}\mathbf{Y}_L}$	$\mathbf{Z}_{\text{out}} = \mathbf{k}_{22}$
$\mathbf{Z}_{\text{in}} = \frac{\mathbf{\Delta}_h + \mathbf{h}_{11}\mathbf{Y}_L}{\mathbf{h}_{22} + \mathbf{Y}_L} = \frac{\mathbf{\Delta}_{h2}}{\mathbf{h}_{222}}$	$\mathbf{Y}_{\text{in}} = \frac{\mathbf{\Delta}_k + \mathbf{k}_{11}\mathbf{Z}_L}{\mathbf{k}_{22} + \mathbf{Z}_L} = \frac{\mathbf{\Delta}_{k2}}{\mathbf{k}_{222}}$

Transmission parameters

$\mathbf{A}_I(\omega)_a = \frac{\mathbf{I}_2}{\mathbf{I}_1} = \frac{-1}{\mathbf{a}_{22} + \mathbf{a}_{21}\mathbf{Z}_L}$	$\mathbf{Y}_{\text{out}} = \mathbf{a}_{21}/\mathbf{a}_{22}$
$\mathbf{A}_I(\omega)_b = \frac{\mathbf{I}_2}{\mathbf{I}_1} = \frac{-\mathbf{\Delta}_b}{\mathbf{b}_{11} + \mathbf{b}_{21}\mathbf{Z}_L}$	$\mathbf{Y}_{\text{out}} = \mathbf{b}_{21}/\mathbf{b}_{11}$
$\mathbf{A}_V(\omega)_a = \frac{\mathbf{V}_2}{\mathbf{V}_1} = \frac{1}{\mathbf{a}_{11} + \mathbf{a}_{12}\mathbf{Y}_L}$	$\mathbf{Y}_{\text{out}} = \mathbf{a}_{11}/\mathbf{a}_{12}$
$\mathbf{A}_V(\omega)_b = \frac{\mathbf{V}_2}{\mathbf{V}_1} = \frac{\mathbf{\Delta}_b}{\mathbf{b}_{22} + \mathbf{b}_{12}\mathbf{Y}_L}$	$\mathbf{Y}_{\text{out}} = \mathbf{b}_{22}/\mathbf{b}_{12}$
$\mathbf{Z}_{\text{in}} = \frac{\mathbf{a}_{12} + \mathbf{a}_{11}\mathbf{Z}_L}{\mathbf{a}_{22} + \mathbf{a}_{21}\mathbf{Z}_L}$	$\mathbf{Y}_{\text{in}} = \frac{\mathbf{b}_{21} + \mathbf{b}_{11}\mathbf{Y}_L}{\mathbf{b}_{22} + \mathbf{b}_{12}\mathbf{Y}_L}$

quantity and its parts are avoided. As an example, we would write the last quantity in the table,

$$\boldsymbol{\mu}_{rc} = \mu_{rcP} + j\mu_{rcQ} = \mu_{rc} \underline{|\theta_{rc}} \qquad \text{(B48)}$$

$$\mu_{rc} = \sqrt{(\mu_{rcP})^2 + (\mu_{rcQ})^2} \qquad \theta_{rc} = tan^{-1} \frac{\mu_{rcQ}}{\mu_{rcP}}$$

With the signs the author has given the quantities in Table 2, all ratio quantities come out with positive signs in numerical computation, which is a great advantage.

TABLE 2

CB:

$$\mathbf{k} = \frac{\mathbf{z}_m}{\mathbf{z}_{22} - \mathbf{z}_{12}} = \frac{\mathbf{z}_{21} - \mathbf{z}_{12}}{\mathbf{z}_{22} - \mathbf{z}_{12}} = \mathbf{a} \doteq \frac{\mathbf{z}_{21}}{\mathbf{z}_{22}}$$

$$\mathbf{A}_I(\omega)\Big|_{\mathbf{z}_L = 0} = \frac{-\mathbf{z}_{21}}{\mathbf{z}_{22}} = -\alpha = -\alpha_{fb} = \mathbf{h}_{fb} \doteq -\mathbf{a}$$

CE:

$$\mathbf{k}' = \frac{\mathbf{z}_m'}{\mathbf{z}_{22}' - \mathbf{z}_{12}'} = \frac{\mathbf{z}_{21}' - \mathbf{z}_{12}'}{\mathbf{z}_{22}' - \mathbf{z}_{12}'} = -\mathbf{b} \doteq \frac{\mathbf{z}_{21}'}{\mathbf{z}_{22}'}$$

$$\mathbf{A}_I'(\omega)\Big|_{\mathbf{z}_L = 0} = \frac{-\mathbf{z}_{21}'}{\mathbf{z}_{22}'} = \beta = \alpha_{fu} = \mathbf{h}_{fu} \doteq \mathbf{b}$$

CC:

$$\mathbf{k}'' = \frac{\mathbf{z}_m''}{\mathbf{z}_{22}'' - \mathbf{z}_{12}''} = \frac{\mathbf{z}_{21}'' - \mathbf{z}_{12}''}{\mathbf{z}_{22}'' - \mathbf{z}_{12}''} = \mathbf{c}$$

$$\mathbf{A}_I''(\omega)\Big|_{\mathbf{z}_L = 0} = \frac{-\mathbf{z}_{21}''}{\mathbf{z}_{22}''} = -\gamma = \alpha_{fc} = \mathbf{h}_{fc}$$

Also note the following open-port quotients:

CB: $\mathbf{k}_{21} = \mathbf{k}_{fb} = \boldsymbol{\mu}_{fb}$	and	$\mathbf{h}_{12} = \mathbf{h}_{rb} = \boldsymbol{\mu}_{rb}$
CE: $\mathbf{k}_{21}' = \mathbf{k}_{fu} = \boldsymbol{\mu}_{fu}$		$\mathbf{h}_{12}' = \mathbf{h}_{ru} = \boldsymbol{\mu}_{ru}$
CC: $\mathbf{k}_{21}'' = \mathbf{k}_{fc} = \boldsymbol{\mu}_{fc}$		$\mathbf{h}_{12}'' = \mathbf{h}_{rc} = \boldsymbol{\mu}_{rc}$

Appendix C
Useful Matrix Tables

TABLE 1 MATRIX RELATIONSHIPS

Network Matrix	Parameter Used					
	z	y	h	k	a	b
$\lvert z \rvert$	$\begin{matrix} z_{11} & z_{12} \\ z_{21} & z_{22} \end{matrix}$	$\begin{matrix} \frac{y_{22}}{\Delta_y} & \frac{-y_{12}}{\Delta_y} \\ \frac{-y_{21}}{\Delta_y} & \frac{y_{11}}{\Delta_y} \end{matrix}$	$\begin{matrix} \frac{\Delta_h}{h_{22}} & \frac{h_{12}}{h_{22}} \\ \frac{-h_{21}}{h_{22}} & \frac{1}{h_{22}} \end{matrix}$	$\begin{matrix} \frac{1}{k_{11}} & \frac{-k_{12}}{k_{11}} \\ \frac{k_{21}}{k_{11}} & \frac{\Delta_k}{k_{11}} \end{matrix}$	$\begin{matrix} \frac{a_{11}}{a_{21}} & \frac{\Delta_a}{a_{21}} \\ \frac{1}{a_{21}} & \frac{a_{22}}{a_{21}} \end{matrix}$	$\begin{matrix} \frac{b_{22}}{b_{21}} & \frac{1}{b_{21}} \\ \frac{\Delta_b}{b_{21}} & \frac{b_{11}}{b_{21}} \end{matrix}$
$\lvert y \rvert$	$\begin{matrix} \frac{z_{22}}{\Delta_z} & \frac{-z_{12}}{\Delta_z} \\ \frac{-z_{21}}{\Delta_z} & \frac{z_{11}}{\Delta_z} \end{matrix}$	$\begin{matrix} y_{11} & y_{12} \\ y_{21} & y_{22} \end{matrix}$	$\begin{matrix} \frac{1}{h_{11}} & \frac{-h_{12}}{h_{11}} \\ \frac{h_{21}}{h_{11}} & \frac{\Delta_h}{h_{11}} \end{matrix}$	$\begin{matrix} \frac{\Delta_k}{k_{22}} & \frac{k_{12}}{k_{22}} \\ \frac{-k_{21}}{k_{22}} & \frac{1}{k_{22}} \end{matrix}$	$\begin{matrix} \frac{a_{22}}{a_{12}} & \frac{-\Delta_a}{a_{12}} \\ \frac{-1}{a_{12}} & \frac{a_{11}}{a_{12}} \end{matrix}$	$\begin{matrix} \frac{b_{11}}{b_{12}} & \frac{-1}{b_{12}} \\ \frac{-\Delta_b}{b_{12}} & \frac{b_{22}}{b_{12}} \end{matrix}$
$\lvert h \rvert$	$\begin{matrix} \frac{\Delta_z}{z_{22}} & \frac{z_{12}}{z_{22}} \\ \frac{-z_{21}}{z_{22}} & \frac{1}{z_{22}} \end{matrix}$	$\begin{matrix} \frac{1}{y_{11}} & \frac{-y_{12}}{y_{11}} \\ \frac{y_{21}}{y_{11}} & \frac{\Delta y}{y_{11}} \end{matrix}$	$\begin{matrix} h_{11} & h_{12} \\ h_{21} & h_{22} \end{matrix}$	$\begin{matrix} \frac{k_{22}}{\Delta_k} & \frac{-k_{12}}{\Delta_k} \\ \frac{-k_{21}}{\Delta_k} & \frac{k_{11}}{\Delta_k} \end{matrix}$	$\begin{matrix} \frac{a_{12}}{a_{22}} & \frac{\Delta_a}{a_{22}} \\ \frac{-1}{a_{22}} & \frac{a_{21}}{a_{22}} \end{matrix}$	$\begin{matrix} \frac{b_{12}}{b_{11}} & \frac{1}{b_{11}} \\ \frac{-\Delta_b}{b_{11}} & \frac{b_{21}}{b_{11}} \end{matrix}$
$\lvert k \rvert$	$\begin{matrix} \frac{1}{z_{11}} & \frac{-z_{12}}{z_{11}} \\ \frac{z_{21}}{z_{11}} & \frac{\Delta_z}{z_{11}} \end{matrix}$	$\begin{matrix} \frac{\Delta_y}{y_{22}} & \frac{y_{12}}{y_{22}} \\ \frac{-y_{21}}{y_{22}} & \frac{1}{y_{22}} \end{matrix}$	$\begin{matrix} \frac{h_{22}}{\Delta_h} & \frac{-h_{12}}{\Delta_h} \\ \frac{-h_{21}}{\Delta_h} & \frac{h_{11}}{\Delta_h} \end{matrix}$	$\begin{matrix} k_{11} & k_{12} \\ k_{21} & k_{22} \end{matrix}$	$\begin{matrix} \frac{a_{21}}{a_{11}} & \frac{-\Delta_a}{a_{11}} \\ \frac{1}{a_{11}} & \frac{a_{12}}{a_{11}} \end{matrix}$	$\begin{matrix} \frac{b_{21}}{b_{22}} & \frac{-1}{b_{22}} \\ \frac{\Delta_b}{b_{22}} & \frac{b_{12}}{b_{22}} \end{matrix}$
$\lvert a \rvert$	$\begin{matrix} \frac{z_{11}}{z_{21}} & \frac{\Delta_z}{z_{21}} \\ \frac{1}{z_{21}} & \frac{z_{22}}{z_{21}} \end{matrix}$	$\begin{matrix} \frac{-y_{22}}{y_{21}} & \frac{-1}{y_{21}} \\ \frac{-\Delta_y}{y_{21}} & \frac{-y_{11}}{y_{21}} \end{matrix}$	$\begin{matrix} \frac{-\Delta_h}{h_{21}} & \frac{-h_{11}}{h_{21}} \\ \frac{-h_{22}}{h_{21}} & \frac{-1}{h_{21}} \end{matrix}$	$\begin{matrix} \frac{1}{k_{21}} & \frac{k_{22}}{k_{21}} \\ \frac{k_{11}}{k_{21}} & \frac{\Delta_k}{k_{21}} \end{matrix}$	$\begin{matrix} a_{11} & a_{12} \\ a_{21} & a_{22} \end{matrix}$	$\begin{matrix} \frac{b_{22}}{\Delta_b} & \frac{b_{12}}{\Delta_b} \\ \frac{b_{21}}{\Delta_b} & \frac{b_{11}}{\Delta_b} \end{matrix}$
$\lvert b \rvert$	$\begin{matrix} \frac{z_{22}}{z_{12}} & \frac{\Delta_z}{z_{12}} \\ \frac{1}{z_{12}} & \frac{z_{11}}{z_{12}} \end{matrix}$	$\begin{matrix} \frac{-y_{11}}{y_{12}} & \frac{-1}{y_{12}} \\ \frac{-\Delta_y}{y_{12}} & \frac{-y_{22}}{y_{12}} \end{matrix}$	$\begin{matrix} \frac{1}{h_{12}} & \frac{h_{11}}{h_{12}} \\ \frac{h_{22}}{h_{12}} & \frac{\Delta_h}{h_{12}} \end{matrix}$	$\begin{matrix} \frac{-\Delta_k}{k_{12}} & \frac{-k_{22}}{k_{12}} \\ \frac{-k_{11}}{k_{12}} & \frac{-1}{k_{12}} \end{matrix}$	$\begin{matrix} \frac{a_{22}}{\Delta_a} & \frac{a_{12}}{\Delta_a} \\ \frac{a_{21}}{\Delta_a} & \frac{a_{11}}{\Delta_a} \end{matrix}$	$\begin{matrix} b_{11} & b_{12} \\ b_{21} & b_{22} \end{matrix}$

TABLE 2 DETERMINANT RELATIONSHIPS

Network Determinant	Parameter Used					
	z	y	h	k	a	b
$\Delta_z =$	Δ_z	$\frac{1}{\Delta_y}$	$\frac{h_{11}}{h_{22}}$	$\frac{k_{22}}{k_{11}}$	$\frac{a_{12}}{a_{21}}$	$\frac{b_{12}}{b_{21}}$
$\Delta_y =$	$\frac{1}{\Delta_z}$	Δ_y	$\frac{h_{22}}{h_{11}}$	$\frac{k_{11}}{k_{22}}$	$\frac{a_{21}}{a_{12}}$	$\frac{b_{21}}{b_{12}}$
$\Delta_h =$	$\frac{z_{11}}{z_{22}}$	$\frac{y_{22}}{y_{11}}$	Δ_h	$\frac{1}{\Delta_k}$	$\frac{a_{11}}{a_{22}}$	$\frac{b_{22}}{b_{11}}$
$\Delta_k =$	$\frac{z_{22}}{z_{11}}$	$\frac{y_{11}}{y_{22}}$	$\frac{1}{\Delta_h}$	Δ_k	$\frac{a_{22}}{a_{11}}$	$\frac{b_{11}}{b_{22}}$
$\Delta_a =$	$\frac{z_{12}}{z_{21}}$	$\frac{y_{12}}{y_{21}}$	$\frac{-h_{12}}{h_{21}}$	$\frac{-k_{12}}{k_{21}}$	Δ_a	$\frac{1}{\Delta_b}$
$\Delta_b =$	$\frac{z_{21}}{z_{12}}$	$\frac{y_{21}}{y_{12}}$	$\frac{-h_{21}}{h_{12}}$	$\frac{-k_{21}}{k_{12}}$	$\frac{1}{\Delta_a}$	Δ_b

NOTE: Variables and parameters listed in these tables are basically transforms, s-domain quantities, or complex quantities. Thus, bold-face type should have been used, such as $\mathbf{z}$, $\mathbf{y}$, $\mathbf{\Delta}_h$, $\mathbf{V}_1$ and $\mathbf{I}_2$. If the voltage sinor, $\mathbf{V}_1$, is a reference quantity, we write it $\mathbf{V}_1 = V_1$. The relation between the parameter subscripts used here and the "irfo" subscripts, used for z, y, h and k parameters, is as follows: 11, or i; 12, or r; 21, or f; 22, or o.

TABLE 3 MATRICES AND EQUATION SYSTEMS

Key diagram, valid for all parameters and all variables

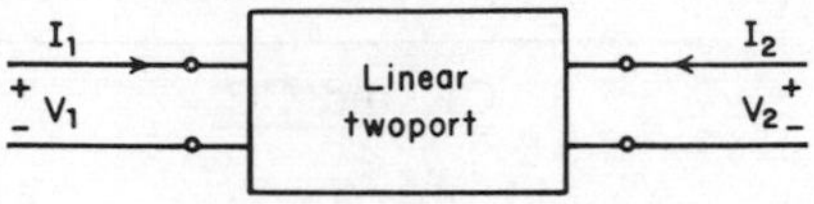

Type of Parameter	Network Matrix	Equation System
Immittance parameters	$\lvert z\rvert \begin{vmatrix} z_{11} & z_{12} \\ z_{21} & z_{22} \end{vmatrix}$ (1)	$V_1 = z_{11} I_1 + z_{12} I_2$ (2) $V_2 = z_{21} I_1 + z_{22} I_2$ (3)
	$\lvert y\rvert \begin{vmatrix} y_{11} & y_{12} \\ y_{21} & y_{22} \end{vmatrix}$ (4)	$I_1 = y_{11} V_1 + y_{12} V_2$ (5) $I_2 = y_{21} V_1 + y_{22} V_2$ (6)
Hybrid parameters	$\lvert h\rvert \begin{vmatrix} h_{11} & h_{12} \\ h_{21} & h_{22} \end{vmatrix}$ (7)	$V_1 = h_{11} I_1 + h_{12} V_2$ (8) $I_2 = h_{21} I_1 + h_{22} V_2$ (9)
	$\lvert k\rvert \begin{vmatrix} k_{11} & k_{12} \\ k_{21} & k_{22} \end{vmatrix}$ (10)	$I_1 = k_{11} V_1 + k_{12} I_2$ (11) $V_2 = k_{21} V_1 + k_{22} I_2$ (12)
Transmission parameters	$\lvert a\rvert \begin{vmatrix} a_{11} & a_{12} \\ a_{21} & a_{22} \end{vmatrix}$ (13)	$V_1 = a_{11} V_2 + a_{12}(-I_2)$ (14) $I_1 = a_{21} V_2 + a_{22}(-I_2)$ (15)
	$\lvert b\rvert \begin{vmatrix} b_{11} & b_{12} \\ b_{21} & b_{22} \end{vmatrix}$ (16)	$V_2 = b_{11} V_1 + b_{12}(-I_1)$ (17) $I_2 = b_{21} V_1 + b_{22}(-I_1)$ (18)

TABLE 4 "FLOATING" TRANSFORMATION MATRIX
(Valid for any connection, any parameter)

CE and CC	CC	CE
z_{22}/Δ_z	$-z_{12}/\Delta_z$	$-z_{12}/\Delta_z$
y_{11}	y_{12}	y_{12}
$1/h_{11}$	$-h_{12}/h_{11}$	$-h_{12}/h_{11}$
Δ_k/k_{22}	k_{12}/k_{22}	k_{12}/k_{22}
a_{22}/a_{12}	$-\Delta_a/a_{12}$	$-\Delta_a/a_{12}$
b_{11}/b_{12}	$-1/b_{12}$	$-1/b_{12}$

CC	CC	CB	CB
$-z_{21}/\Delta_z$	z_{11}/Δ_z	z_{22}/Δ_z	$-z_{12}/\Delta_z$
y_{21}	y_{22}	y_{11}	y_{12}
h_{21}/h_{11}	Δ_h/h_{11}	$1/h_{11}$	$-h_{12}/h_{11}$
$-k_{21}/k_{22}$	$1/k_{22}$	Δ_k/k_{22}	k_{12}/k_{22}
$-1/a_{12}$	a_{11}/a_{12}	a_{22}/a_{12}	$-\Delta_a/a_{12}$
$-\Delta_b/b_{12}$	b_{22}/b_{12}	b_{11}/b_{12}	$-1/b_{12}$

CE	CB	CB and CE
$-z_{21}/\Delta_z$	$-z_{21}/\Delta_z$	z_{11}/Δ_z
y_{21}	y_{21}	y_{22}
h_{21}/h_{11}	h_{21}/h_{11}	Δ_h/h_{11}
$-k_{21}/k_{22}$	$-k_{21}/k_{22}$	$1/k_{22}$
$-1/a_{12}$	$-1/a_{12}$	a_{11}/a_{12}
$-\Delta_b/b_{12}$	$-\Delta_b/b_{12}$	b_{22}/b_{12}

NOTE: This complex "floating"-matrix table was developed by the author in 1962 and was made part of the Transistor Electronics courses EE 427 and EE 428 at Lowell Technological Institute, Lowell, Mass., during the academic year 1962-1963. Thanks to the "built-in" parameter formulas, consultation of matrix tables such as Table 1 can generally be avoided. The above table was published in *Electro-Technology*, vol. 72, no. 3, Sept. 1963.

Table 5 Transistor Parameter Definitions

Immittance Parameters				
z parameters				
$z_{11}=z_i=V_1/I_1$	2op	Open-port input (or driving-point) impedance	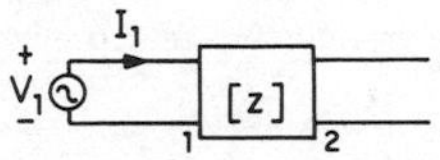	(1)
$z_{12}=z_r=V_1/I_{20}$	1op	Open-port reverse transfer (or coupling) impedance	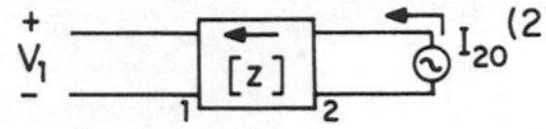	(2)
$z_{21}=z_f=V_2/I_1$	2op	Open-port forward transfer (or coupling) impedance	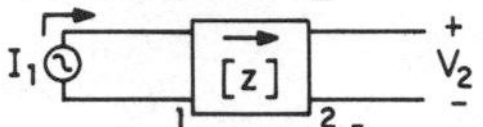	(3)
$z_{22}=z_o=V_{20}/I_{20}$	1op	Open-port output impedance	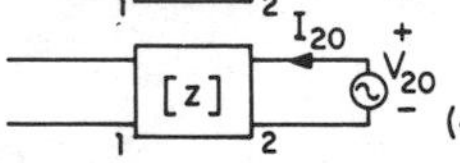	(4)
y parameters				
$y_{11}=y_i=I_1/V_1$	2cl	Closed-port input (or driving-point) admittance	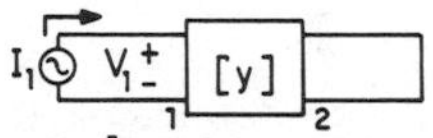	(5)
$y_{12}=y_r=I_1/V_{20}$	1cl	Closed-port reverse transfer (or coupling) admittance	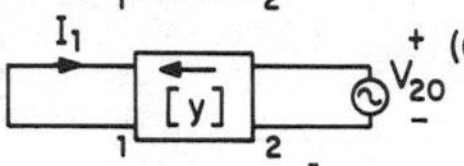	(6)
$y_{21}=y_f=I_2/V_1$	2cl	Closed-port forward transfer (or coupling) admittance	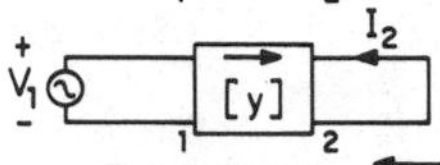	(7)
$y_{22}=y_o=I_{20}/V_{20}$	1cl	Closed-port output admittance	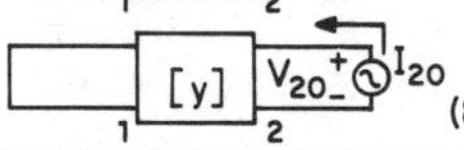	(8)
Hybrid Parameters				
h parameters				
$h_{11}=h_i=1/y_{11}$		Closed-port input (or driving-point) impedance	See y_{11} diagram*	(9)
$h_{12}=h_r=V_1/V_{20}$	1op	Open-port reverse voltage-transfer ratio	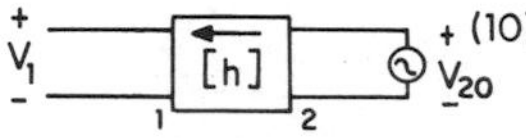	(10)
$h_{21}=h_f=I_2/I_1$	2cl	Closed-port forward current-transfer ratio, or forward current-amplification factor	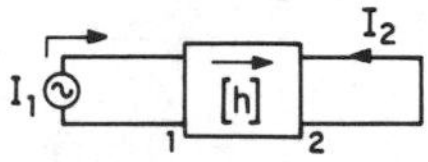	(11)
$h_{22}=h_o=1/z_{22}$		Open-port output admittance	See z_{22} diagram	(12)
k parameters				
$k_{11}=k_i=1/z_{11}$		Open-port input (or driving point) admittance	See z_{11} diagram	(13)
$k_{12}=k_r=I_1/I_{20}$	1cl	Closed-port reverse current transfer ratio	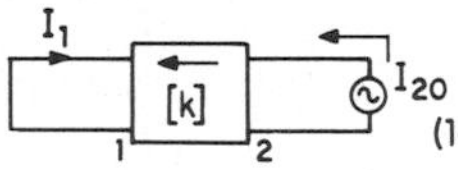	(14)
$k_{21}=k_f=V_2/V_1$	2op	Open-port forward voltage-transfer ratio, or forward voltage-amplification factor	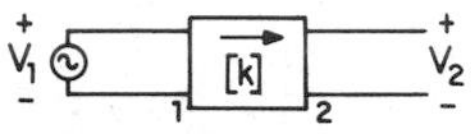	(15)
$k_{22}=k_o=1/y_{22}$		Closed-port output impedance	See y_{22} diagram	(16)

*In this and following references to other parameters and key diagrams, for example by the formula $h_{11}=1/y_{11}$, note that complete equality is not at hand since one key network may be current-driven while the other is voltage driven

Table 5 (Cont.)

Transmission Parameters For diagram, see above key diagrams with reference to given quantity, such as k_{21} in formula 17		
a parameters		
$a_{11} = 1/k_{21}$	Inverse open-port forward voltage-transfer ratio, or inverse forward voltage-amplification factor	(17)
$a_{12} = -1/y_{21}$	Negative inverse closed-port forward transfer (or coupling) admittance	(18)
$a_{21} = 1/z_{21}$	Inverse open-port forward transfer (or coupling) impedance	(19)
$a_{22} = -1/h_{21}$	Negative inverse closed-port forward current-transfer ratio, or negative inverse forward current-amplification factor	(20)
b parameters		
$b_{11} = 1/h_{12}$	Inverse open-port reverse voltage-transfer ratio	(21)
$b_{12} = -1/y_{12}$	Negative inverse closed-port reverse transfer (or coupling) admittance	(22)
$b_{21} = 1/z_{12}$	Inverse open-port reverse transfer (or coupling) impedance	(23)
$b_{22} = -1/k_{12}$	Negative inverse closed-port reverse current-transfer ratio	(24)

Table 6 Network sections ($\Delta_a = 1$)

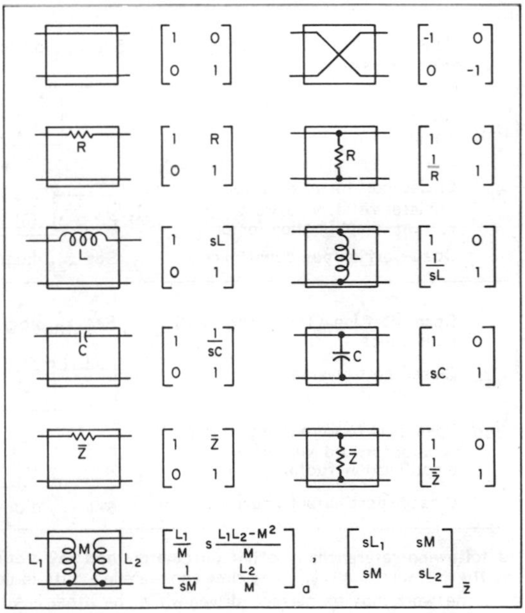

Index